GCSE CDT

LONGMAN REFERENCE GUIDES

Series editors: Geoff Black and Stuart Wall

TITLES AVAILABLE
CDT
English
French
Mathematics
Science
World History

FORTHCOMING
Biology
Chemistry
Geography
Physics

CDT

LONGMAN REFERENCE GUIDES

David Rees

Longman

Longman Group UK Limited,
Longman House, Burnt Mill, Harlow,
Essex CM20 2JE, England
and Associated Companies throughout the world.

First published 1989

British Library Cataloguing in Publication Data

Rees, David, 1932–
CDT. – (Longman GCSE reference guides).
1. England. Secondary schools. Curriculum subjects:
Design. G.C.S.E. examinations
I. Title
745.4′07

ISBN 0–582–05075–8

Designed and produced by The Pen and Ink Book Company Ltd, Huntingdon, Cambridgeshire.

Illustrated by Chris Etheridge

Set in 9/10pt Century Old Style

Printed and bound in Great Britain

HOW TO USE THIS BOOK

Throughout your GCSE course you will be coming across terms, ideas and definitions that are unfamiliar to you. The Longman Reference Guides provide a quick, easy-to-use source of information, fact and opinion. Each main term is listed alphabetically and, where appropriate, cross-referenced to related terms.

- Where a term or phrase appears in **different type** you can look up a separate entry under that heading elsewhere in the book.
- Where a term or phrase appears in **different type** and is set between two arrowhead symbols ◀ ▶, it is particularly recommended that you turn to the entry for that heading.

ABRASIVES

Abrasives are used to improve the smoothness of a surface. By rubbing the surface to be made smooth the rough parts are worn away, leaving a smoother finish to the surface being treated. The material used for the abrasive should be much harder than the material being rubbed, so that the wearing away action is greater on the material than on the abrasive being used. Of course some materials are harder than others, so it is important to select the appropriate abrasive for the material being smoothed.

ABRASIVES FOR WOOD

Glass paper

Glass paper is a man-made product specially designed for smoothing wood surfaces. Very small pieces of ground glass are glued onto a paper backing. The size of a sheet is 280mm × 230mm and there are ten grades of 'cut'. The *larger the size* of the pieces of ground glass, the *coarser* the cut; the *smaller* the sizes of ground glass, the *finer* the cut. See the table below.

Garnet paper

Garnet Paper is similar to glass paper but can be recognised by its reddish colour, whereas glass paper is yellowish in colour. The abrasive grit is obtained by crushing garnet, a glass-like mineral that is very hard. The grit is graded into different size grains and glued onto a paper backing. The finished product is of a higher quality than glass paper and is more expensive. There are two types of garnet paper. *Open coated paper* has the abrasive grains spaced apart so that when rubbing softwoods, that are often resinous, or painted surfaces, the paper does not become clogged. The second type is *close coated paper*. Here the grains are packed close together to provide an even and regular surface, i.e. the same as glass paper. This paper is ideal for use on hardwoods, producing a high quality finish.

Aluminium oxide

Aluminium oxide is also a raw material from which a very hard abrasive is obtained. The specially tough, hard wearing grits are bonded to either a metal or rubber backing for use on either a disc- or belt-sanding machine. Again these are graded according to grit size (Table A.1).

Grit size		Glass paper	Garnet paper
220 180	Extra fine	Flour 00	6/0 5/0
150 120	Fine	0 1	4/0 3/0
100 80 60	Medium	1½ F2 M2	2/0 0 ½
50 40 36	Coarse	S2 2½ 3	1 1 ½ 2

Table A.1 Abrasives

Sand paper

The term *sand paper* is commonly used to include abrasive papers used on wood and is not strictly an accurate name. If you can be more specific and accurate in naming an appropriate abrading paper in your Design Folio, or in your answer to an examination question, you will gain far more credit.

Wire wool

Wire wool or *steel wool* is an excellent fine abrasive to use when polishing. The wool does not become clogged so easily as in the case of glass papers and the fine dust of polish can be shaken out or blown out in between rubbings. Always check that there are no fine strands of wire left on the surface before applying the next layer of polish.

ABRASIVES FOR METAL

The two main abrasives used on metal are 'emery cloth' and 'wet and dry paper'. A third type of abrasive is one that is suspended in a liquid or paste, and comes under the heading of metal polish or lapping compound.

Emery cloth

Emery cloth is the name frequently given to small grains of corundum bonded to a cloth 230mm × 280mm. As with glass papers, the grains are graded into sizes to produce the fine coarse grades of emery cloth. The most frequently used are 'F', 'M' and 'C' (Fine, Medium and Coarse).

Wet and dry paper

Wet and dry paper refers to small grains of silicon carbide bonded to a waterproof paper. The sheets are 230mm × 280mm in size. This abrasive is used mainly for very fine or highly finished surfaces. To keep the very fine grains from becoming clogged, the paper can be rinsed in running water. This keeps the grains exposed and able to make direct contact with the metal surface being rubbed. Wet and dry is also suitable for use on some plastic materials, such as acrylic, and hardened polyester resins. The coarseness of cut is graded by 'Grit Numbers'. The higher the number, the finer the cut; 400 is an exceptionally fine grade and is used as a final stage in rubbing down. Grades between 220 and 80 are available and are used in the earlier stages of abrading a surface.

Metal polishes

Metal polishes are very fine abrasive grains suspended in a liquid. The most commonly known trade brands are *Brasso* and *Silvo*. They are applied with a cloth and rubbed vigorously to give a shine to brass or silver. They can also be used on copper, aluminium and nickel.

Grinding compounds

Grinding compounds are fine abrasive grains mixed in a paste and are mainly used for providing a polished surface to mechanical components, e.g. piston and cylinders, valve seatings, etc.

ABRASIVES FOR PLASTICS

In general the surface of many plastics will not require abrading. The two most common situations where they do require some abrading are in Glass Reinforced Plastics work and in acrylic work where edge finishing is necessary. Though *Brasso* or *Silvo* can be used as a substitute for edge polishing acrylic, there are other special polishes. An abrasive polish for cutting is Perspex Polish Number 1. Perspex Polish Number 2 is used for producing a highly polished finish. Perspex is the ICI trade name for acrylic.

Points to remember

1. Select the correct abrading product for the material being abraded.
2. Start with the coarser grades first.
3. Do not change from a coarser grade to a smoother grade until the best possible finish has been obtained from the one being used.
4. Abrade a surface in *steady stages* and do not be tempted to jump from a coarse grit abrasive to a very fine grit abrasive. Use the intermediate grades where possible.
5. Always abrade *along* the grain when smoothing a wood surface for polishing. Going *across* the grain or rubbing in a circular motion will produce scratches that will show through any transparent or translucent polish. It is only acceptable to go across the grain when the surface is to be painted and the scratches will not show.

ACCELERATOR

A cobalt octoate solution is sometimes known as an *accelerator* or *activator* since it can be used to speed up the curing process of a synthetic resin. Some resins are already pre-activated when purchased. This means that they will cure in room temperature at a rate that will allow a reasonable working time for the user. A pre-active resin will cure in approximately 20–30 minutes after a catalyst has been added and mixed with the resin. This means that no more accelerator needs to be added and the resin is ready for use. Too much accelerator will not only speed up the curing process but will also cause the resin to get too hot and craze.

ACID RAIN

Much industrial waste is allowed to filter into the air, e.g. through very tall chimneys. When this mixes with water vapour in the air, some of the industrial waste is absorbed. For instance, sulphur dioxide dissolves in water vapour in the air so that the rain which falls becomes acidic, damaging trees and harming animal life in rivers and lakes. Many forests in Norway have been affected by such rain, and it is believed that much of the industrial waste has come from England. Indeed, countries throughout the world, including England, have now identified acid rain as a problem for forests and lakes.

ACTIVATOR

An alternative name for **accelerator**.

ACTIVE TRANSDUCERS

Those **transducers** that generate an emf (electro magnetic force), e.g. **microphone, thermocouple.**

ACUTE ANGLE

An angle less than 90 degrees. ◀ **Angles** ▶

ADHESIVES

An adhesive is a substance that will bond two or more pieces of material together. The pieces of material may be similar or dissimilar. Most bonding processes are intended to be *permanent*, i.e. once glued, the parts are not intended to come apart. There are occasions when the bonding is required to be *temporary*, i.e. held together for a short period and able to be parted without damage. There are many varying situations where materials require bonding, and adhesives have been designed to cope with a wide range of materials and situations. Table A.2 should help you to find an adhesive that will suit your needs.

AESTHETICS

When something is said to be attractive, pleasing to look at, etc., an *aesthetic* judgement is being made. When you evaluate an object you are expected to make a comment about its appearance. If your judgements are favourable then you could say that the object is aesthetically pleasing.

SITUATION	MATERIAL							
	Wood/ wood	*Wood/ metal*	*Acrylic/ acrylic*	*PVC rigid/ PVC rigid*	*PVC flex/ PVC flex*	*Fabric/ fabric*	*Paper card/ paper card*	*Balsa*
Contact (allows adjustment by sliding the joint)	PVA	Epoxy	Tensol Nos. 12 and 70				Copydex, PVA	Cement
Contact made directly (adjustment cannot be made)	Epoxy contact	Epoxy contact		Contact cement			Copydex contact	
Construction of models	PVA	Epoxy	Tensol No. 12	PVC Contact cement, Glue gun, PVC	Contact cement	PVA, Plastisol	Copydex	Cement
Hand pressure	Epoxy rapid	Epoxy rapid	Tensol No. 12, Super Glue	Contact cement		PVA	Copydex	Cement
Jewellery	PVA	Epoxy	Tensol No. 12	Contact cement				
Long setting time (more than 5 mins)	PVA	Synthetic	Tensol No. 70 1 hr Tensol No. 12 3 hrs	Contact cement		PVA	PVA	
Quick setting time (less than 5 mins)	Epoxy rapid 3–5 mins, Glue gun 20–60 seconds	Epoxy rapid	Super Glue	Glue gun, PVC Grey 80–90 seconds		Glue gun, black	Copydex contact	Cement
Strength	Synthetic	Epoxy	Tensol No. 12, Super Glue	Contact cement		Plastisol		
Sustained pressure, vice clamp, etc.	PVA	Synthetic						
Temporary	Masking tape	Masking tape	Masking tape	Masking tape	Masking tape	Masking tape	Masking tape, Blue Tack	Masking tape, Blue Tack
Units storage	PVA	Epoxy	Tensol No. 12	Contact cement				
Wet	Synthetic	Epoxy, synthetic	Tensol No. 70	Contact cement		Plastisol		Cement

Table A.2 Adhesives

AIR BLEEDING OCCLUSION

Another word for *bleeding* is *draining*, and another word for *occlusion* is *blocking* or *stopping*. Therefore a circuit in which air is allowed to drain and to be stopped when required, is called an 'air bleed circuit'. In a circuit that has two air pressure supplies, double air pressure valves (3-port or 5-port) have to be used.

A *double air pressure valve* is one that is operated by a change of air pressure. An increase, caused by an occlusion in the air bleed, is sufficient to move a spool that is attached to a diaphragm, which then operates the valve (Fig A.1).

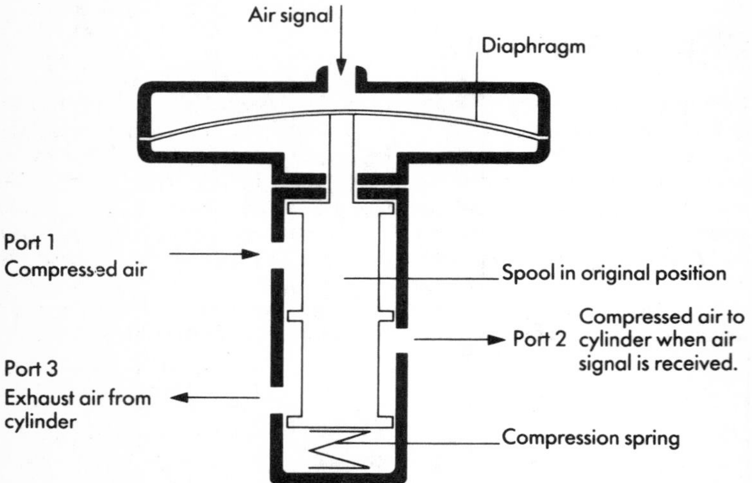

Fig A.1 Diaphragm 3-port valve

When the occlusion is *removed*, the air bleeds from the circuit, the pressure is no longer acting on the diaphragm, and the spool is returned to its original position by the pressure of a spring.

Such circuits are used to signal that a car has arrived at a garage forecourt. The weight of the car going over a flexible tube squashes the tube and stops the air bleed. This activates a valve that makes a cylinder go positive, i.e. giving an outward stroke to strike a bell. Another use of such circuits is in the closing of a machine guard. The air bleed circuit only allows the main air supply to the machine when the guard is closed.

ALARM

There are two main types of alarm system, 'audible' and 'visual'. The *audible* is a high pitched sound and the *visual* is a coloured light, often red. In both systems the signals are given in repeated short bursts because these are more readily noticed than a continuous signal.

ALLOYS

Some metals are alloys. This means that they will fuse with others and become a single material; e.g. copper and zinc will fuse together when heated to melting point and produce *brass*. By varying the ratios of copper to zinc, different grades of brass may be produced. *Steel* is an alloy of carbon and iron and by increasing the amount of carbon, different types of steel may be produced e.g. mild steel and carbon steel (sometimes called tool steel because many cutting tools are made from this type of steel). Table A.3 shows you examples of ferrous (iron-containing) alloys; Table A.4 shows you examples of non-ferrous (non-iron-containing) alloys.

ALLOYING MATERIAL

By fusing two or more metals together, the resulting alloyed material takes on new characteristics. You know that iron rusts very easily when exposed to moisture; but by alloying nickel and chromium with the iron, stainless steel is produced, which does *not* rust. Stainless steel is therefore suitable for making washbasins, cutlery, medical instruments, etc. The *ratios* of the metals being alloyed is critical to obtain the desired properties, so considerable care has to be taken at the preparation stage to ensure that the correct quantities are used.

Because of the high cost and the facilities necessary for the alloying of metals, industrial methods must be used. However, if you are case-hardening

Name	*Alloy of:*	*Properties*	*Uses*
Mild steel	Carbon 0.1–0.3% Iron 99.9–99.7%	Tough. High tensile strength. Can be case hardened. Rusts very easily	Most common metal used in school workshops
Carbon steel	Carbon 0.6–1.4% Iron 99.4–98.6%	Tough. Can be hardened and tempered	Cutting tools and punches
Stainless steel	Iron, nickel and chromium	Tough. Resistant to rust and stains	Cutlery, medical instruments
Cast iron	Carbon 2–6% Iron 98–94%	Strong but brittle. Compressive strength very high. Has a natural lubricant	Castings, manhole covers, engines
Wrought iron	Almost 100% iron	Fibrous, tough, ductile, resistant to rusting	Ornamental gates and railings. Not in much use today

Table A.3 Examples of ferrous alloys

Name	*Colour*	*Alloy of:*	*Properties*	*Uses*
Aluminium	Light grey	Aluminium 95% Copper 4% Manganese 1%	Ductile, soft, malleable, machines well. Very light	Window frames, aircraft, kitchen ware
Copper	Reddish brown	Not an alloy	Ductile, can be beaten into shape Conducts electricity and heat	Electrical wiring, tubing, pans, kettles, bowls
Brass	Yellow	Mixture of copper and zinc 65%–35% most common ratio	Hard. Casts and machines well. Surface tarnishes. Conducts electricity	Parts for electrical fittings, ornaments
Silver	Whitish grey	Mainly silver but alloyed with copper to give sterling silver	Ductile, malleable, solders, resists corrosion	Jewellery, solder, ornaments
Lead	Bluish grey	Not an alloy	Soft, heavy, ductile, loses its shape under pressure	Solders, pipes, batteries, roofing

Table A.4 Examples of non-ferrous alloys and metals

a steel, you will be introducing carbon into the surface of the steel; this is an example of alloying a material in school workshop conditions. Increasing the amount of carbon by a very small quantity will make the surface hard.

ALTERNATING CURRENT

A flow of electricity which is constantly changing its direction and magnitude in a regular way is called an alternating current. The value of the current increases to a maximum value in *one direction*, then smoothly decreases to zero before moving in the *opposite direction* and smoothly increasing to a maximum of identical value to the previous maximum. This can be presented graphically as a sine wave (Fig A.2).

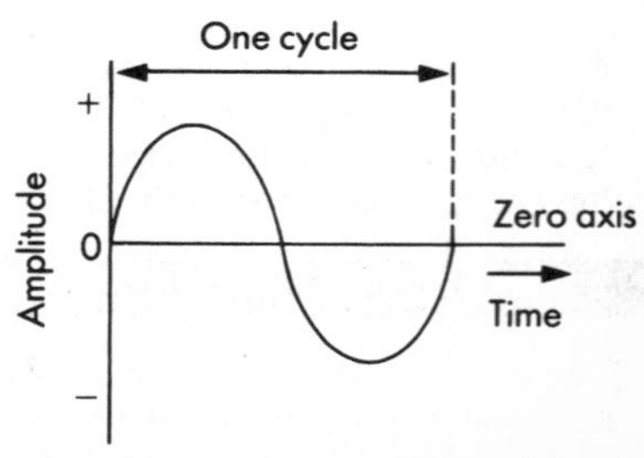

Fig A.2 Sine wave

The flow from zero to zero and back again is known as a *cycle*. The number of cycles per second is known as the **frequency**. Alternating current is the most commonly used form of electricity. In Great Britain the frequency is 50 Hz (Hertz being a unit of frequency; 1 Hz is equal to 1/50 cycles per second).
◀ Frequency ▶

ALTERNATING VOLTAGE

Alternating voltage is where the polarity keeps reversing negative to positive to negative to positive. The rate at which this is done is known as the **frequency**. A coil rotating in a magnetic field will produce a *positive* polarity in the first half of its rotation, but a *negative* polarity in the second half of its rotation. The rotating coil in the magnetic field generates an alternating voltage. If the coil rotates 50 times in one second, the alternating current voltage will have a frequency of 50 Hz.

ALTERNATIVE IDEAS OR SOLUTIONS

When attempting to solve a problem you are asked to think of a number of alternative ideas. This means looking at the problem broadly and developing ideas that are different from each other. Looking at a wide range of possible solutions gives you more choice in selecting the *particular* solution you wish to develop for realisation. This should increase your chances of developing an idea that will be successful. If you start with a *single theme* and look at the possible variations on this theme, then the success or failure of your final solution will depend very much upon the single theme adopted at the outset. This could be very risky. You are much more likely to succeed by looking at a variety of alternative ideas and you will certainly gain more credit in the final assessment.

AMMETER

An ammeter is an instrument for measuring a current. It measures the flow of electrons in a circuit in units called **amperes**. The ammeter that you are most likely to use in your projects is designed to measure low levels of direct current. It has a positive terminal and a negative terminal which enable it to be connected in series into a circuit.

An ammeter is an expensive and highly sensitive instrument. Remember first, to select an ammeter that is able to measure within the current range that you are testing; second, to connect the negative supply to the negative terminal and the positive supply to the positive terminal; and third, to connect the ammeter in series in the circuit.

AMPERE

The ampere (A) is a unit of current flow in a circuit. It is measured by an instrument called an **ammeter**. The instrument is based upon the principle first developed by André Ampere in 1821, namely, that a compass needle mounted inside a coil would be deflected when a small current flowed in the wire. You may need to measure in one of three units, two of which are smaller than one ampere. They are; the *ampere* (A), the *milliampere* (mA) which is one thousandth of an ampere, and the *microampere* (μA) which is one millionth of an ampere.

AMPLIFIER

Amplify means to make larger, and in this context an amplifier is a device for converting small electrical signals into large electrical signals. Such devices form an important part of most circuits that emit sound waves; e.g. radios, televisions, hi-fi systems, electric guitars, etc.

Transistors can also be used to amplify a current in a circuit.

◀ Darlington pair amplifier, Transistor ▶

AMPLIFIER VALVE

◀ Valves ▶

AMPLITUDE

The peak value of an alternating current or the wave form in the positive or negative direction is called *amplitude* (Fig A.3)

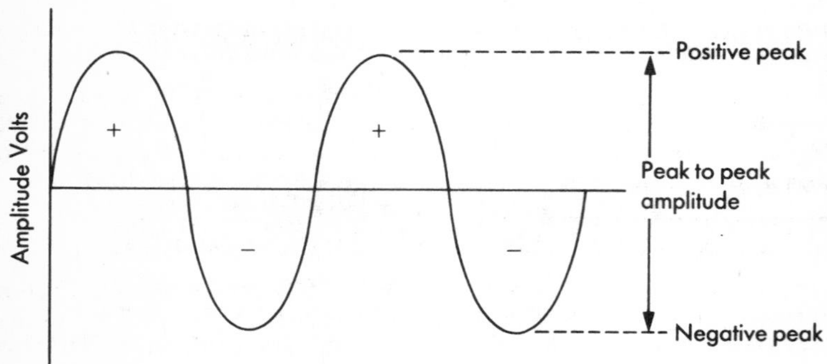

Fig A.3 Amplitude

The difference between the two extreme values in a complete cycle is the *peak to peak amplitude.*

AMPLITUDE MODULATION

Changing the amplitude of a carrier wave to keep in step with a signal produced at a lower frequency is called *amplitude modulation* (AM) (Fig A.4).

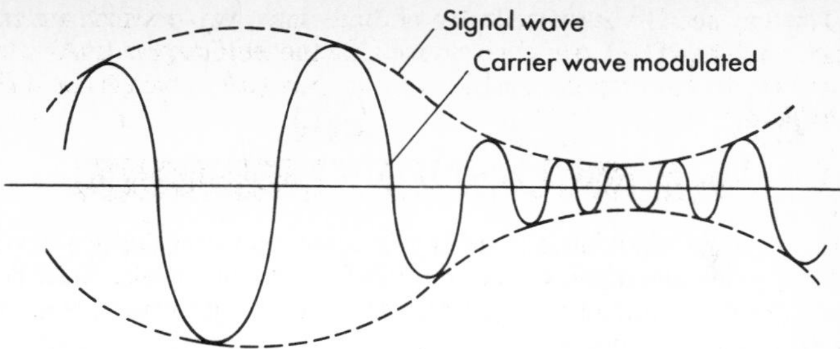

Fig A.4 Amplitude modulation

ANALOGUE

Analogue systems change from one state to another *gradually*. For example, the daily temperature gradually rises as the day proceeds and gradually falls as the night draws near. The mercury thermometer is an analogue device; as the temperature rises so the mercury expands, and as the temperature falls so the mercury contracts.

It should be noted that the alternative is an 'on' – 'off' state, with no in-between stages. When you press a switch to turn the light on , it comes on immediately; when you switch the light off, it goes out immediately.

ANALOGUE DIGITAL CONVERTER

A system for converting a continuously varying signal such as voltage or frequency into numbers (digits) for use by computers is called an *Analogue Digital Converter*. If a 1V analogue input equals a digital binary output of 0001, then a 5V analogue input would equal a digital binary output of 0101.

ANALOGUE SWITCHES

Analogue switches are electronic Integrated Circuits that replace mechanical switches. They are either SPST (Single Pole Single Throw) or SPDT (Single Pole Double Throw), normally open or normally closed. When the switch is at logic 1 the switch is 'on'. When the switch is at logic 0, the switch is 'off'.

ANALYSIS

To *analyse* something is to break it down into smaller parts and to consider each part separately. In order to gain a fuller understanding of a design problem it is necessary to look at it in detail. Each detail that is considered forms part of the analysis. Though all the parts are interrelated with each other and with the **Design Brief**, they can be considered on their own. This will help you to concentrate on one particular part at a time. You can prepare a *list* that will later serve as a guide for the things that will need investigating and developing as possible solutions. *After the realisation* of a solution, the list of points in the analysis can form the basis for your *evaluation*, e.g.:

Analysis
The container must:
a) be portable;
b) be able to contain brushes, pencils, sketch pad, paints, rubbers, inks, etc;
c) be able to store the items so that they are easily identified;
d) have some means of security;
etc.

Evaluation
Is the container:
a) portable?
b) able to contain brushes, etc?
c) able to store the items so that they are easily identified?
d) able to keep the items secure?
etc.

A clearly tabulated analysis helps you to communicate your thinking clearly and allows an assessor to readily follow and understand your work. Such an approach will often bring you credit in the assessment of your work.

ANCILLARY MATERIALS

Suppose, when you choose the materials for the realisation of a solution, you find that the main material is wood. Yet you intend that some small part of the solution should be made from metal or plastics, etc. In this case, these materials are said to be *ancillary* to the wood. They are still, however, important and may have been chosen for their characteristics, special properties or appearance.

AND GATE

This is a digital logic circuit that produces a 'High' output of 1 only when all inputs are at 1. ◀ Logic gates ▶

ANGLE

An angle is the inclination of either two planes or two lines. The space between them is measured in degrees. There are four named types of angle (Fig A.5): *Acute* that has an angle less than 90 degrees; *Right angle* that has an angle of 90 degrees; *Obtuse* that has an angle between 90 degrees and 180 degrees; and *Reflex* that has an angle between 180 degrees and 360 degrees.

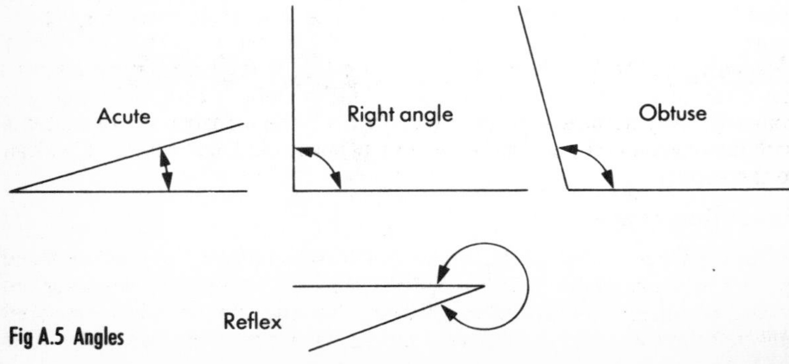

Fig A.5 Angles

ANIMATION

Animation refers to the process of bringing something to 'life', i.e. making it move. Many cartoon characters start off as still drawings, but by filming the many hundreds or thousands of drawings, the characters can be seen to move when projected on to a screen. Puppets can be 'brought to life' by careful manipulation of strings.

The illusion of movement can be created in a number of ways; one example is to do a number of drawings of a 'stick man' walking. Each drawing must be identical in size, but the arms and legs can be drawn in varying stages of movement. The more gradual the stages, the greater the number of drawings that will be necessary, but the result will be much smoother. The movement is obtained by placing the drawings on top of each other and then flicking through the sheets, bending them sufficiently to just show each of the drawings.

ANNEAL

To anneal a material means to make it soft. Materials such as steel, copper and aluminium are known to be relatively hard, yet can be made softer through a process called annealing. Suppose you have two pieces of identical material, one which has been annealed and the other which has not. It will not be too difficult to determine which has been annealed, even though in appearance they seem to be the same. Hold the two pieces in a vice, with part of each standing just above the vice jaw. Gently hit each piece with a mallet or hammer; one piece will bend more readily than the other. The piece that bends easily is the annealed piece of metal.

ANNEALING PROCESS

To anneal metals, heat is required. However, the amount of heat varies for different metals, and so it is important to carry out an **annealing process** that is appropriate for the metal being treated.

Annealing mild steel

Heat the metal to a cherry red colour and allow it to cool slowly in a brazing hearth. The slower the process of cooling, the better the results. For *small section* material this could mean one or two hours; for *large section* material this could mean ten or twelve hours. Once the metal is cool, the process is complete. Any surface scale produced through the oxidation of the material with the oxygen in the air can be removed with an old file to restore the shine to the surface.

Annealing copper

When copper is repeatedly hit with a mallet or hammer it becomes hard and difficult to work. Therefore to be able to continue working it is necessary to soften the copper by an annealing process. The copper is heated to cherry red and quenched in water. A dull grey scale will have formed on the surface. This can be removed by placing the copper in a pickling bath of dilute sulphuric acid. Depending upon the strength of the pickle, the removal of the scale will take as little as 3 or 4 minutes. Do not be tempted to leave the copper in the pickling bath too long, because the dilute sulphuric acid will continue to attack the copper as long as it remains in the bath.

Annealing aluminium

Aluminium, like copper, becomes hard if repeatedly hit with a mallet or hammer. This work-hardening process can reach a stage where the aluminium becomes brittle and begins to crack. It may be necessary to anneal the material several times during a beating process. Because aluminium has a much lower melting point than either copper or mild steel it cannot be heated to cherry red colour. The annealing temperature for aluminium is only 350°C and therefore it is not necessary to go any higher. To do so would bring the danger of melting the aluminium and spoiling whatever was being made. To avoid getting the aluminium *too hot,* a thin layer of soft soap is smeared over the surface and then heated with a gentle flame from a brazing torch. The flame is kept moving over the surface so that an even temperature is maintained. When the appropriate temperature has been reached, the soft soap will begin to change to brown. As soon as the brown colour appears, stop applying the heat to the aluminium. The aluminium can be cooled quickly by quenching in cold water. The brown soft soap should easily wash away. After the aluminium has been wiped dry in a cloth, it is soft and ready for further work.

Other metals such as *gilding material* also respond to annealing treatment, and you are advised to check the details of the process for each material that is to be annealed.

ANODISING

Most metals *corrode* and for some metals, such as iron or mild steel, a protective coating (e.g. a lead-based paint) has to be used to prevent rusting. However some metals, such as aluminium, have a very slow rate of corroding due to a surface film of oxide. The thickness of this protective layer can be increased by an electrolytic process to improve the metal's resistance to corrosion. The process is called *anodising.*

The process can be done either in a school workshop or science laboratory. A piece of work, constructed in aluminium, is suspended in a tank containing a solution of sulphuric acid, sodium sulphate and water electrolyte. With two *cathodes* also suspended in the solution, a DC electric current is passed through the solution. For practical purposes, a 12V car battery can be used. The cathode connected to the negative terminal of the battery is a sheet of lead (two cathodes help to produce an even layer of oxide). The *anode* is the piece of work in question and this is connected to the positive terminal (Fig A.6).

The current is supplied at a rate of approximately 2 amps. For a piece of work with a surface area similar to half this page this process may take

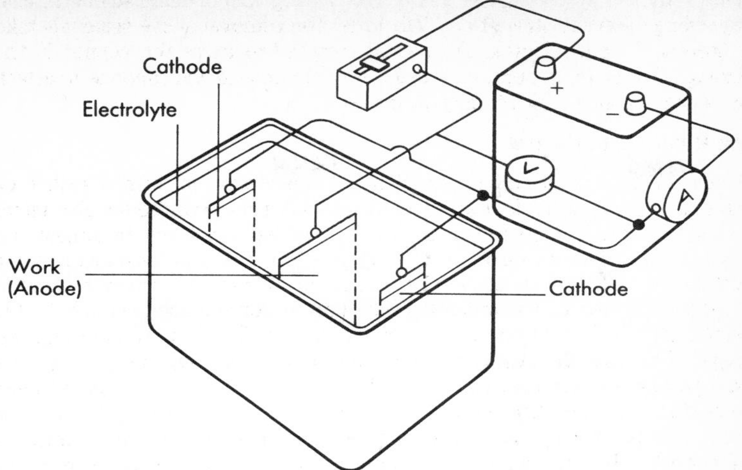

Fig A.6 Anodising

approximately 45 minutes. The newly anodised layer, which may be many hundred times thicker than the original layer, is porous, but can be sealed by placing the work in boiling water. This converts the oxide into its monohydrate, $Al_2O_3H_2O$, which, being bulkier, fills in the pores.

However, the newly-anodised layer in its porous state allows dyes to be used, so that a coloured surface finish is achieved. By impregnating the porous film with silver halides, a plate of aluminium can be used as a photographic plate, or in printing processes.

ANTHROPOMETRICS

This word is make up of two words; *anthropos* meaning man and *metrics* meaning measurement. Man measurement is therefore concerned with the size of man. In more practical terms this really means human beings, so *anthropometrics* is to do with the measurement of small children through to adulthood, whether male or female.

Knowing the average size of humans means that artefacts can be made to a size that is appropriate for the user. The proportion and size of a chair, table, car, hand drill, hammer, spoon, etc. are all influenced by the size of human beings. It is helpful to know both the space occupied by a human and the space required to work or perform specific functions when designing a room, or a piece of equipment such as a desk or work station. Such information is available and can be obtained from publications such as; *'Anthropometrics' An introduction for schools and colleges,* by S.T. Pheasant, published by the British Standards Institution, PP7310.

A 1/10 scale model known as a 'manikin' is also helpful when designing artefacts. ◀ Manikin ▶

ANVIL

The most commonly known anvil is perhaps the Blacksmith's Anvil (Fig A.7). The anvil essentially provides a working surface on which a metal worker can bend, shape and form metal. Gold and silversmiths also use very much smaller anvils. The work surface of a micrometer is also known as an anvil.

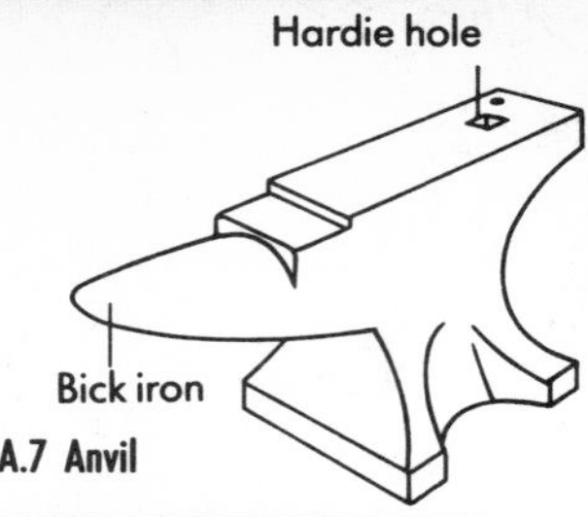

Fig A.7 Anvil

APPRAISAL

Appraisal is another word meaning 'to make judgements'. It is similar to **evaluation** in which you also make one or more judgements about a product or a process. To say that a product does the job *well,* you are saying that it is *satisfactory.* If you say that it is doing its job *very well,* you are saying that it is *more than satisfactory.* Similarly, you may wish to say that it is *not doing the job very well,* in which case you are saying that it is *not satisfactory.* Other appraisals could include varying levels of excellence or weakness.

For an appraisal to be really valuable to you in an examination or coursework project you should always state a *reason or reasons* why you believe that the product is, or is not, doing its job well.

◀ Evaluation, Aesthetics ▶

ARC

In geometric terms, an arc is a curved line that forms part of a circle. It is usually smaller than the circumference of a semi-circle. Arcs are drawn with the aid of a compass when constructing geometric shapes. In electrical terms, an arc is a luminous discharge that occurs when an electric current flows between two electrodes that are separated by a small gap.

◀ Arc-welding, Circle, Construction ▶

ARC-WELDING

Arc-welding is a process used to join metals. The heat necessary to melt the welding rod and to melt the surface of the pieces of metal to be joined is obtained electrically. A transformer is used to increase the amperage (i.e. increase the flow of current) so that an electrical arc is obtained when the welding rod (which is connected via a lead to one terminal of the transformer) is brought near to the work (which is connected via a lead to the other terminal of the transformer) (Fig A.8).

The arc provides enough heat to melt the rod and the surface of the work. It also produces a very strong light, so it is necessary for the user to wear very dark goggles. The brightness of the arc and the rays given off can be harmful to the eyes if the correct goggles are not worn. Protection for other people nearby is also necessary and this is why arc-welding is either done behind a

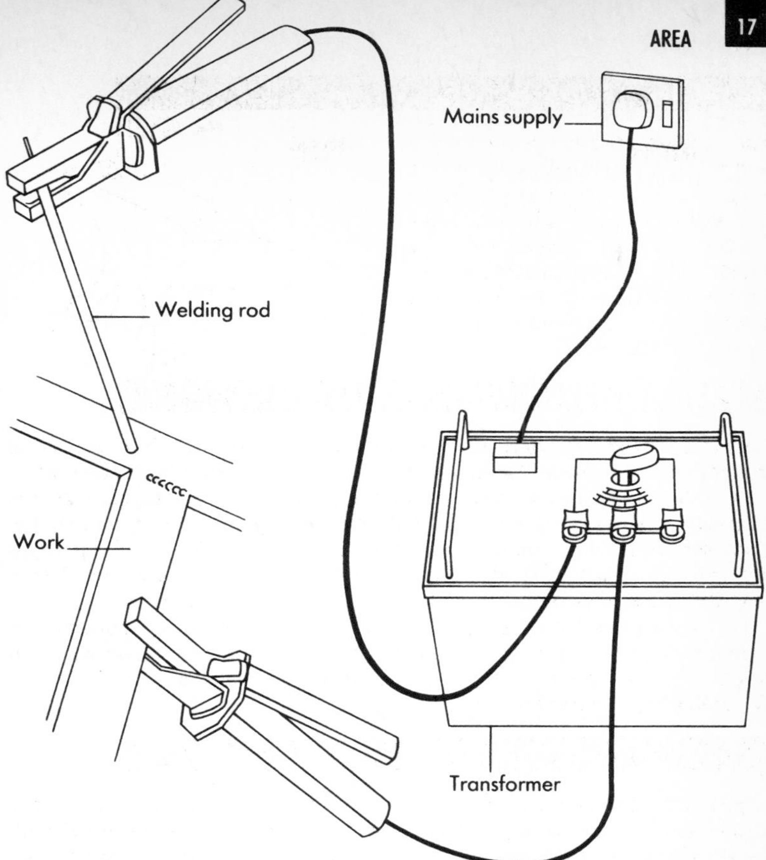

Fig A.8 Arc welding

protective screen or in a protective welding booth. 'Arc eye' is often the result of exposure to too much of this light. It is very painful and feels as though sand has been thrown in your eyes. In severe cases, temporary blindness is caused.

Arc-welding is especially useful for joining iron or steel. Little or no preparation is necessary to the surfaces and the process is fairly quick.

AREA

Area is the measurement of a surface. To calculate an area of basic shape (e.g. Rectangle, Parallelogram, Triangle, and Circle) it is necessary to know two dimensions or one dimension and a formula (Fig A.9).

Another method of finding areas is to change the more complicated shape into a simple shape with equal area, such as a rectangle into a square (Fig A.10); *or* a triangle into a rectangle (Fig A.11) *or* a polygon into a triangle (Fig A.12).

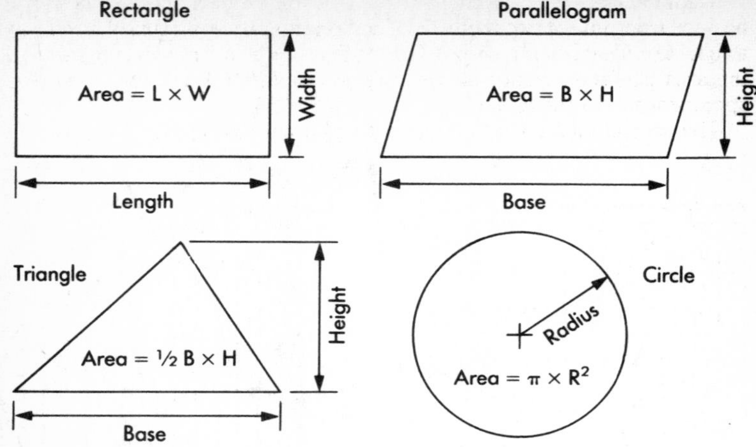

Fig A.9 Area

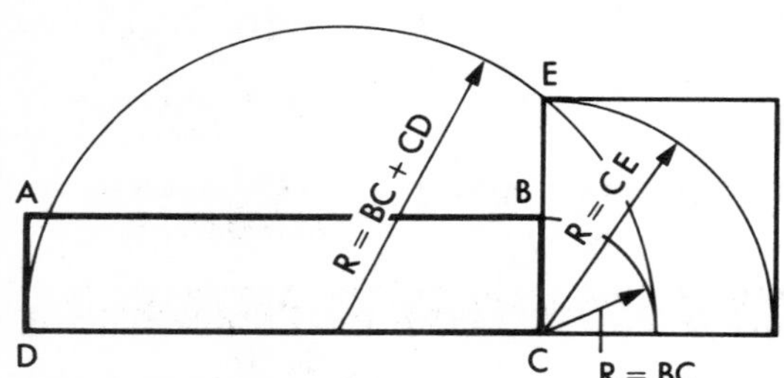

Fig A.10 Changing a rectangle into a square

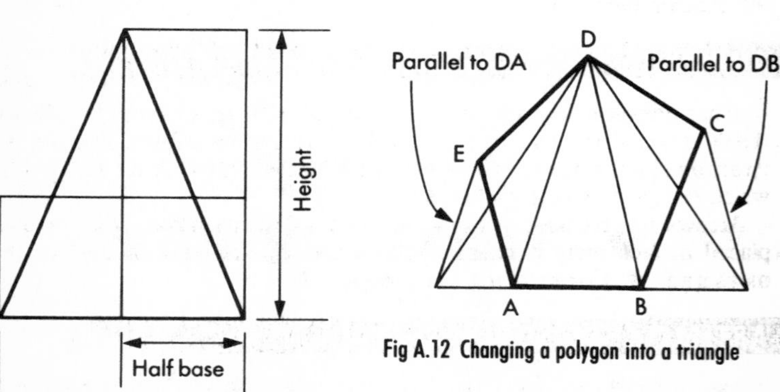

Fig A.11 Changing a triangle into a rectangle

Fig A.12 Changing a polygon into a triangle

Graphical methods of finding out an area with very complicated shapes can be done using one of two methods. The first method is to count the squares of a suitable grid laid over a shape. The number of *whole squares* contained within the area plus the number of *half squares divided by 2* will give you a close approximation to the area of the shape (Fig A.13).

The second method is to construct mid-ordinates (Fig A.14).

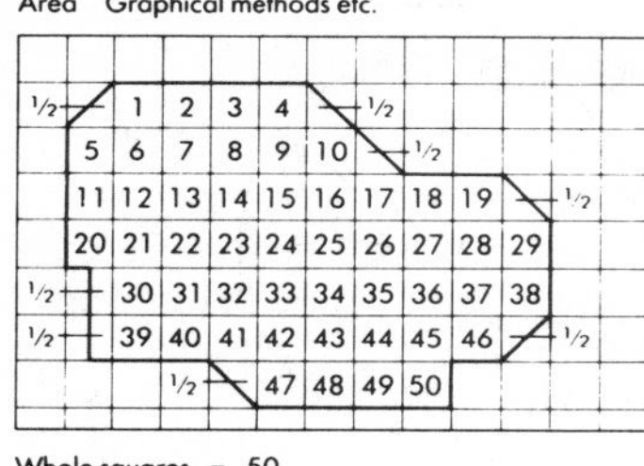

Area Graphical methods etc.
Whole squares = 50
Half squares = 8 ÷ 2 = 4
Total = 54 squares
If one square = 1 cm × 1 cm
Area of shape = 54 square cms

Fig A.13 Approximate area measured by grid

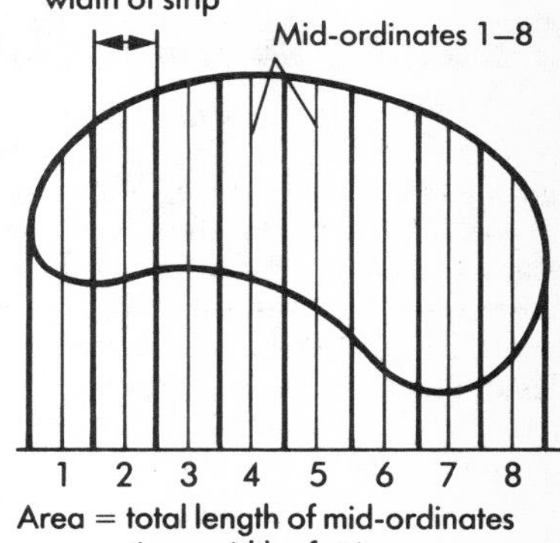

width of strip

Area = total length of mid-ordinates times width of strip

Fig A.14 Approximate area measured by mid-ordinates

ARMATURE

The central moving part of a dynamo or electric motor is called an armature. It usually has a coil of wire wound on a core of iron that is free to rotate.
◀ Electric motor ▶

ARROW

In most graphical language an arrow indicates the direction to be followed or the direction of a moving object. In a *flow diagram* the arrow indicates the next direction to go, while in a diagram of a *gear train* it can indicate the direction in which the gear wheels will rotate.

Arrows are also used to show the *end* of a dimension line. When arrows are placed at *both* ends it indicates the length of the edge or surface that is measured. ◀ Conventions, Line, Vector ▶

ARTIFICIAL SEASONING

In the artificial seasoning of wood, the timber is stacked in kilns and an artificial means is used to control the temperature, moisture content and flow of air. The process is very quick and is commonly used.
◀ Natural seasoning ▶

ASSESSMENT

To assess a situation is to estimate the amount of progress that has been made. This may apply to the particular project you are working on, or to your course as a whole. A *written assessment* is a record of such estimates that can be logged in your Design Folio, or it can be a written record of your personal progress. The 'personal progress' assessment is very important and helps to determine the grade you will get in a subject.

ATOM

The atom was at one time believed to be the smallest particle on earth. The atom is *not* solid. It is made up of space in which electrons are constantly moving. This movement is extremely rapid and forms a 'cloud' of electrical charge which is visible under a very powerful microscope in the form of light. The movement of the electrons gives an impression that the atom is a small 'ball'. At the centre of each atom is a *nucleus* which contains the *protons* which give it a positive electrical charge. It is this positive charge that stops the electrons (which have a negative charge) from flying away (Fig A.15).

Hydrogen is the simplest atom. It has one electron and a nucleus which has one proton. *Carbon* has six electrons and a nucleus which has six protons. More complicated atoms include *Uranium*, which has 92 electrons and a nucleus which contains 92 protons.

Though there is still much more to learn about the atom, if you understand what has been written here you will have a sufficient depth of understanding for the 'Technology' strand of C.D.T. ◀ **Elements, Protons** ▶

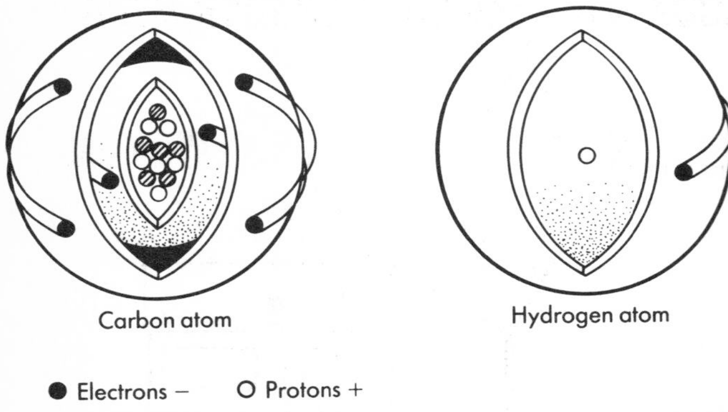

Fig A.15 Atoms

AUDIBLE

That which can be heard.

AUDIO

The reproduction or production of sound. Recordings in the form of tape, disc, etc, when played on the appropriate audio equipment *reproduce* the sounds that are stored. Equipment used in alarm systems, in electronic circuits such as micro-wave ovens, in computer key-boards, etc, also *produces* sound to draw the attention of the user so that he/she can take the appropriate action.

AUTOMATIC CIRCUITS

In a *pneumatic* circuit, when the air is switched on, a double acting cylinder produces a reciprocating movement until the air supply is switched off. This is done by having a plunger or push button switch, which, when a cylinder becomes positive (outward stroke), strikes the button which sends a pressure signal to a pressure-sensitive valve. The piston then goes negative (inward stroke) and strikes a roller-trip operated 3-port valve. This sends a signal to the pressure-sensitive valve and the reciprocating movement is repeated.

Automated circuits can include both pneumatic and *electrical* circuits, which require microswitches and solenoid-operated valves.

AUTOMATIC RECIPROCATION

Automatic control circuits are used where a repeated backward and forward (reciprocation) movement is required. Such functions as stamping, sawing, sanding, etc. are all examples of **reciprocating** movements. When such movements operate continuously, without the help or interference of a human being, the system is said to be *fully automated.* ◀ Automatic circuits ▶

AUXILIARY VIEWS

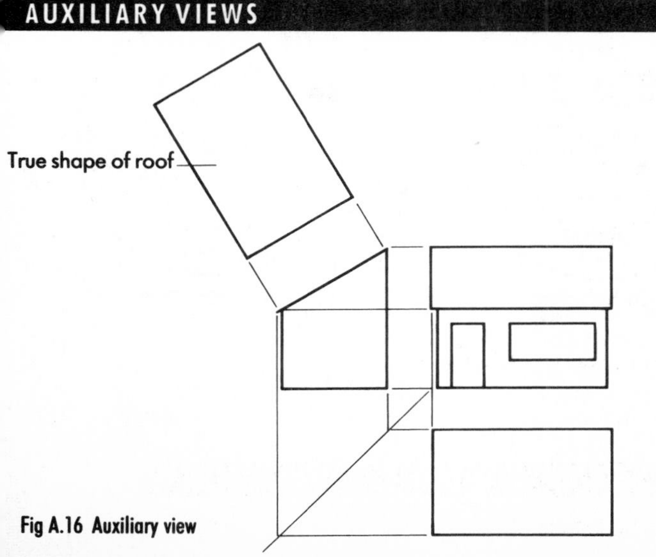

Fig A.16 Auxiliary view

Most **Orthographic Projection** drawings are able to provide all the information that is necessary in two or three views, i.e. side view, front view, front view and plan. If, however, a true shape of one of the surfaces *cannot* be obtained by using these views, then an extra or auxiliary view can be projected from the views already drawn (Fig A.16).

AXIS

An axis is a line about which a geometric figure is constructed. Where more than one axis is required, the larger axis is called a *major* axis and the smaller axis is called the *minor* axis. This is shown in the construction of an ellipse.

AXLE

In practical terms, an axle is a round bar to which wheels may be attached at either end (Fig A.17). The method of attachment will be influenced by the design of axle that is chosen, i.e. fixed or free to rotate. If a *fixed* design is chosen, then the wheels must be free to rotate on the axle. If a *free running axle* is chosen, then the wheels must be fixed firmly so that they do not rotate. Remember, a free running axle with free running wheels will not produce a drive forward or backwards. It is even more obvious that a fixed axle and fixed wheels will not work.

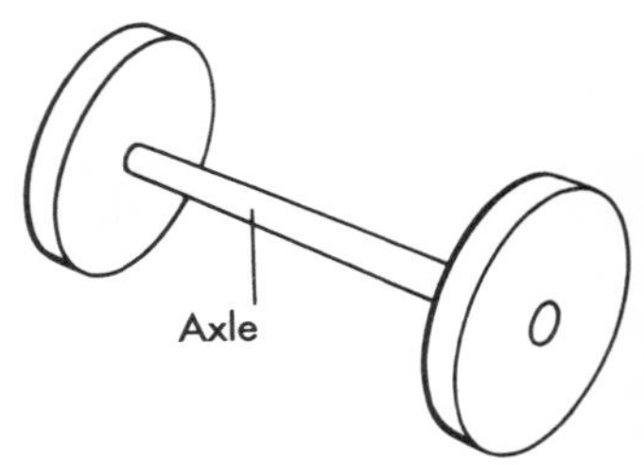

Fig A.17 Axle

AXONOMETRIC PROJECTION

An Axonometric Projection is used to produce a three-dimensional image of an object. The most commonly used is **Isometric Projection**. There are two other types known as *Dimetric* and *Trimetric*, but these are much less well known and not often used except in sketching (Fig A.18).

Though these types of projection show three views of an object, the drawing will appear distorted. This is because in real life, things that are near to you *appear* larger than those of the same height or length that are further away. This foreshortening effect is not allowed for in Axonometric Projection. In the three illustrations in Fig A.18, you will see that the vertical lines are of *equal length*. The lines near to you are the same length as those that are further away from you. For those who find **perspective** drawing too difficult, Axonometric Projection is an excellent alternative method of drawing in three dimensions.

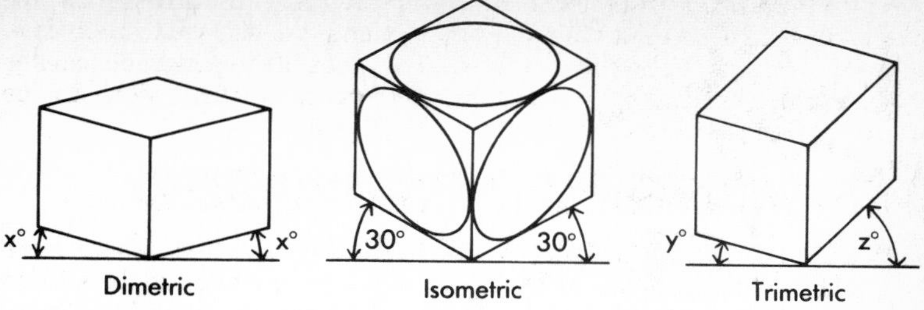

Fig A.18 Axonometric projection

BALANCE

In general terms, balance is to do with things that are equal. When one weight or load on a beam is the same as another load, and the loads are an equal distance from the fulcrum, they are said to be *in balance*, or *in equilibrium*. When looking at a structure it can look in balance; this is especially true of symmetrical shapes. The one half is the same as the other half.

In electrical circuitry, instruments and bridges are used to obtain a balanced state. ◄ **Symmetry** ►

BALLOON DIAGRAMS

These are used to present thoughts that stem from a central problem or condition (Fig B.1).

The balloon diagram is a very useful method of presenting thoughts that come from a **brain storming** session.

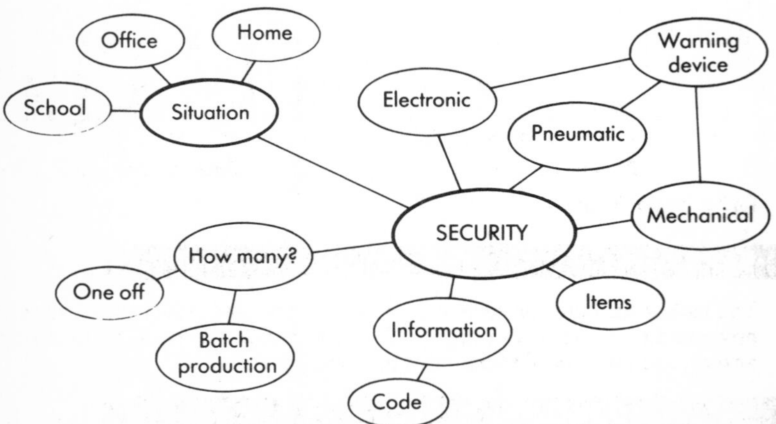

Fig B.1 Balloon diagrams

BAR

The bar is a unit of measurement for air pressure. One bar is approximately the same as atmospheric pressure i.e. 14.72 pounds per square inch, 0.1 Newtons per square millimetre, or 1.03 kilograms per square centimetre. Low pressures are measured in *millibars,* i.e. one thousandth of a bar.

BAR CHARTS/GRAPHS

Bar charts are used to graphically represent figures. Instead of having to plough through lots and lots of figures to understand the information being conveyed, a bar chart can convey the information simply and quickly in visual form. It is particularly useful for showing comparisons.

For instance, a bar chart illustrating the quantities of rainfall for each month of a year can quickly show the months in which there was heavy rainfall, as opposed to those in which there was little rain. The actual quantities can be read from the vertical side of the chart and the months can be read from the bottom line of the chart (Fig B.2).

These bar charts can be *coloured* to make the information stand out from the paper. A second way of adding to the appearance is to draw *three dimensional* bars and to add the appropriate tones to show one side receiving most light and another side in shadow. Remember that the importance of a chart is to *communicate information clearly and easily,* so only use colouring and shading techniques that will assist in this function.

◀ Organisation chart ▶

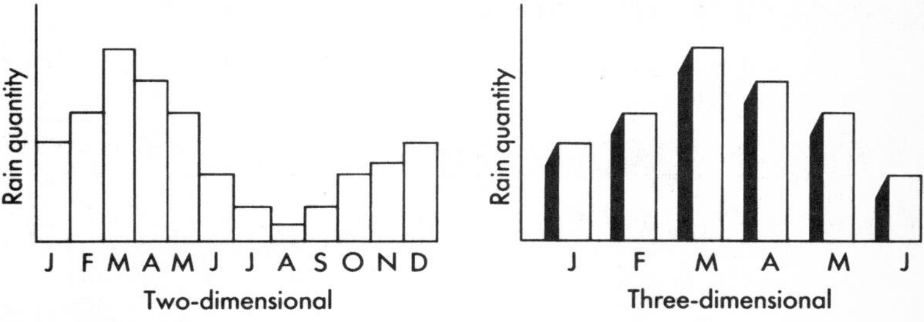

Fig B.2 Bar chart/graph

BARK

The bark is the outer protective layer of the trunk and branches of a tree. It protects the growing cells from the frost and damage that could be caused by animals and man. ◀ Cellular structure ▶

BATCH PRODUCTION

When an artefact is being designed it is helpful to know whether one or more artefacts are to be produced. If it is known that a batch of ten identical artefacts are to be produced, then an appropriate process can be chosen. The important factors that will need to be considered in batch production are:

a) that all the items produced are identical;
b) the type of jigs, moulds, etc. that will be necessary to ensure that all the artefacts are similar in size and form;
c) how to use time and materials economically.

Most *moulding processes*, such as injection moulding, blow moulding and vacuum forming, and *casting processes* such as sand casting, resin casting, and investment casting, are processes by which the production of *identical forms* can be achieved. Once a mould is made (except for the sand casting process), the process can be repeated many times without the need to make a fresh mould. So when you are assessing how economically time is being used, it is necessary to take into consideration how long it would take *to make a mould.* An example might be the production of wheels for a small toy. To produce a batch number of *ten* wheels in nylon using injection moulding techniques would not be an economical use of time and material. This is because it would take much longer to make the metal mould on the lathe than it would to either use a hole saw on a drilling machine, or a parting tool on a bar of nylon on a centre lathe. However, if the batch number was between *50 and 100* then, because the injection moulding process is quite simple and quick, it could be economical to spend time making the metal mould. So details such as the time needed to make the mould, the number in the batch, etc, have to be considered when selecting an appropriate process. They should be clearly stated in any project or answer to questions in a technology examination.

BATTEN

A batten is a narrow strip of timber. It is generally used to provide added support. Battens are used to hold the roofing felt in position on a roof.

BATTERY

A battery is a dry cell that will produce a Direct Current supply. For many projects in which DC electric motors are used it is necessary to have a 6 to 9 volt supply, but for smaller motors a 1 to 5 volt supply is more than enough.

Some batteries are rechargeable and although the initial cost is higher than for a non-rechargeable one, their life is considerably longer. Because of the constant demand for using batteries in school projects, many schools prefer to use the rechargeable type since *the cost per unit of use* is much more economical.

BEAM

A beam is a piece of material used to support a load. It is important that the *material* be suitable for withstanding the particular load, so considerable care should be taken to select the appropriate type and form that the material should take. A beam under a *downward load* will have to withstand a *compression force on the upper surface* and a *tension force on the under surface.*

However, along the central axis of the beam there should be little or no forces acting upon it. The design of a beam should be such that the bulk of the material should be in the positions where the forces are greatest with as little material as possible where the forces are minimal or non-existent. In order to make a beam as light as possible, material can be removed along the line of the **neutral axis.** The 'I' section girder is an excellent example of a design for a beam. The material is thick at the top and the bottom where it is needed most, and thin where it is needed least of all. ◀ **Neutral axis** ▶

BEARINGS

Bearings are designed to reduce the friction between moving surfaces. Remember *friction* is a resistance to movement, and the greater the load to be moved the greater the resistance there will be to movement. The ancient Egyptians were well aware of this when moving the massive stones used to build the pyramids. Though many hundreds of slaves were available to move the stones, it was soon appreciated that the use of logs as rolling bearings would mean that far fewer slaves would be required to move the stones, with the movement much smoother and quicker. In mechanical terms this means that *far less effort* was required to move a load, and the system was more *mechanically efficient.* Today, *roller bearings* work on the same principle but are precision mechanisms.

TYPES OF BEARING

There are *four* types of bearing that you are likely to have to recognise and know how they should be used. If you can say *why* they are suitable for a particular application, so much the better. The four types are Plain, Ball, Roller and Thrust.

Plain bearing

A plain bearing is the simplest mechanism. It consists of a bronze sleeve in a metal casing. Bronze is noted for its low level of friction, i.e. it feels slippery. Today, *nylon* is used in plain bearings and is a cheaper material than bronze. Plain nylon bearings are used where cost is low. Work takes place in cool conditions and a lubricant such as oil is not essential.

Ball bearings

Ball journal bearings are precision made. They consist of an *inner race* which fits on a shaft, and an *outer race* which keeps the steel ball bearings in a cage (Fig B.3). To reduce metal fatigue and to increase the working life of a bearing, a lubricant must be used, either oil or grease. Ball bearings are mainly used in light precision mechanisms such as power drills, the turn-table of a music centre, bicycle hubs, etc.

Roller bearings

Roller bearings are similar to ball bearings in that they are precision made, have an inner and outer race, a cage and require lubrication (Fig B.4). They differ in that they can carry greater loads, but are generally more expensive.

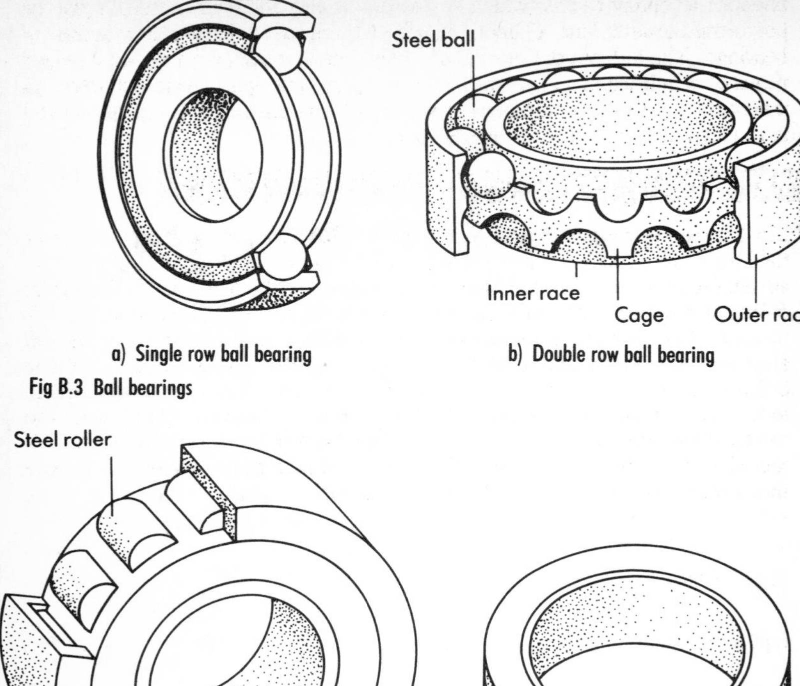

a) Single row ball bearing

b) Double row ball bearing

Fig B.3 Ball bearings

Fig B.4 Roller journal bearing

Fig B.5 Thrust bearing

As a result they are to be found in heavy machinery, such as the wheel hubs of cars, gear boxes, centre lathes, etc.

Thrust bearings

Thrust bearings are designed to carry the same type of loads as those already described, i.e. a load that is at a right angle and radial to the axis of a shaft. However, they can also carry loads that are *not* at right angles to a shaft. To withstand this sideways thrust, the roller bearings are tapered (Fig B.5). They are mainly used in car wheel hubs.

Today there has been considerable development in the variety of *plastic* materials. This has allowed the application of bearings to be extended and improvements to be made in the design of artefacts. Such materials as phenolic or epoxy resins (which are usually reinforced with a fibre), nylon or polytetrafluoroethylene (Teflon or PTFE) are used in the production of bearings. These have the advantage over metal bearings in that they do *not* require a lubricant. This means that they are particulary suitable in mechanisms that come into contact with food, so such bearings are often used in modern food processors, egg whisks, etc.

BELTS

Most drive systems in machines include a belt and a **pulley**. The function of the belt is to transfer the motion of the *driver pulley* to the *driven pulley*. The advantage of the belt system over a **sprocket** is that the belt will slip if *too great a load* is placed at the working end of the machine. The *slipping action* will mean that no damage is then done to the machine and the working end will stop working. Think of a drilling machine where the working end is the drill drilling into a piece of steel. If the drill bit is a large one, quite considerable force can be applied to the lever that lowers the drill bit as it cuts through the metal. If too great a force is applied, either the drill bit will break or the belt will slip on the pulley. Though this situation should not really occur, it does mean that a safety factor has been built into the system.

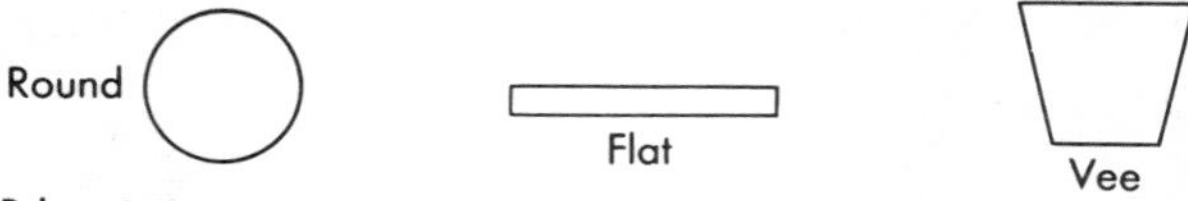

Fig B.6 Belt sections

There are *round, flat* and *vee* section belts (Fig B.6). The important thing is that the type of belt must be appropriate for the type of pulley system being used. The *vee belt and pulley* system means that the belt is continually running in a groove and it is difficult for it to come off the pulley. By contrast the flat belt can slip sideways and come off a flat pulley, perhaps because the belt was too slack or the pulleys were not in line. The vee pulley also allows for a larger surface contact between belt and pulley, so improving the quality of grip. The most common application of the vee belt and pulley system can be found on drilling machines and centre lathes in the school workshops and on the water cooling fans in cars. ◀ Pulleys ▶

BEND

This is a property of a limited number of materials. When a force is applied to a material it will be either flexible and bend or rigid and remain unmoved.

Bending wood

Most woods have a low level of flexibility and for bends of 90 degrees and over it is necessary for the wood to be made soft and flexible. This can be done by *steam bending* or by cutting the timber into thin slices so that they are thin enough to bend without breaking. The thin slices (f209lamina) can be bonded together using an *adhesive* and a *bending former* to achieve a bent form (Fig

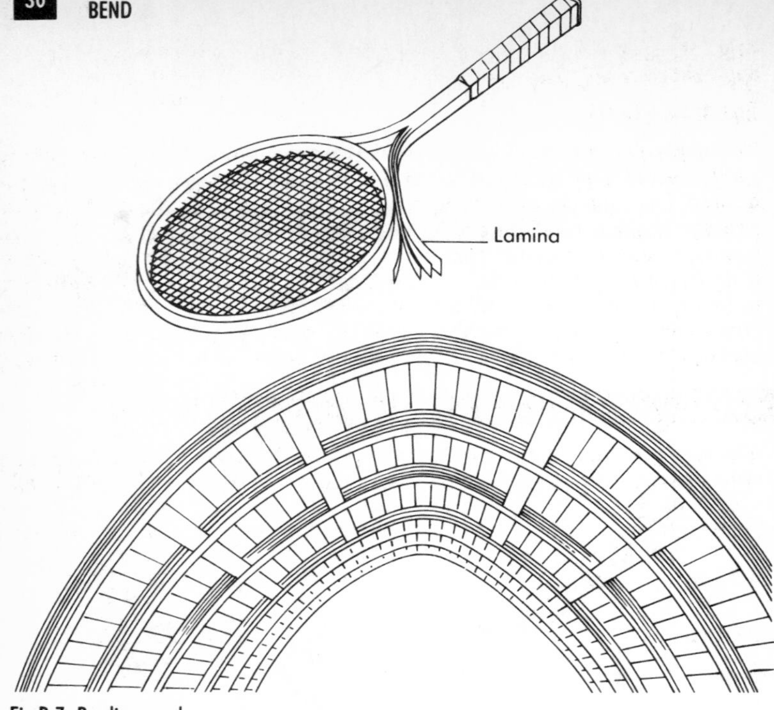

Fig B.7 Bending wood

B.7). However some timbers are not sufficiently pliable for even the lamina to bend. In this case it may be necessary to make the timbers more pliable by soaking them in steam before attempting to bend them in a bending former. Bent forms in timber using this process can be seem in chairs, tennis rackets, modern roof structures, etc.

Some timber such as ash and willow are quite flexible and can be easily bent. But to make them *keep* their bent form, as in a walking stick or hockey stick, the timber needs to be soaked in steam, placed in a bending former and allowed to cool and dry. The principle here is that the wooden fibres are bonded together by a substance that becomes soft and fluid when hot and moist, so that they are able to slide over each other when they have been forced to form a curved shape. On cooling, the substance sets again and locks the fibres into the curved position.

Bending metal

The molecular structure of most *metals* often means that they are more flexible than timber. Even so, before some metals are bent it is necessary for them to be **annealed** (softened). *Small section* material can often be bent cold, but *larger section* material may need heating to red heat before bending can take place (e.g. mild steel and wrought iron).

Aluminium is a soft material that, when annealed, bends very easily while cold. It must not be heated because of its low melting point, which is approximately 660 degrees Celsius.

Bending plastics

Thermoplastics also bend easily, but for a curvature to be permanent it is gently heated over an electric strip heater along the line where the bend is desired. Once the plastic feels pliable (ready to bend) the material can be bent into the position required and held until it has cooled; this will only take approximately one minute. Then the pressure can be released and the plastic material will keep its new shape. If the bend is reheated, the plastic will return to its original flat state. This property is called 'elastic memory'. The most commonly used thermoplastic material is *Acrylic*, and this process is often applied in the production of small stands, book rests, photograph holders, etc.

BEVEL

A bevel is the meeting of two inclined planes. Examples can be found in a sliding bevel, a bevel edged chisel, bevel gear, bevel gauge etc. (Fig B.8).

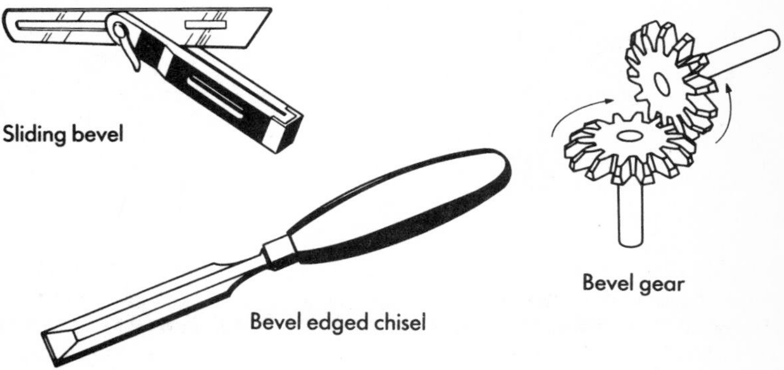

Fig B.8 Bevels

BIBLIOGRAPHY

The bibliography is a *list* of the books you have used to obtain your information for a project. Whenever you are engaged in **secondary** research (reading work that someone else has produced), it is helpful to know *where* the information came from. Should you wish to check a piece of information, you can then easily find its source from your list. Examiners like to see a Bibliography because it tells them a little about how widely you have read.

BICK IRON

This is the main working part of an anvil. It is believed that the name 'bick' came from the word 'beak' because the bick iron looks like the beak of a bird.

◀ Anvil ▶

BIMETALLIC STRIP

The bimetallic strip is made by welding together two metals that have a different **coefficient of linear expansion** (i.e. one expands more than the other when heated by the same amount). When such a bimetallic strip is heated the strip is forced to bend. In our example, the side made of copper will expand the most and cause the strip to curve towards the brass, the side that will expand least (Fig B.9).

Bimetallic strips are commonly used in room thermostats in central heating systems. The bimetallic strip forms part of the electric circuit. As the temperature in the room rises, so the bimetallic strip bends *away from* the electrical contact, cutting off the power supply to the system. When the temperature in the room drops, the bimetallic strip bends *towards* the electrical contact and completes the circuit again, so switching on the heating system. This principle of temperature control can be applied to many projects involving the maintenance of set temperatures, e.g. heating a greenhouse or small propagating units.

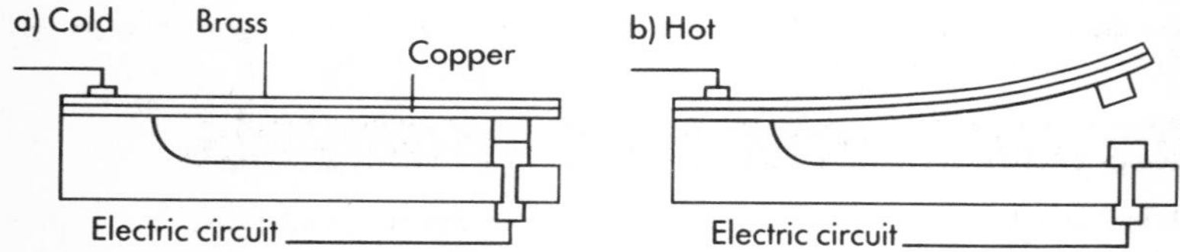

Fig B.9 Bimetallic strip

BINARY

A system of using only two numbers, 0 and 1 is called a binary system. The system uses a yes/no principle. A 1 indicates a 'yes' and a 0 indicates a 'no'. The binary system can be used to show the presence or absence of certain decimal numbers. The numbers 1, 2, 4, 8, 16, 32 are shown below:

32	16	8	4	2	1		
0	0	0	0	0	1	=	1
0	0	0	0	1	0	=	2
0	0	0	1	0	0	=	4
0	0	1	0	0	0	=	8
0	1	0	0	0	0	=	16
1	0	0	0	0	0	=	32

The binary number 110101 equals the decimal number 53
(32 + 16 + 4 + 1) = 53

Using this system enables a counting system to be punched on paper tape. the tape can then be fed into a computer. The punched hole represents a 1 or 'yes', and the space, where no hole exists, represents a 0 or 'no':

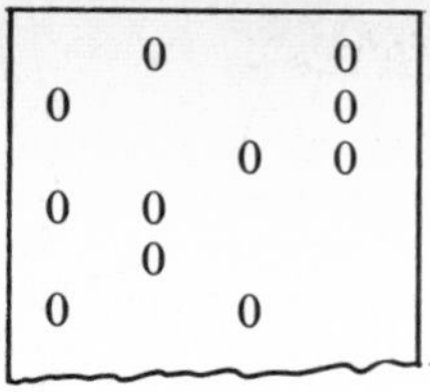

	0		0
0			0
		0	0
0	0		
	0		
0		0	

no	yes	no	yes	0101	=	5
yes	no	no	yes	1001	=	9
no	no	yes	yes	0011	=	3
yes	yes	no	no	1100	=	12
no	yes	no	no	0100	=	4
yes	no	yes	no	1010	=	10
						43

Punched tape

The tape could then be used in the electronic digital computer.

BINARY BITS

The digits 1 and 0 of the binary system are known as 'bits'. Computers are capable of storing 'bits' but the 1 and 0 here are referring to the ability to pass or not to pass a pulse of an electric current in an electronic circuit. A group of approximately 8 'bits' are known as a 'byte', and the storage capacity of a computer is measured in 'bytes'. The letter K is used to indicate 1000 so 2K 'bytes' means approximately 2000 bytes. ◀ Nibble ▶

BIODEGRADABLE

When *plastics* were first developed as a material for general use they were seen as almost indestructible. They did not rust like metals and they did not rot or decay like wood. They were seen as a material that could *not* be recycled like glass or paper. So the problem of disposing of the millions of used plastic containers, bottles and bags every year was seen as a serious environmental issue. As a result, many of the plastic bags and other containers that have a short, useful life have been developed so that they will decay and break down when attacked by microorganisms. This *biodegradable* property helps avoid the problem of creating mountains of unwanted plastic materials.

BIO-TECHNOLOGY

Bio-technology looks at *biological* (plant and animal life) and *technological* (mechanical, electronic, control systems) areas of study *together*, to see how they can be related and so assist in future technological development. The technological approach to the propogation of certain plant forms (such as algae/bacteria), and to providing natural colouring in a food chain are just two areas of study.

It is also the title of a module set by one of the Regional Examining Groups, namely the Welsh Joint Education Committee (W.J.E.C.)

BIRD'S EYE VIEW

This term could not be more explicit. It means to view something from a

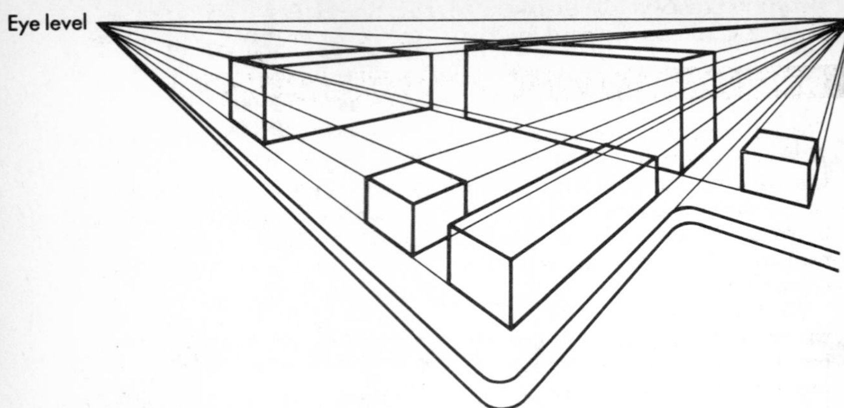

Fig B.10 A bird's eye view

height. You could imagine flying in a hot air balloon which drifts slowly at a height of several hundred feet over a city and think what might be seen from this position. This can of course be done today, but before aerial photographs could be taken, an artist had to *imagine* what could be seen in order to draw a 'bird's eye view'. If you are required to draw a bird's eye view of a future development for a dockland area or a derelict site, you will need to have a knowledge of two point perspective and an ability to present your ideas graphically (Fig B.10).

BISECT

Bisect means to cut in half. The term is most commonly associated with the bisection of lines and angles. Though it is possible to use a *ruler* to divide the length of a line by two, or a *protractor* to measure the degrees of an angle and divide by two, you are expected to do the bisection of each by **construction**. This means using a compass and drawing a series of arcs as shown in Fig B.11.

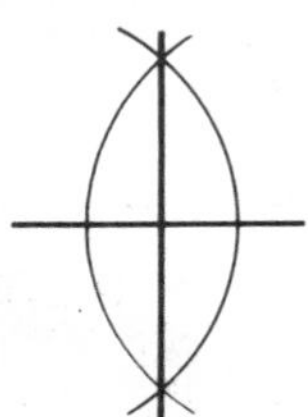

Fig B.11 Bisection of a line

Remember that it is very important that you draw the construction lines clearly (but using a thin line) and leave all construction lines on the diagram. Examiners like to see *how* you constructed the bisection.

BIT

Bit is a general term used to include a variety of drills that have specific names. 'High Speed Jobbers Twist Drill Number 10' is a specific name and detail of a drill bit. Though the term 'bit' can be used, you are advised to be as

specific as possible in the examinations and in the details you offer in projects.
Note: 'Bit' can also be used for binary digit ◀ **Binary bit, Centre bit** ▶

BLOCKBOARD

This is a manufactured board that is available in standard sheets of 2440 mm × 1220 mm, and in varying thicknesses of 12 to 25 mm. *Blockboard* is built up with a core of softwood strips bonded together with an adhesive and covered with a sheet of plywood on either side. *Laminboard* is also a manufactured board and is built up in the same way, except that the softwood strips are narrower. The strips are glued together with the annual rings curving in opposite directions to counteract any warping (Fig B.12).

Blockboard is fairly stable, i.e. it will not warp very much. It can also be used in furniture, though its exposed edges will need lipping (glueing a thin strip of wood to the edge), and the surfaces will need veneering, painting or staining etc.

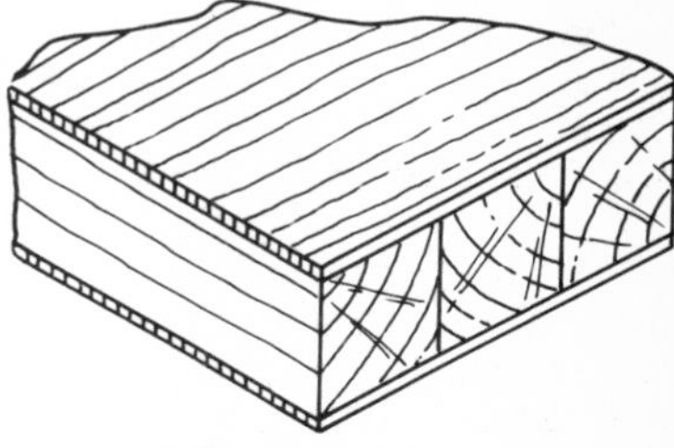

Fig B.12 Blockboard

BLOCK GRAPHICS

This is a form of graphics that has developed since the introduction of computers. However, block graphics can be done using a suitable size grid graph paper. By shading in certain squares, shapes can be achieved even if a curved or angular line appears to be a series of steps. The smaller the grid, the smaller the steps and the smoother and less angular the flow of the curved outline (Fig B.13).

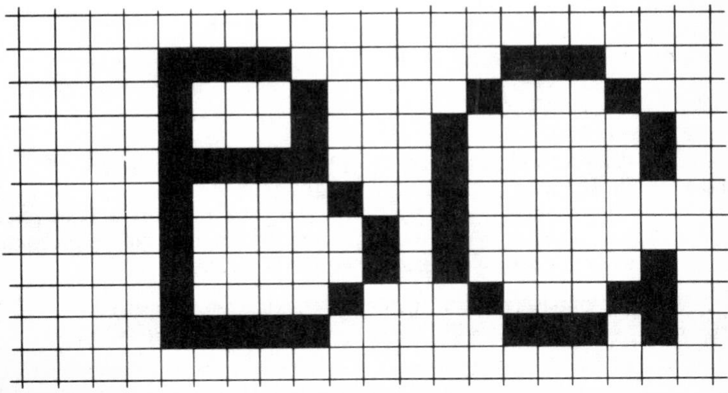

Fig B.13 Block graphics

In a computer it is possible to apply the appropriate code to gain access to the 'blocks' so that shapes and forms can be created on the screen. With a printer, the result can be reproduced on paper. ◀ Graphics ▶

BLOW MOULDING

Some plastic materials can be blown into shape when they are soft. To be able to do this effectively some specialised equipment is necessary. The principles employed in blow moulding are quite simple and are borrowed from the glass blowing industry. When the softened plastic tube is placed in a mould and air is forced into the tube, it expands and takes on the shape of the mould. Most plastic bottles are formed by this process. *Extrusion blowing* and *injection blowing* are two methods used commercially (Fig B.14a and b).

Blow moulding can be done in the school workshop with some basic equipment; an electric oven in which to heat the plastics, a mould and a car foot pump. With a supply of acrylic (thermoplastic) bowls, a range of dishes, food covers, etc can be produced (Fig B.15).

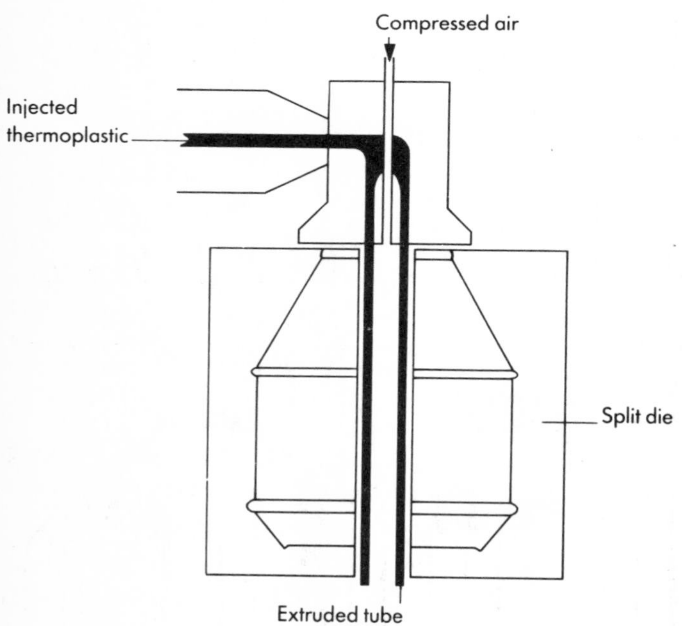

Fig B.14a Blow moulding (extrusion) i) Tube extruded

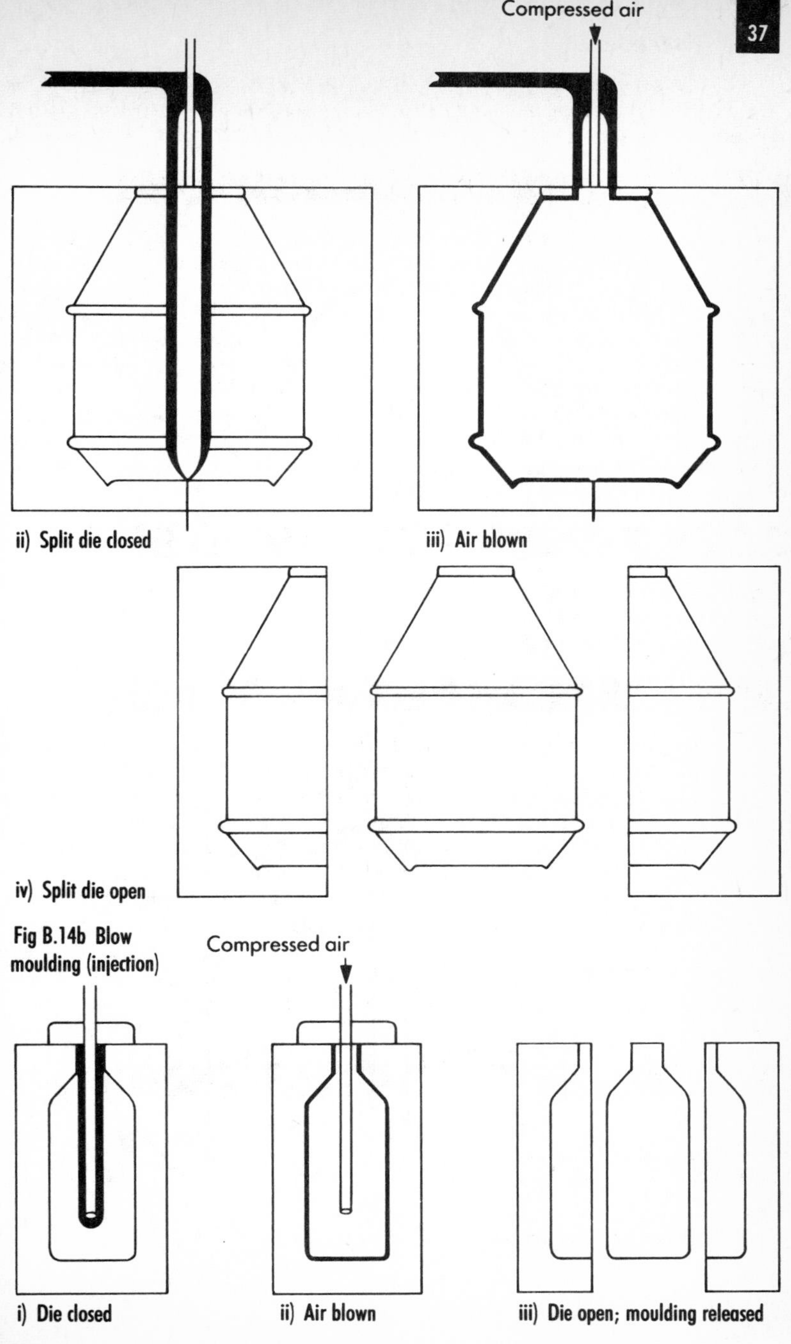

Fig B.14b Blow moulding (injection)

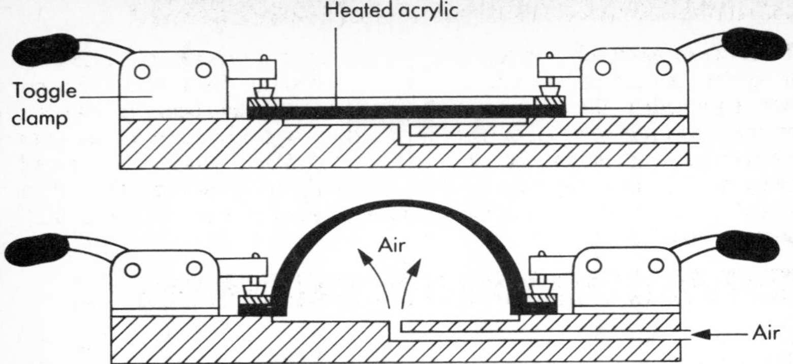

Fig B.15 Blow moulding; using a jig to make bowls

BOARD

Board is a general term used to refer to a large piece of wood. It is next down in size to a 'plank' and next up in size to a 'strip'. Boards are up to 40 mm thick and are available up to 500–600 mm wide.

BONDING

This is the process of holding together. In practical terms, bonding in CDT means the holding together of two pieces of like or unlike materials by using an adhesive. Another situation where bonding is important is in the sand casting process. The grains of *casting sand* (a mixture of fine sand and three per cent clay) need to be held together so that after removing a pattern, a cavity for casting can be formed. The bonding medium here is water. The water and the clay bond the sand grains but have the disadvantage of creating pockets of steam when the hot metal is poured into the cavity. Excessive steam often causes damage to the casting. A commercially prepared oil-bonded sand is preferred, since it has the properties of holding grains together *without* the danger of producing steam during the pouring of molten metal into the cavity of the mould.

BOW'S NOTATION

This a clear method for lettering force diagrams. The letters are printed in the spaces of the diagram (Fig B.16).

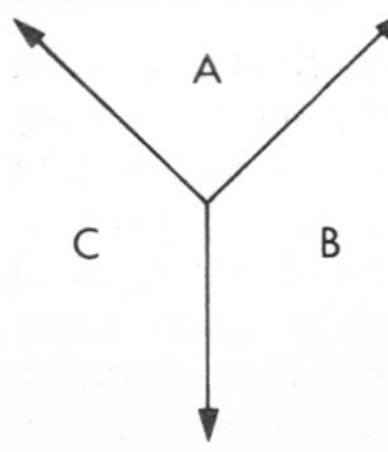

Fig B.16 Bow's notation

BRAIN STORMING

This is a process where a group of people get together to try to develop ideas. It consists of each person writing down a list of ideas. Then, with everyone working together, the ideas are read out to the group and someone makes a complete list. It is helpful if the list can be written on a board or projected onto a screen so that everyone can see it. The 'storm' of ideas should continue until everyone feels that they have no more to contribute. What may start out as 'crazy' ideas are often an excellent stimulus leading to what may eventually become 'good' ideas.

BRAKES

There are a variety of brakes used to stop a mechanical motion. They include disc, drum, pad and shoe brakes which can be either cable or, hydraulically operated. *Cable systems* are used where the energy required to stop a motion is not high, e.g. on a bicycle. *Hydraulically operated systems* are used where the energy required to stop a motion is not high, e.g. on a bicycle. *Hydraulically operated systems* are used where the energy required is high and the human energy has to be amplified in order for the braking system to be effective, e.g. power-assisted braking on a car. The principle of most braking systems is to apply a stationary surface to a moving surface, so that friction between the two will affect the speed of the moving surface. With increased contact pressure the frictional value is increased, further slowing down the motion (Fig B.17).

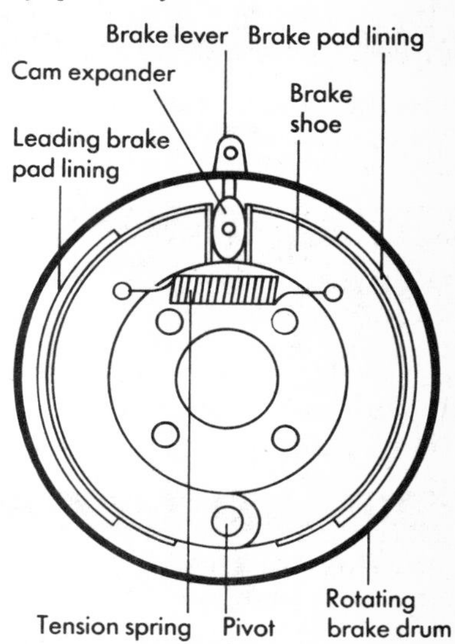

Fig B.17 Drum brake

BRAZING

Brazing is a method or process of joining metals together using a composition of brass as the solder. Brazing is sometimes referred to as a *hard* soldering process. This is to distinguish it from *soft* soldering, where solders such as tin and lead melt at much lower temperatures.

The process of brazing is carried out by first making sure that the surfaces where the join is to take place are clean, and all oxides have been removed. The *brazing rod* or *spelter* must also be clean and free from oxides. A preparation of *borax* is applied to the surfaces to be joined, as well as to the rod or spelter. The area of the join is gently heated with a brazing torch. The borax melts first, 'wetting' the join and creating a barrier between the air and the clean surface of the metal. This prevents any oxides forming and ensures that the metal remains clean throughout the process. If spelter is used, the snippets will be already placed along the join. If a rod is being used, it can be given a final coating of borax and gently warmed in the flame. As the borax melts it can be brought near to the join and heated until the metal and the rod have reached the melting point of the solder. The solder will 'run' as soon as this temperature has been reached. The 'wet' surface of the join will help the solder to run and flow into the join. The heat source is removed and the work allowed to cool. The main application of brazing is joining mild steel. ◀ Soldering ▶

BREADBOARD

These are boards on which electrical circuits are mounted. The layout makes it easy for circuits to be understood and for components to be easily connected and disconnected by using terminal pins (Fig B.18). There are different types of printed circuit boards (pcbs). All have the advantage of being quick and easy to use and do not require components to be soldered in position. The main purpose for these boards is to enable you to *test* a circuit that you have designed for a project on which you are working.

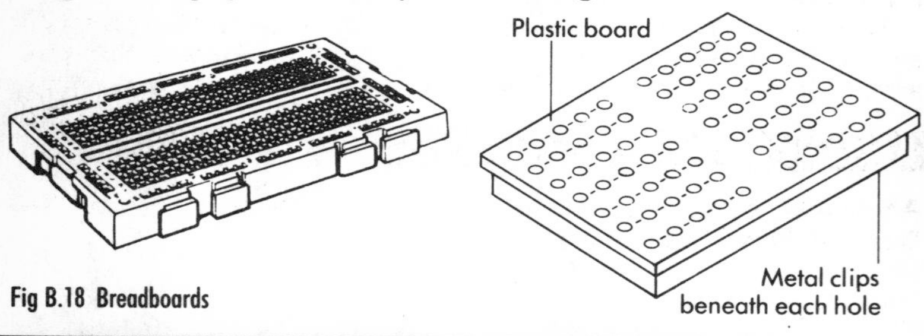

Fig B.18 Breadboards

BRIEF

The term brief is often used as a shorter way of saying **'design brief'**. ◀ Design brief ▶

BRITISH STANDARDS INSTITUTION (BSI)

All products that are produced must be of an acceptable standard before they can be used by the public. The BSI have, over the years, laid down standards that are required to protect the user from poor quality and dangerous goods, e.g. toxic materials in paints, shoddy electrical insulation, inadequate safety standards in the design of toys, outdoor play equipment, playpens, office furniture, etc. The list of publications containing British Standards is very long, but you may have come across BSI Publications related to Engineering Drawing Practice that have the code number pp 7308, or pp 7307. These are about Graphic Symbols. You should also be familiar with such titles as

Compendium of British Standards for Design and Technology in Schools; Anthropometrics, An Introduction for Schools and Colleges, pp 7310; *Construction Drawing Practice for Schools,* pp 7320; and so on.

You cannot be expected to learn everything in these publications. They are *reference* books which you can use. The one area where you may be expected to know and use the information correctly is when communicating through drawing. Correct use of lines, symbols, layouts, dimensioning, etc. is just as important in CDT as being able to use the correct spelling and ordering of words. ◀ PP number publications ▶

BRITTLENESS

Materials have a variety of properties, including the important aspect of *brittleness.* One material that is noted for its brittleness is *glass.* The type of glass used in bottles, drinking glasses, windows, etc., will often shatter into small pieces if hit or dropped. Some *metals* can also be brittle, e.g. cast iron or carbon steel that have not been tempered. Files are made from cast steel, and if these are banged or dropped they will have a tendency to break, and this is true for carbon steel drills as well. In order that these tools are able to cut, it is important that they be hard, but this is often obtained at the expense of being brittle. Materials can however, be *treated* so that they will not break easily, e.g. toughened glass, but the process is costly.

There is a distinction between being tough, hard and brittle. Quite often students get these properties of materials muddled and lose marks when answering questions in an examination. ◀ Toughness, Hardening ▶

BYTE

A byte is eight binary bits of information. One byte equals two 'nibbles' (four 'bits'). ◀ Binary bits, Nibble ▶

CABINET DRAWING/PROJECTION

This refers to a pictorial method of representation that is drawn using a parallel motion or tee square and a 45 degree set square. On the *front view* all lines that are horizontal and vertical on the object will be *drawn* horizontally and vertically. On the *side views* all lines that are horizontal on the object will be drawn at an angle of 45 degrees and half scale. This reduction by half on the side views helps to give the impression of **perspective**, which helps to make the object look more real (Fig C.1).

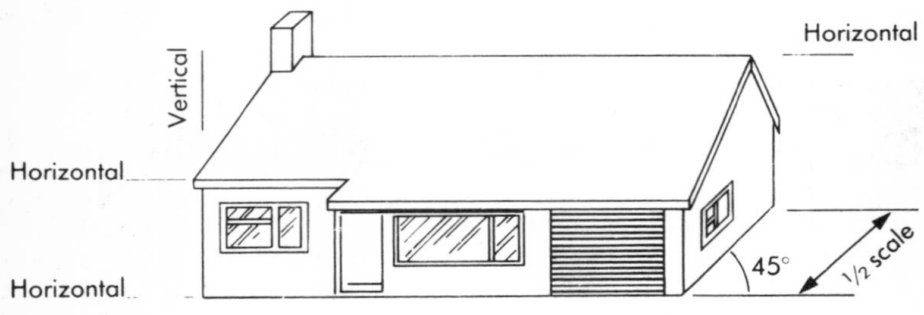

Fig C.1 Cabinet drawing

CALCULATION

Most detail involving size or weight, can be expressed using figures. To determine *sizes* involving gear ratios, forces, speeds, etc., it is usually best to calculate mathematically. To determine *areas*, you could divide a line into an equal number of parts and also calculate the areas mathematically. However, you are often asked to determine such information by **construction**. It is important that you do achieve the results by construction when asked. Even so, if you are an able mathematician, you can *check* the results of your construction mathematically. Remember to show all the details when you are performing a calculation since you will then gain credit, even if you make a mathematical error.

CALIPERS

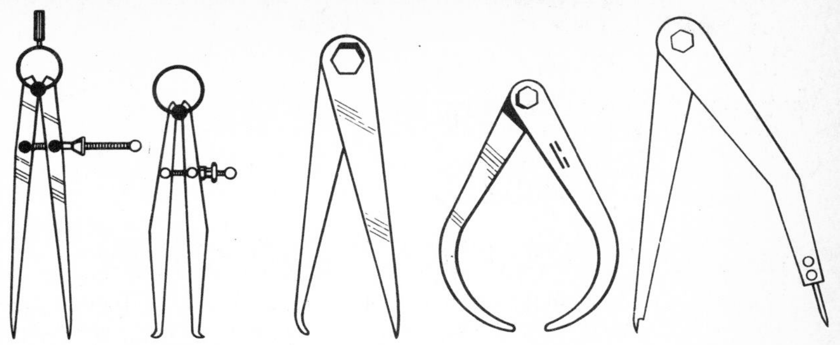

Fig C.2 Calipers

Calipers are familiar measuring or marking out tools. *Dividers* are a close relative and are designed to be used on metal or paper. The 'firm joint pattern' is most common, though the 'spring pattern' is also widely used, but more expensive. The 'spring pattern' type are more accurately controlled by turning a threaded knurled nut (Fig C.2).

CAMS

A cam is a part of a mechanism that is designed to change rotary motion into **reciprocating** motion. The cam is fixed to, or is part of, a shaft that rotates. The outer edge of the cam is in contact with a *follower* that is forced to keep in contact by a compression spring. During one rotation of the cam, the follower will rise and fall. The *amount* the follower rises and falls is determined by the *size of the cam and the position of the shaft.* If the cam is circular in profile and fitted to the shaft so that the centre of the shaft and cam are shared (*concentric*), then the follower will *not* rise or fall, even though the cam and the shaft are rotating. To bring about a rise and fall movement, it is necessary for the cam and shaft to be *eccentric* (not sharing the same centre). The *amount* of rise and fall will be equal to the *distance* the centres are apart.

Most cams are *pear-shaped.* This means that its rotation will cause a rise and fall movement of the follower as well as a variation in the *speed* of movement. When the follower is in contact with the cam along the part of the profile that is sharing the same concentricity, there is no movement in the follower. Where the profile does not share the same concentricity, the follower moves. The smaller the arc of the profile, the quicker the movement of the follower. A follower can be made to rise and fall by going through three phases of movement; slow, quick, and rest. The pear-shaped cam in Fig C.3 shows a cam designed to create such a pattern of movement.

The mechanical device in Fig C.4 is a common feature of car engines, but can only be seen when an engine has been dismantled.

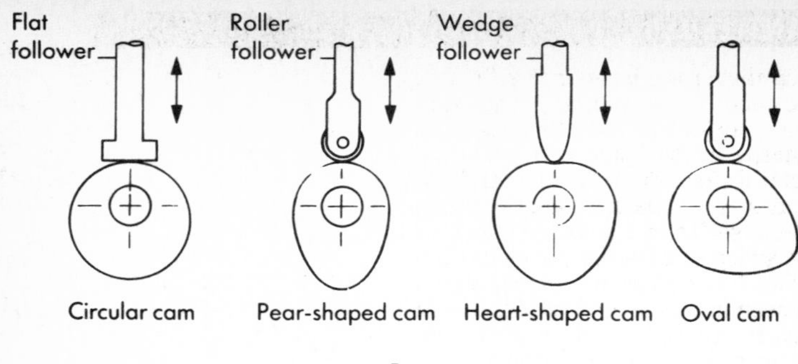

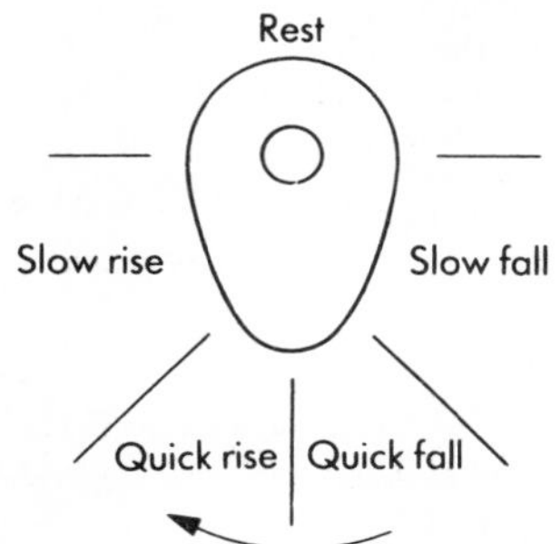

Fig C.3 Cams

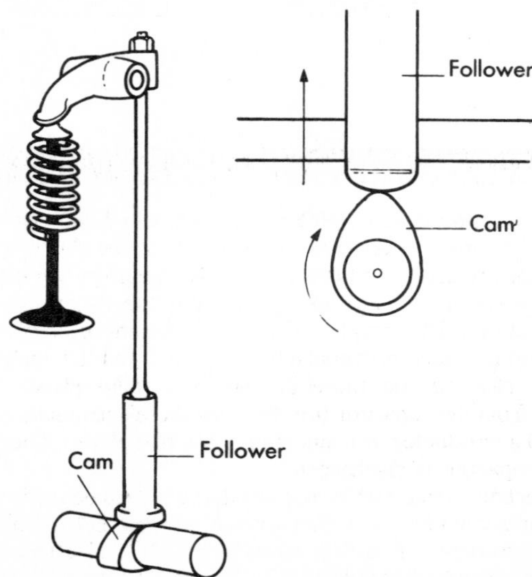

Fig C.4 Cam and follower in a car engine

CANTILEVER

A cantilever is a beam that is fixed at one end to a support, and free (unsupported) at the other end. An example in the home is a towel rail that is fixed to the wall at one end and protrudes outwards. Most designs have a set of two or three rails that can swing in different positions (Fig C.5a). An example in engineering can be seen in cantilever bridges. These bridges are supported on piers; the extreme ends of the bridge may appear to be supported by the banks, but they are not carrying a load at all. In fact, the bridge is exerting an upward pull at either bank, so if the banks were removed the bridge would remain undamaged.

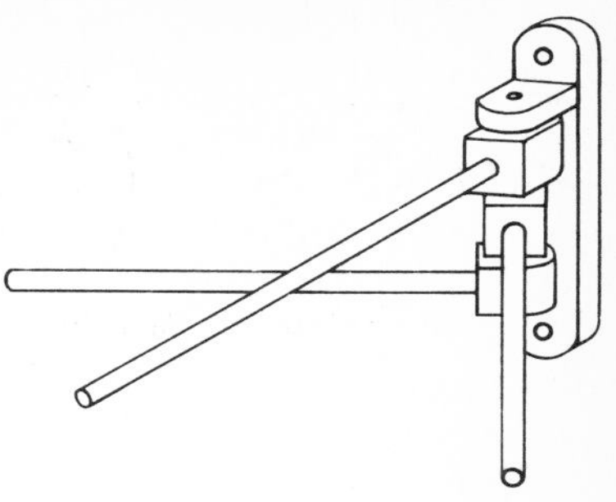

Fig C.5 Cantilevers
a) Towel rail

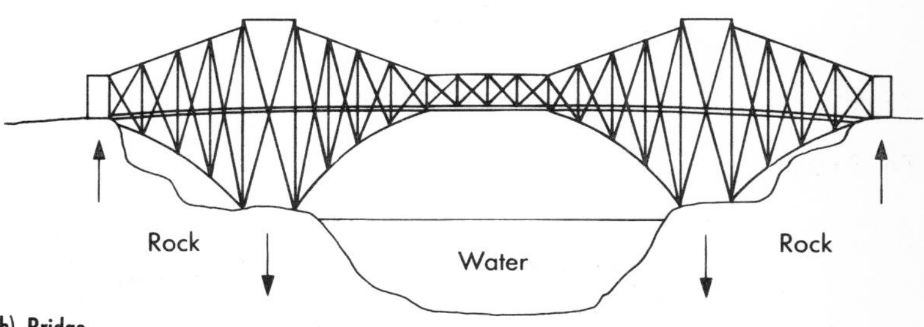

b) Bridge

CAPACITOR

A capacitor, sometimes called a **condenser**, is a device for storing an electric charge. The capacitor consists of two metal plates separated by an insulator. If the plates are connected to a DC supply, the negative terminal will supply a surge of electrons to one plate and from the other plate to the positive terminal of the DC supply. This displacement of electrons charges the capacitor to the same potential difference (p.d.) as the supply. Once this level has been reached, no more charging can take place. To *discharge* the electrons from the capacitor (i.e. to make the electrons flow from one plate to the other) a **conductor** is connected to the two plates. The electrons will flow until the capacitor is discharged.

The electric charge (Q) is measured in units called *coulombs*. One coulomb is the quantity of electricity that flows in one second when the current is one ampere. An *ampere* is a flow of 6.28×10^{18} electrons per second. One *coulomb* is equal to a charge of 6.28×10^{18} electrons. A capacitor's ability to store a charge is referred to as its *capacitance*. Capacitance is measured in *farads*, but since this is rather a large unit it is usual to use the *microfarad* (μF or 10^{-6}F), one millionth of a farad, or the *nanofarad* (nF or 10^{-9}F), a thousand millionth of a farad, or the *picofarad* (pF or 10^{-2}F), one billionth of a farad.

The *dielectric* is an insulator, but since there is no such thing as a perfect insulator, a flow of electrons occurs between the two plates. This flow is referred to as a 'leakage'. A good quality capacitor should have a low level of leakage.

► 'breakdown voltage' of a capacitor is the maximum working voltage and is usually written in the form '100V wkg'. If this breakdown voltage is exceeded, the capacitor is usually permanently damaged.

► 'tolerance' of a capacitor is the range of values it can have above and below its stated value. Tolerance values of commonly used capacitors range from 10% to 50%, but you should check the values since they are not always symmetrical, e.g. −25%, +50%.

Capacitors are made in a variety of shapes and from a variety of materials, e.g. polyester, polystyrene, ceramic, polycarbonate, tantalum and electrolytic (Fig C.6). They can also be designed to perform a variety of functions, e.g. variable capacitors used for tuning radio receivers. When choosing a capacitor you must check that you choose the correct values for working voltage, capacitance, tolerance, etc. It is important to note that the values for a capacitor can change with age, temperature, etc.

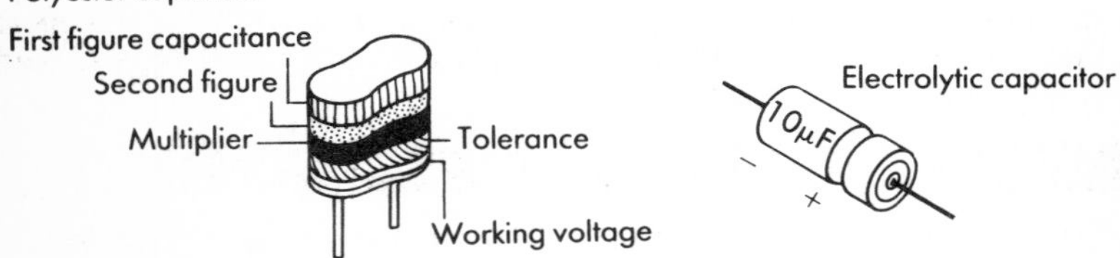

Fig C.6 Capacitors

CARBON

Carbon is an element that is unique. Its atoms can bond with other carbon atoms in chains or rings almost indefinitely. The compounds known as the 'paraffin hydrocarbons' or 'alkanes' are those of carbon and hydrogen. Methane is a natural gas given off from the decay of carbon-based materials and has been the cause of explosions in mines.

Dr L.H. Baekland (1863–1944), a Belgian-American scientist, specialised in organic chemistry, in particular the element carbon. In 1909 he discovered a reaction between a coal tar substance called phenol and formaldehyde. He observed that a thick, sticky resin was produced. When allowed to cool after the reaction, it hardened; but if it was heated it would soften so that it could be moulded into a desired shape. On cooling again, however, it would become hard (set) with any further attempts to soften it by heating proving impossible. Baekland realised the commerical use of this substance and patented it under the name of *Bakelite*. So, from this study of carbon, the first *synthetic plastic material* was born. Bakelite became a commercial success, but more importantly the discovery led the way to a whole new range of plastic materials being developed. The plastic materials that we know and use today are developed through a knowledge and understanding of the properties of *carbon atoms* and their unique ability of bonding. ◀ Polymerisation ▶

CARBON IN STEELS

The presence of the smallest quantities of carbon in *steel* affects its properties, i.e. its toughness, brittleness and hardness. By accurately controlling the amounts of carbon in steel, carbon steels with *particular properties* can be produced for special purposes. *Low carbon steel,* which contains less than 0.15% carbon, is fairly soft and suitable for the production of rivets. *Mild steel,* which is a general purpose steel, contains between 0.15% and 0.25% carbon, and is one you commonly use in the school workshop. *Medium carbon steel* contains between 0.25% and 0.5% carbon and is used in mild steel castings. *High carbon steels* vary between 0.75% and 1.5% carbon and are used to give the steel varying levels of hardness and toughness. At the *lower end* of this range, steels are produced to make blacksmith's tools, such as cold sets, swages, fullers, etc. In the *middle* of this range, carbon steel is produced for the production of chisels, punches, dies, drills and various cutting and turning tools. At the *higher end* of this range, high quality cutting tools, such as razor-sharp tools, are produced from the steels containing 1.5% carbon. This carbon steel is also referred to as 'cast steel' or 'tool steel'. You are most likely to use this type of steel in the production of cutting tools that need hardening and tempering.

CARCASE CONSTRUCTION

This is a term used to distinguish between the two major families of construction in cabinet making. A cabinet could either be made by constructing a *carcase* (box) or a *frame*. The carcase is generally made from wide boards and can be seen in cabinets for television, for storing clothes, books, etc. Cabinets made from *natural timber* often include joints such as common through, lapped or mitred dovetail for the outer construction, and housing through or stopped joints for dividing the internal space into manageable units. If manufactured boards are used, the jointing is done by dowelling, screwing, etc., and the internal divisions are joined by dowelling, screwing or (for adjustable shelving) by drilling and inserting a peg.

CARTRIDGE PAPER

This is the most commonly used paper in school drawing offices. It probably gets its name from the fact that this type of paper was used in the production of cartridges, which are cases that contain an explosive. Cartridge paper is generally regarded as a medium quality paper and is available in the standard sizes, A1, A2, A3 and A4.

Paper is graded according to its '*tooth*'. The heavier a paper is, the thicker the paper will be. The weight of paper is measured in grams per square metre, i.e. gsm. Thin drawing paper is about 60 gsm; cartridge paper is between 100 and 120 gsm. The 'tooth' refers to the texture of the paper surface. Smooth surfaces are good for pen and ink drawings; rougher surfaces are good for pencilwork, especially for sketching with a B grade (soft) pencil.

◀ Paper sizes ▶

CASE-HARDENING

Some mild steels can be given a 'skin' or case of a hardened surface by introducing more carbon into the alloy. When the metal is red hot the surface can absorb carbon, so increasing its carbon content to a level that will enable it to be heat treated again, i.e. hardened and tempered. This means that it will have many of the characteristics and properties of *tool steel*.

The case-hardening process is done by packing the mild steel into metal box that contains a carbon-rich compound. The box is sealed tightly (to prevent air from reaching the mild steel and allowing oxidation to take place), and heated to a temperature of 950°C. The longer the piece of mild steel can be left to 'soak' in the carbon rich compound at this temperature, the more carbon will be absorbed and the thicker the case will be. This process is called '*carburizing*'. Once the process is completed, the mild steel can be heat treated in the same way as tool steel, i.e. it can be heated and quenched in cold water for hardening and it can be tempered by further heating and quenching in the normal way.

A cheaper and quicker way of case hardening is to heat the mild steel to a cherry red colour with a brazing torch and to put it into a carbon-rich compound called Kasenit. This process can be repeated several times to increase the amount of carbon being absorbed and to increase the thickness of the newly formed skin. This skin can be hardened by heating the steel to red heat again and quenching it in water.

The purpose of case hardening is to provide a component that is able to stand a lot of frictional wear on its surface, and at the same time to have a softer core that is able to withstand shock or impact. This combination of properties is important in some mechanisms, such as the gudgeon pin that holds the piston on a connecting rod. Here, the surface of the pin has to withstand the frictional wear of the piston as well as sudden force created by the ignition of fuel vapour in the cylinder.

◀ Hardening and tempering ▶

CAST IRON

Cast iron is a brittle material which easily shatters under impact. But properties of being able to 'flow' when heated to melting point have made it a very popular material for the production of just about everything that has to be hard wearing during the 17th and 18th centuries. Most kitchen ware was made of cast iron and all the pots, pans, ovens, stands and even table and chairs were made from cast iron. Large structures such as bridges (the Iron Bridge at Coalbrookdale being the first and most well known), have used cast iron, and large buildings were constructed of iron and glass, e.g. Crystal Palace and many large railway stations. Cast iron was seen by many as a material that was suitable for just about everything, in a similar way to our view of plastics today.

The use of cast iron today is much more selective. Its property of being a heavy, hard wearing, self-lubricating material (it contains graphite in its structure), makes it ideal for the manufacture of machine beds for lathes, milling machines, grinding machines, etc. A visit to Coalbrookdale would be a valuable experience, and it would certainly help you understand how the production and application of cast iron influenced the lives of the local people.

CASTING

This is a process in which a liquid state material is poured into a mould. The material takes up the form of the mould, solidifies and is removed. The final solidified form is known as a casting. ◀ Cope and drag, Flask ▶

CASTING PROCESSES

There are two groups of casting processes.

Hot casting

Hot casting is when a material is heated until molten before it is poured into a mould. Hot casting processes are suitable for metals and cold casting processes are suitable for resins (thermosetting plastics).

Cold casting

In *cold casting*, the material is already in a liquid state and requires a chemical to be added to bring about a reaction that will solidify the material when it is in the mould.

Cold casting, as the name implies, means that the heating of the material is not a necessary part of the process. The mould therefore does not have to be heat-resistant. This means that the moulds can either be made of rigid materials, such as wood, rigid polythene and glass fibre reinforced plastics, or of flexible materials, such as rubber. Using flexible moulds means that complicated and finely detailed castings can be made, including places where 'under cuts' may occur.

In both types of casting the preparation of the *resin* is similar. A quantity of resin, sufficient to fill the mould (and perhaps a little more), is prepared by mixing a catalyst, that will cause the polymerisation (curing of the resin to make it go solid) to take place. The resin is then poured into the mould that has been prepared with a release agent and allowed to cure. Once the casting has solidified, it can be removed. The release agent, usually a silicone wax, ensures that the resin does not bond to the sides of the mould so that the casting can be removed without damage. Though many practical applications are possible, this process has been mainly used for embedding or encapsulation of objects in a clear resin. Chess pieces have been produced using this process.

METAL CASTING IN SCHOOLS

Many metals or alloys of metals are suitable for casting, e.g. gold, silver, brass, aluminium and lead. Aluminium is perhaps the most common metal used for casting in schools and colleges. It has a melting point of about 650°C, which is a temperature easily reached in a small gas-air fired furnace. The aluminium, while still in the crucible (a plumbago pot), has to be degassed and cleaned with a flux. The molten metal should look bright and silvery. It is at this stage that the crucible is raised, using specially designed tongs, and tipped steadily into the pouring basin of the sand mould. The metal then spills from the basin into the pouring hole, and into the cavity left by the pattern, then up the rising hole until it emerges just above the level of the sand. The pouring from the crucible stops immediately this happens and the casting is left to cool and to solidify. The casting is removed after approximately three hours, using tongs in case it is still quite hot, and then cleaned, ready for the next stage.

APPLICATIONS OF CASTING IN SCHOOLS

The main application of casting in schools is for the production of components for lampstands, handles for hacksaws, and adjustable brackets on photographic enlargers, but more recently for the production of sculptural forms.

CATALYST

A catalyst is a substance which brings about a chemical change in another substance while remaining unchanged itself. The practical application you are likely to encounter in the school workshops is in the **curing** (hardening) of polyester or epoxy resins. The term 'hardener' is more commonly used by the manufacturers since it seems to describe the function of the substance. There are two forms in which the catalyst is available, paste and liquid. The paste form is an organic peroxide (cyclohexanone peroxide) and must be very carefully applied to the resin. It is more difficult to weigh and measure the correct quantity for a paste than for a liquid catalyst, but it does avoid the chance of splashing. Special safety precautions have to be taken when dealing with these chemicals. ◀ **Encapsulation** ▶

CELLULAR STRUCTURE

All living material depends for its growth on having a cellular structure. The cells take on a different function and between them they fulfil the needs of the plant or animal to survive. In CDT you need to be concerned with various materials, including *wood*. Though no longer a living organism, the cell structure of wood is still there to be seen. A basic knowledge of cell structure will help you to appreciate how well a tree is able to survive and the ways in which the end product, wood, may be identified and used for specific purposes.

The growth of any living thing is dependent upon *cell division*. In this way the new cells are formed, adding to the size of the plant or animal. In trees the process of cell division is almost continuous, though more active in spring than summer, and relatively dormant in the cold months of winter. This can be

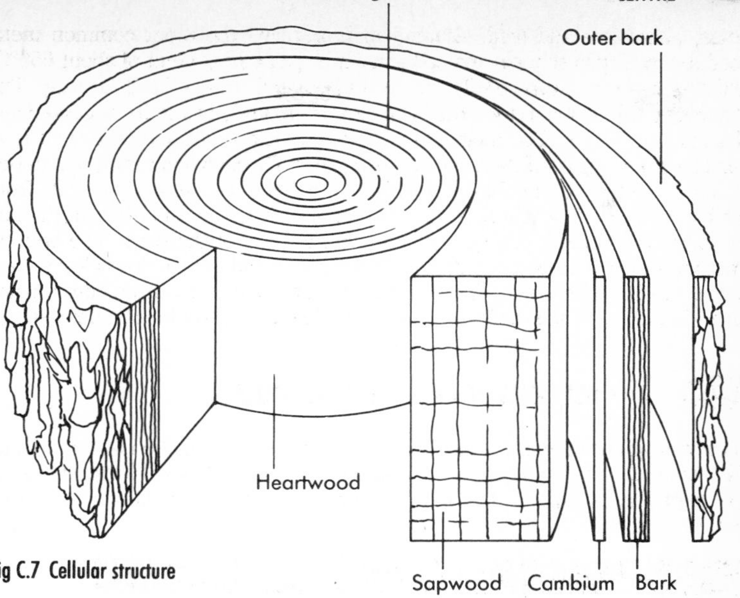

Fig C.7 Cellular structure

seen by looking at the end grain of a piece of wood. The larger and thin-walled pores (tubular cells) are the cells that were formed in the spring. The smaller and thicker-walled pores are the cells that were formed at the end of the growing season, and can often be recognised by their darker colour when compared with the lighter colour of the spring cells. Together they show the growth that has taken place in one year, and are known as *annual rings*.

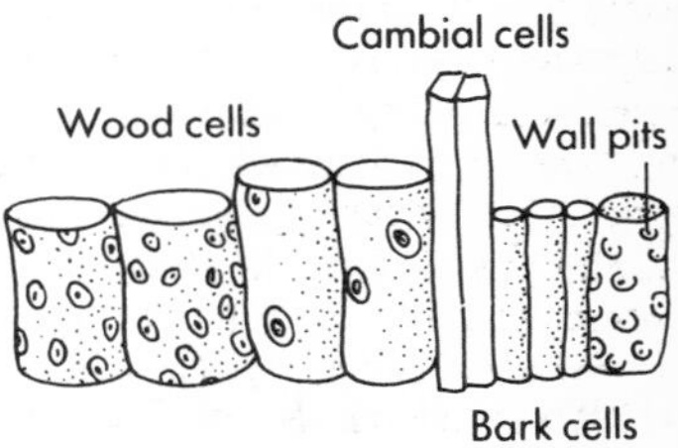

The growth cells in a tree form in the *cambium layer* (Fig C.7), a layer of cells just between the bark and the wood cells (the ones that have finished growing). It consists of a single layer of cells that divide; the cells on the *wood side* grow quickly and form the cells that will eventually become wood; the cells on the *bark side* form slowly and make up the inner *bark layer*. The bark layer protects the sensitive growing cells from the cold and from damage by falling branches, animals and children who love carving initials in trees. The wood cells act to support the tree, and it is because of their considerable strength that a tree can grown to a height that no other living thing can reach. The Sequoia, an American tree, is one of the tallest trees, growing to a height of 90 metres (almost the length of a football pitch).

There are two families of wood. *Softwood* comes from cone-bearing trees, also known as 'evergreens' or 'coniferous' trees. The term softwood is purely a botanical classification. The other member of the family is the ***hardwood***, which comes from the 'deciduous trees' that lose their leaves in winter. Again the term 'hardwood' is purely a botanical classification.

◀ Coniferous, Deciduous, Hardwood, Softwood ▶

CENTRE

The centre of anything is the middle. It is the point or position that is equidistant (equal distance) from its outside shape or form. The centre of a circle or a sphere, square or cube are examples. The centre of a cylinder, rod, bar, etc., is the *axis* that is equidistant from the outer surface (Fig C.8).

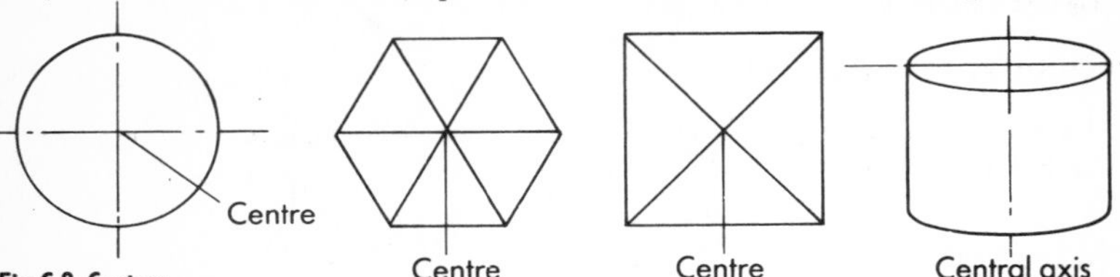

Fig C.8 Centres

The term 'centre' is often used as a prefix to many tools and instruments, e.g. Centre Lathe (Fig C.9), Centre Drill, Centre Bit, Centre Square, etc. The connection is related to the *function* that each has to perform. To turn a bar on a lathe, the central axis of the bar has to be the same as the central axis of the *live centre* and *dead centre* of the lathe. The central axis of the centre drill has to be the same as the central axis of the hole to be drilled.

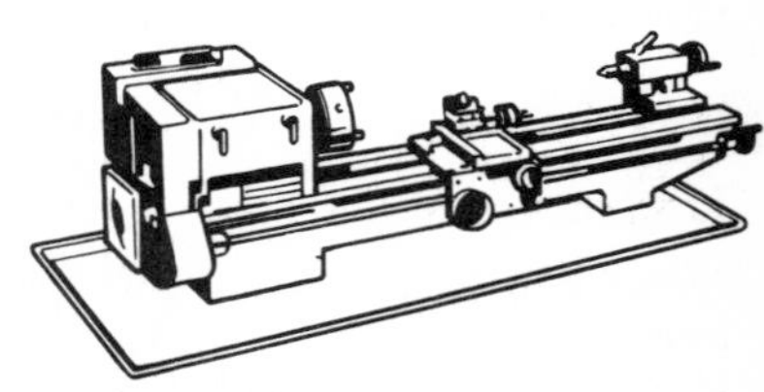

Fig C.9 Centre lathe

CENTRE BIT

The term centre bit is a generalised name for a range of drill bits. Centre bits are specifically designed to fit in a brace with a chuck which takes a four-sided, tapered shank. It is better if you can be *specific* about the type of 'bit' required for a particular task.

TYPES OF CENTRE BIT

There are six types of centre bit which you should know.

Auger twist bit

Used to bore deep holes along and across the grain (Fig C.10).

Fig C.10 Auger bit

Jennings pattern twist bit

Used for boring deep holes along and across the grain (Fig C.11).

Fig C.11 Jennings bit

Forstner bit

Used for boring flat bottomed blined holes (a hole that does not go all the way through) (Fig C.12).

Fig C.12 Forstner bit

Countersunk Rose bit

Used to countersink a hole to accept a screw with a countersunk head and to enable it to fit flush with the surface (Fig C.13).

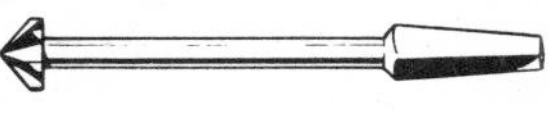

Fig C.13 Countersunk Rose bit

Centre bit

Used for boring holes in thin wood (Fig C.14).

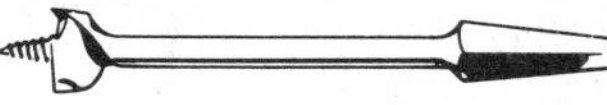

Fig C.14 Centre bit

Expanding bit

Used for boring holes in thin wood, but the cutter can be adjusted to cut larger holes. Sizes range from 12.5 mm to 75 mm. A change of cutter is necessary for boring the larger range (Fig C.15).

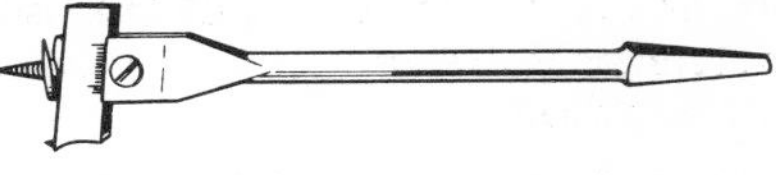

Fig C.15 Expanding bit

OTHER BITS

Many of the bits are also designed for use in *power drills.* These have a triangular, parallel-section shank for fitting into a three-jaw chuck. The range of bits is very extensive but the four most commonly used are: *Flat bit,* for boring flat bottomed holes or through holes in thin boards (Fig C.16); *power auger bits,* for boring deep accurate holes; *counter sinking bits,* for cutting a hole to accept the countersunk head of a screw; *dowel bits,* for drilling a flat-bottomed hole for receiving a dowel.

Reading about and seeing the variation of the types of bits should help to show you why it is important to be specific. Imagine the confusion of a shop assistant if you asked to buy a 'bit'. You must be able to *name* the type of 'bit' you require.

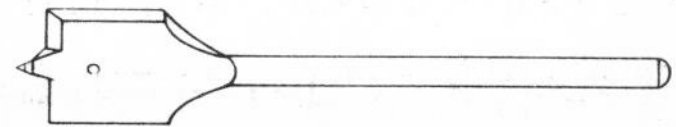

Fig C.16 Flat bit

CENTRE DRILL

This is a drill designed specifically for drilling a tapered hole that matches the taper of a lathe centre (Fig C.17).

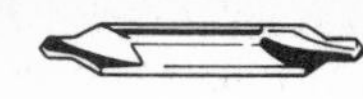

Fig C.17 Centre drill

CENTRE OF GRAVITY

A point about which an object, person or animal is in balance. A beam resting in a horizontal position on a pivot is in balance, and the **centre of gravity** is at the *point of contact* of the pivot with the beam. This need not necessarily be at the mid-point of the beam! If a load is placed at one end of the beam, the point of contact for the pivot will need to be nearer the end carrying the load to make the beam and the load remain horizontal. We then say the beam is in **balance** or in **equilibrium**.

Products with a *low* centre of gravity are often more stable than products with a mid-way or higher centre of gravity. A pyramid has a very low centre of gravity and is a very stable structure. Tall buildings have a centre of gravity that is much higher and they are less stable. When designing an artefact it is important to consider the centre of gravity, especially in tall structures such as a standard lamp, aerial, or wind-powered electricity generating tower. To *lower* the centre of gravity, the *lamp* may need to have the base sizes increased to a point where the lamp could withstand side forces without falling over. The *aerial* may need to have guys attached to increase the base area of contact. The *tower* will need to have sloping sides, so that its height: base contact area ratio is small enough to make it a stable unit.

CENTRE PUNCH

A small hand tool for marking the centre of a hole on metal. The centre punch is struck cleanly with a hammer (Fig C.18). There are more expensive centre punches that are spring loaded so that as pressure is applied at the top, the punching end is released suddenly, causing a mark to be made in the metal.

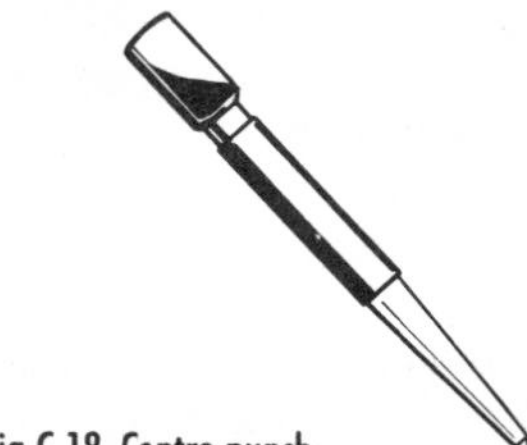

Fig C.18 Centre punch

CENTRE SQUARE

It is often necessary to drill a hole in the centre of the end of a piece of round bar. A centre square is used to *find* the centre by placing the centre in three different positions, so that a very small triangle can be drawn using a scriber (Fig C.19).

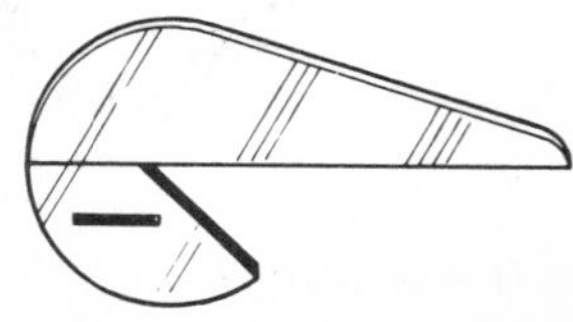

Fig C.19 Centre square

The centre of the triangle is the centre of the bar. One of the most common reasons for wanting to find the centre of a round sectioned bar is so that a hole may be drilled with a centre drill. The bar may then be set in a centre lathe and can rotate, sharing a common central axis.

CERAMIC

Ceramic objects are objects made from clay and fired at a very high temperature. The general term for objects made this way is *pottery*. The fired piece may be treated with a glaze and fired again. The process has been used for many years and some of the earliest made examples are known to be over 7000 years old. Pots and various shaped containers have been made for many thousands of years. However, the techniques of making pots by building up the walls and by coiling a roll of clay round and round in a spiral have not changed very much. Only the more controlled methods of firing, using electricity, have been responsible for influencing the design of kilns.

CHAIN DRIVES

The transfer of a motion from a source of power to another part of a mechanism can be done in a number of ways. The chain drive is made up of links that are held together by pivoting rivets so that the chain can follow the curvature of the circumference of a wheel. The wheels have sprockets so that the wheel cannot slip and maximum force can be transmitted from one sprocket wheel to another. A common application of this mechanism can be found on a bicycle (Fig C.20).

On a smaller scale, chain drives can be used in construction kits such as those produced by Fischertechnic and Economatics for the assembly of a plotter or a buggy robot, etc (Fig C.21). The advantage of such a mechanism is the ability to transfer a motional force *without slip*. The links and the sprockets, when properly engaged, cannot slip, so ensuring the maximum mechanical efficiency.

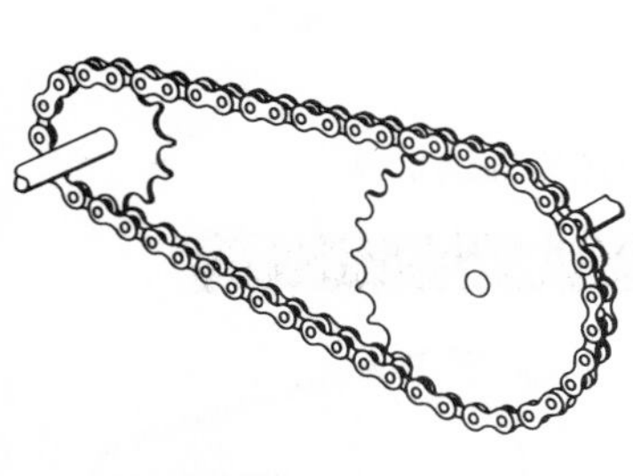

Fig C.20 Chain drive on bicycle

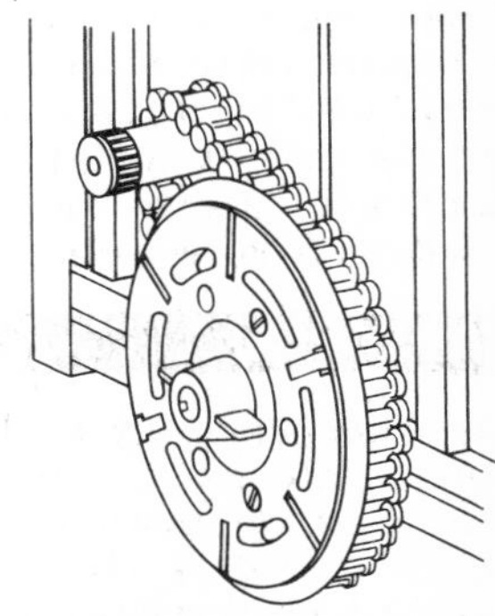

Fig C.21 A kit chain

CHAIN MOLECULES

A chain molecule is a linear chain of molecules. Every substance or material is built up of millions of minute particles called **atoms**. The atoms have a distinct number of **protons** and a matching number of **electrons**. This number is known as the *atomic number* and is used to identify one element from another. The element hydrogen has one proton and one electron and has the periodic table number 1, while carbon has six electrons and six protons and has the periodic table number 6.

The bonding of the atoms of the elements hydrogen and carbon forms the structure of synthetic materials commonly known as *plastics*. The long molecule that is peculiar to plastics is a string of smaller molecules linked end to end, very much like a chain. The discovery that carbon was the main element in natural plastics, such as cellulose, led scientists to apply the **bonding** principle to developing plastics artificially. Today nearly all the artificial (synthetic) plastics are developed on the bonding characteristics of the carbon atom.

The long chain molecular structure gives the feature of plasticity. The molecules are able to move when heated but, because of their long thread-like structure, are unable to untwine, and so remain in contact with each other. This enables the plastic's material *to change its form while hot* (when the molecules are free to move). On cooling, the molecules become locked in the form they have adopted, and so the material can be shaped (while hot) and allowed to set in the position that is desired. The plastic materials that are able to be shaped when heated and, if necessary, reheated, are known as **thermoplastics**. Those that can be heated only once to form the desired shape are called **thermosets**.

CHAMFER

Because wood was always weak along the exposed corners and edges, it regularly became damaged in use. So craftsmen decided to *remove* the corners with a chisel or plane to make a feature and, of course, to stop the corner being damaged (Fig C.22). The angle of 45° for the chamfer was convenient, since it took even amounts of wood away from both adjacent surfaces and fitted in well where **mitred** joints (angled at 45°) were used. In

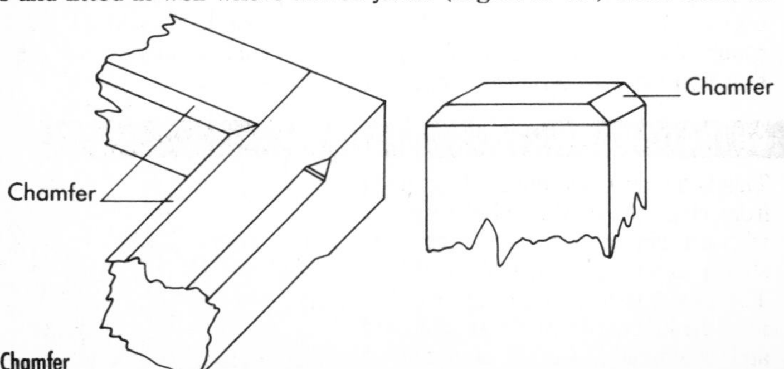

Fig C.22 Chamfer

old furniture, the chamfer became an important decorative feature, especially in church furniture.

Although chamfering is still an acceptable feature, you must remember that it can only be successfully done on *natural timber*. Manufactured boards are sometimes veneered with a decorative wood, or laminated with a plastic lamina. If the corner was removed in this case, the composition of the manufactured board would be exposed, the appearance spoilt, and the edge of the veneer or lamina liable to be damaged.

CHARTS

Much use is made today of charts in order to convey information graphically. The visual image of facts and figures is often much more easily and quickly understood than information presented using the written word or figure alone. There are a variety of ways in which information can be conveyed graphically and they can all be referred to as a chart. The most common charts you are likely to use are: **Bar charts** (Gantt Charts), **Flow charts, Graphs, Pictorial graphs, Organisation charts, Networks** and **Circuit diagrams.**

CHIP

A *chip* is a term derived from the production of integrated circuits on slices ('chips') of silicon. A chip is a complete integrated circuit containing **diodes, transistors, resistors,** etc (Fig C.23). You will find that the term **Integrated Circuit** is the preferred term to use in examinations and when buying such items. The Integrated Circuits usually carry a manufactured code number, e.g. LM555, NE555V, CA555CG, etc. All these have identical circuits. The letters distinguish the manufacturer.

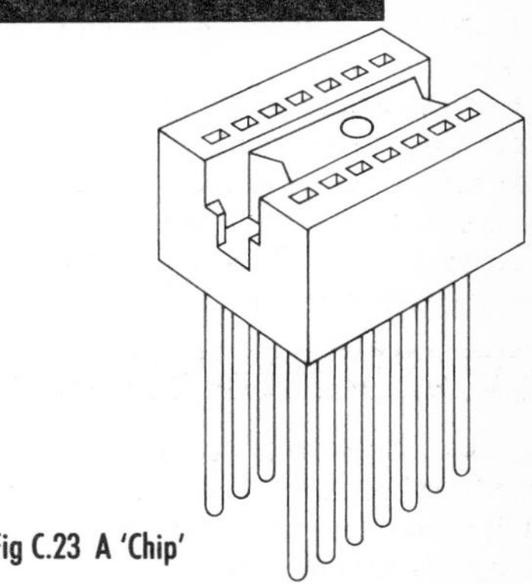

Fig C.23 A 'Chip'

The advantage of using Integrated Circuits (ICs) is that they take up very little space and are generally very efficient and reliable. When a fault does occur in a circuit it is usually because of the wiring or soldering and not the result of a faulty IC. Remember to always use an IC socket and to make sure that you insert the IC the correct way round.

CHIPBOARD

This is a man-made board. It is made from chips of wood bonded together with a resin adhesive and formed in sheets under pressure (Fig C.24). The board is not as strong as other man-made boards such as plywood and blockboard, but is also not as expensive.

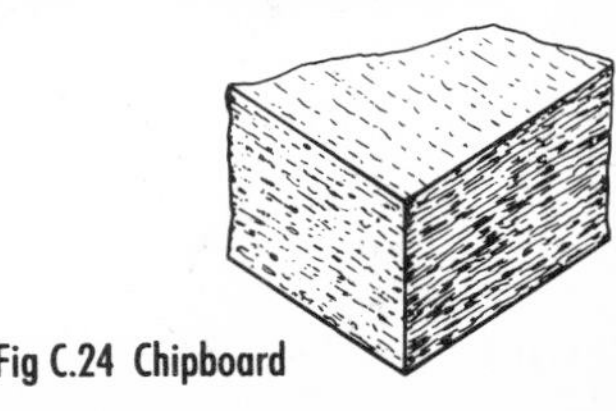

Fig C.24 Chipboard

Where appearance is *not* important the boards can be used as they are. But where appearance *is* important then veneered or laminated chipboard is available, though of course it is more expensive. Veneered and plastic-laminated boards are much used in the making of furniture. Chipboard is available in sheet sizes 2440 mm × 1220 mm, and in varying thicknesses; 18 mm is a commonly used thickness.

The *advantages* of using chipboard are: it is available in large sizes; it has a uniform strength in all directions; it does not warp; it is not likely to be attacked by wood beetle.

The *disadvantages* of using chipboard are: it is not attractive to look at; it tends to swell in very moist conditions; it stains very easily; and it is difficult to clean up.

CHISELS

One of the earliest tools developed by man was one which could be used to chip away at wood and which we now call the chisel. As such tools have evolved over many thousands of years, so various types of chisel have been developed.

TYPES OF CHISEL

The particular type of chisel used today is governed by its function. A *cold chisel* is designed to cut *metal* and is quite different in its appearance and arrangement of material from a chisel designed to cut wood.

Cold chisels

Cold chisels are designed for cutting metal while it is cold. There are a variety of cold chisels, each designed to perform a particular function. They are made from a hexagonal bar of carbon steel which has been **hardened** and **tempered** at 280°C. The end which is to be struck by a hammer is ground to a short taper, to lessen the 'mushrooming' effect caused by the hammer blows. This end is 'soft' so that the impact of the hard hammer face does not result in fracture. The cutting end is tempered to be sufficiently hard and tough to cut mild steel and softer metals such as aluminium and copper. The cutting edge is curved to avoid strain on the corners (Fig C.25).

Wood chisels

Wood chisels are designed to cut natural timber *across* the grain. Attempts to cut *along* the grain usually result in the wood splitting. There are three main types of wood chisel:

- those designed to be held in hand, with pressure carefully applied to produce a cutting action;
- those that are struck with a mallet to produce a cutting action;
- those that have a curved section blade.

The last type is more often referred to as a **gouge** and more detail is given under that heading.

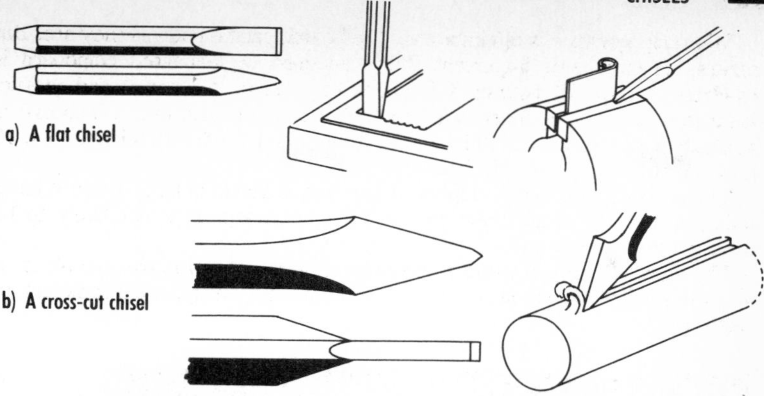

Fig C.25 Types of cold chisel

Firmer chisels

Firmer chisels are designed to cut wood *without* the need for a blow from a mallet. There are two patterns, and the difference is in the cross-section shape of the blade. The Firmer chisel is rectangular in section and the bevelled edge has the upper edges ground away to produce a bevel. The bevelled edge tool has the added advantage of being able to chisel cuts into corners where the angle is less than 90° (Fig C.26). These chisels are not designed to be hit with a mallet or hammer. The chisels with wooden handles split easily, and the lightness of the blade is such that it will not withstand the shock of the blows. There are, however, chisels that have sturdy blades and plastic handles that *can* withstand the impact of a blow from either a mallet or a hammer.

Fig C.26 A firmer chisel

Bevelled edge chisel

The Bevelled edge chisel has the upper surfaces of the blade ground away (Fig C.27). This makes the blade lighter and less strong but makes it possible for paring and cleaning corners with an angle less than 90°. It is therefore specially suited for the cleaning up of dovetail joints.

Fig C.27 A bevelled edge chisel

Mortice chisel

The Mortice chisel is specially designed to withstand the blows from a mallet. The design features include a *steel ferrule* fitted to the wooden handle where

Fig C.28 A mortice chisel

the mallet strikes the handle. This prevents the handle from splitting. There is also a *leather washer* fitted at the other end to absorb the shock between the handle and the blade. The cross section shape of the blade is much thicker than the Firmer chisel, so that it will withstand the blows and be suitable for levering the chips free from the mortice hole (Fig C.28).

Having an understanding and knowledge of the design features of tools helps in the selection of the correct tool for the job. Using the correct tool for the job is likely to produce better results than improvising with a tool that is not specially designed to do the job.

CHORD (OF A CIRCLE)

The chord is a straight line that divides a circle into two segments (Fig C.29). Note that if the straight line passes through the *centre* of the circle, the line is called a **diameter**, and divides the circle into two semi-circles.

Fig C.29 Chord of a circle

CHOSEN SOLUTION

During a designing activity you will have considered a number of possible solutions to a problem. Only *one* of your ideas needs to be developed for what will be the final solution. If it is difficult to choose one, it may be because each of your ideas has something about it that may be worth developing. In this case try to select aspects of each idea and to put them together to form a single solution. It is quite possible that you will now have found a solution that will become the chosen solution.

The chosen solution is the one that you think will satisfy the **design brief**. But before you can go further you will need to *develop* your idea by working out how it could be made and possibly by making a model.

CIRCLES

A circle is the path of a moving point that is equidistant from a fixed point. The fixed point becomes the centre, and the *path* of the moving point the **circumference**. Circles are measured by the length of a straight line that passes through the centre and touches the circumference at both ends (Fig C.30). This line is known as the **diameter**, and the diameter of a circle is the size of a circle.

Concentric circles are circles of different diameter sharing the same centre. **Eccentric circles** are circles of different diameters, usually one inside the other and not sharing the same centre (Fig C.31).

Circumscribed circles are circles that go outside another geometric shape but remain in contact with it, i.e. it is the smallest circle in which that shape can fit without the circumference of the circle cutting through any lines (Fig C.32). The prefix 'circum' means 'to go around' and is used in the name of the line that forms a circle, i.e. **circumference.**

An **escribed circle** is one that is drawn to touch the two sides of an angle (Fig C.33).

An **inscribed circle** is one that is drawn inside a geometric figure and touches all sides of that figure (Fig C.34).

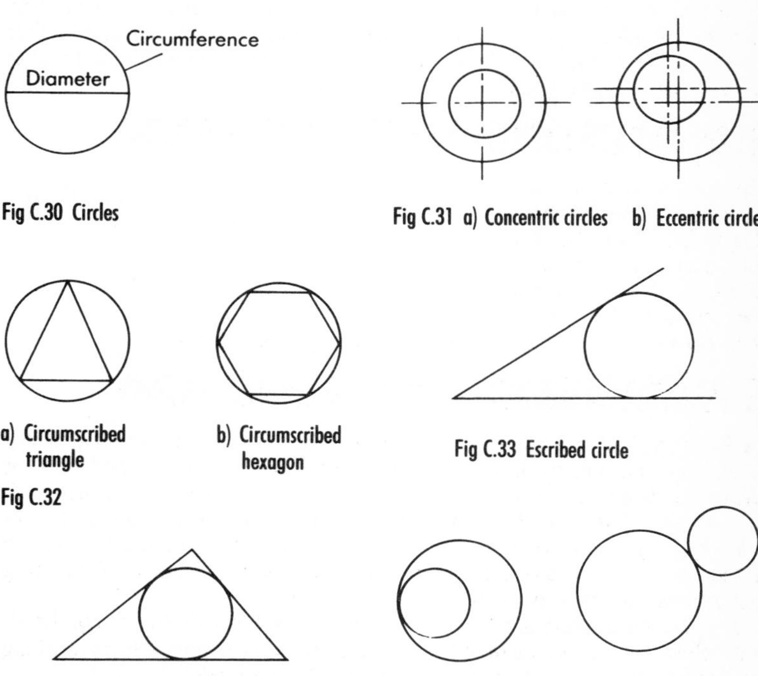

Fig C.30 Circles

Fig C.31 a) Concentric circles b) Eccentric circles

a) Circumscribed triangle

b) Circumscribed hexagon

Fig C.32

Fig C.33 Escribed circle

Fig C.34 Inscribed circle

Fig C.35 Circles in contact

CIRCLES IN CONTACT

There are two possible arrangements. One circle inside the other or one circle outside the other (Fig C.35). When you are required to do any geometric construction involving circles, the most important point or position is the *centre.* If you can establish the position for the centre of a circle you are well on the way to solving most problems that involve circles or arcs.

CIRCUIT

A circuit is a means by which an electric current or a liquid, etc, may flow from one position to another. A *complete* circuit is one that is unbroken and in which a current or liquid may flow (Fig C.36).

Circuits are most commonly associated with electrical and electronic devices. The flow of water in a central heating system or the flow of hydraulic fluid in a car braking system are also forms of circuitry.

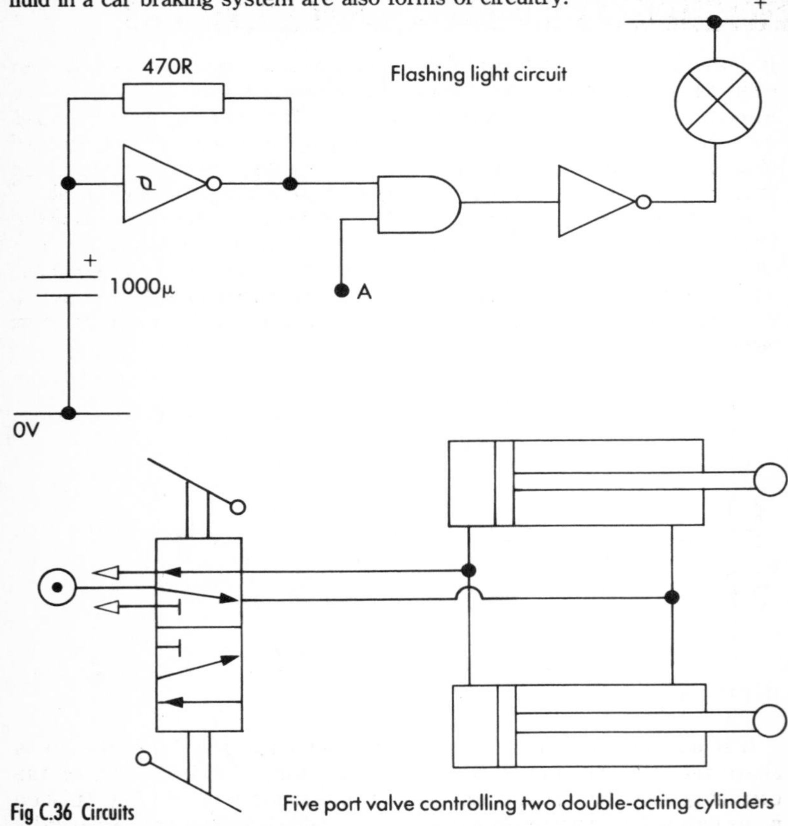

Fig C.36 Circuits

CIRCUIT DIAGRAMS (ELECTRICAL)

A circuit diagram has two main functions. One is to communicate clearly and precisely the details of a circuit so that it may be understood by the reader. The second is to work out possible solutions for a problem involving circuits.

To make the drawing of a circuit easy, *symbols* have been developed so that a two-dimensional diagram can be drawn. These symbols are nationally accepted and the British Standards Institution have published booklets specially for schools and colleges. The publication you will find helpful is PP7307, Graphical Symbols. It contains all the symbols you are most likely to need.

When you are designing and drawing circuits it is important that what you put down on paper can be easily followed, so always try to use vertical and horizontal lines and to show clearly the appropriate symbols of the components included in the circuit.

CIRCUIT WAVE FORMS

Just as silence is a rare experience, so too is absolute stillness. Almost everything is moving, even though the movement may not be detected without the help of very sensitive equipment. The electrons in an atom are constantly on the move (they are vibrating) and with an increase of temperature, the movement or vibration increases. Electric circuits can produce vibrations, an effect which is used to generate pulses or waves.

An **oscilloscope** is an instrument that is able to display the vibrations in the form of waves. The variation of current in a mains supply produces a 'sinusoidal' variation. This means that it produces a **'sine' wave** (Fig C.37). The time taken for the voltage to change from its maximum positive value to its maximum negative value, and back again, is called the 'period' of the sine wave.

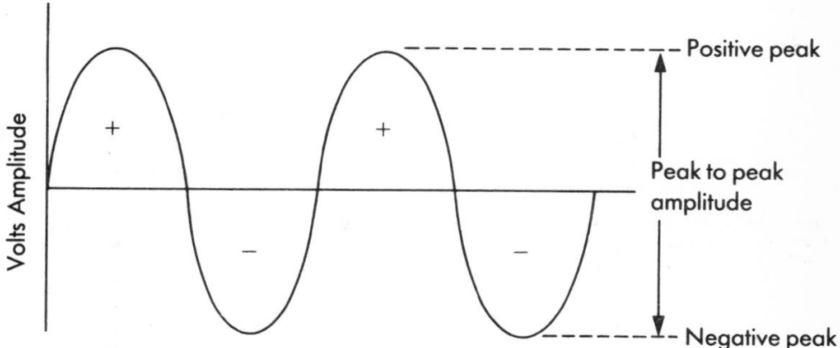

Fig C.37 Sine wave

A steady flow of direct current will show a straight line. When the line is above zero it is indicating that a current is flowing. As time moves on the current gets weaker and the line moves nearer to the zero line. Any variation in the flow will be indicated by a rise and fall. Sudden changes will be shown by pointed peaks and troughs, while gradual changes will be shown by wavey or undulating lines (Fig C.38) ◀ Oscilloscope ▶

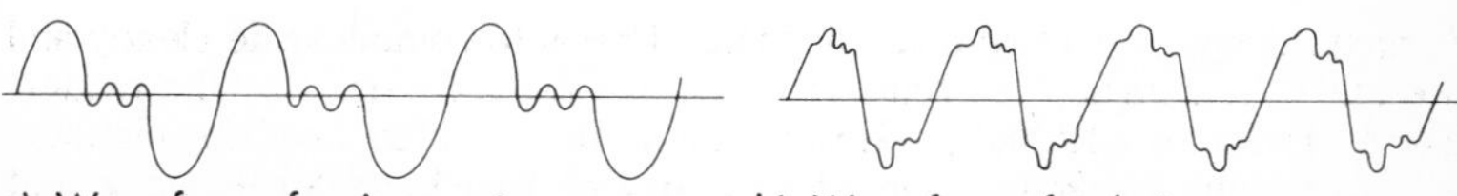

a) Wave form of a piano note b) Wave form of a clarinet tone

Fig C.38 Circuit wave forms

CIRCUMFERENCE

The prefix 'circum' means to go round. To *circumnavigate* the world means to go round it. *Circumference* means to go round a point. The circumference of a circle then is the line that goes round the circle at an equal distance from a centre.

CLEARANCE ANGLES

These are the parts of a cutting tool that are ground away so that the cutting action is efficient. The two most common situations where clearance angles are to be found are on **twist drills** and **lathe** tools (Fig C.39). Though you would not necessarily be expected to learn the different angles for different materials shown in Table C.1, you should be aware that they do exist. You should also appreciate that the correct angle on the appropriate material will give the best results.

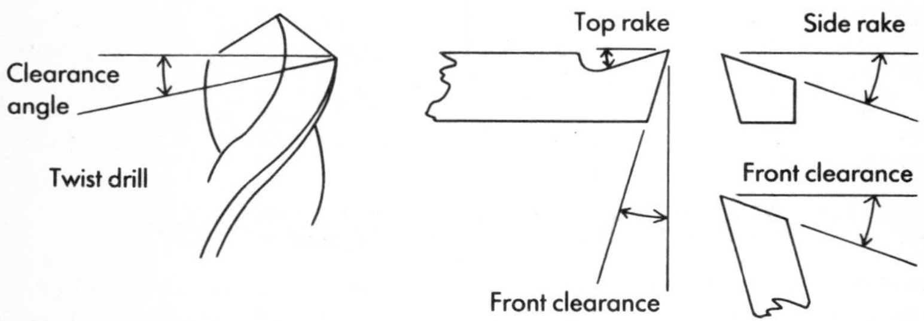

Fig C.39 Clearance angles

Table C.1 Clearance angles for different materials

MATERIAL	*HIGH SPEED STEEL*			
	Top rake	*Front clearance*	*Side rake*	*Side clearance*
Acrylic	2°	8°	2°	6°
Aluminium	30°	8°	15°	6°
Brass	0°	8°	0°	6°
Mild steel	20°	8°	15°	6°
Nylon	2°	8°	2°	6°
Carbon steel	10°	8°	5°	6°

CLEARANCE HOLE

When preparing two pieces of material to be joined together by using a screw, one piece must have a clearance hole so that the two pieces can be held closely together. The size of a clearance hole is determined by the diameter of the shank of the screw being used (Fig C.40). In the case of *wood screws*, you can hold the screw up to the light, hold the drill in line with it and select the drill that just masks the outline of the screw. If in doubt, drill a variety of sizes of holes in a spare piece of wood and try the screw in each hole until you find one that just passes through without wobbling from side to side. In the case of *machine screws* you can refer to a table that has a list of tapping sizes and clearance sizes. You can then make your selection straight from the table.

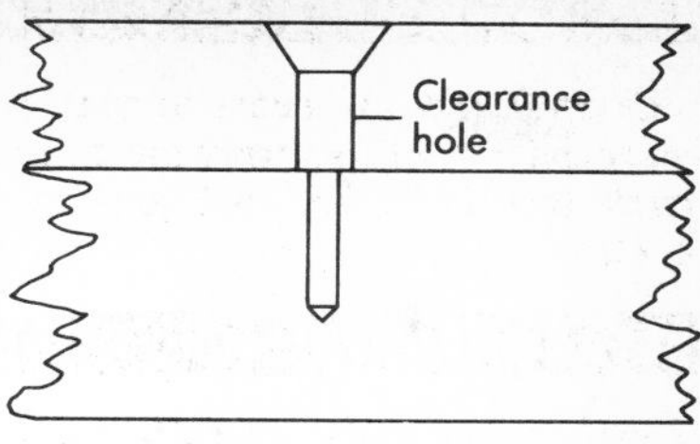

Fig C.40 Clearance hole

CLOCK PULSE GENERATOR

This is an electronic device that generates regular signals which are used to synchronize with (work at the same time with) operations in a logic circuit. The frequency is generated by a clock and is known as the *clock frequency*. The regular pulses sent to the logic circuits are called the *clock pulses*.

The obvious application of such a device is in digital clocks and time-operated mechanisms such as video recorders, electric cookers, central heating control systems, time switches, etc.

CLUTCHES

A *clutch* is a mechanical device for linking and disconnecting a driving source under control with a component that is to be driven. The most common and well known application is in the driving mechanism of a car. When the clutch is *disengaged*, the engine can be going while the car remains stationary. When the clutch is activated to become *engaged*, the rotational speed of the engine is transferred to the clutch, which in turn is linked, via shafts, to the driving wheels. As the two parts of the clutch become synchronized so the transmission of energy to the wheels is complete.

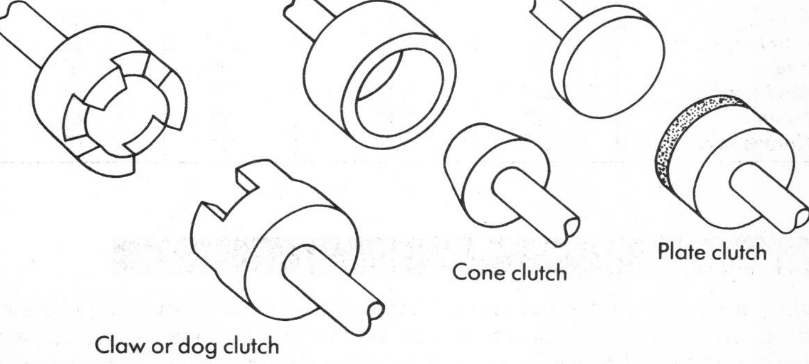

Fig C.41 Clutches

The principle of connecting a driver to a driven mechanism via a clutch is applied in many mechanical devices, such as lathes, shaping machines, etc. The need to *gradually transfer* the force of a rotating shaft from an electric motor to a heavy load of a large machine is necessary if damage is to be avoided. It is widely recognized that clutches wear out before the other components, but while they can be readily replaced, damage to a gear box could be more difficult and expensive to resolve.

Some common types of clutch are the *cone, single plate centrifugal* and *dog* (Fig C.41).

CMOS DIGITAL INTEGRATED CIRCUIT

This is a *logic gate* designed to improve speed of operation, to increase reliability and to prevent unplanned or unintended electrical impulses that may reach the input lines. The logic systems are based on a double transistor type of gate, e.g. TTL (Transistor-Transistor Logic), or on a couple of complementary MOS transistor gates, e.g. CMOS Logic. The CMOS is an improvement of the TTL gates and is the preferred standard gate.

These integrated circuits contain **diodes, transistors, resistors,** etc., and can be easily damaged if handled too much and exposed to static electricity, so do remember to handle them only when absolutely necessary and to avoid rubbing that would produce static electricity.

COEFFICIENT OF LINEAR EXPANSION

Metals have a variety of characteristics, one of them being that they expand when heated and contract when cooled. However, they do not all expand and contract at the same rate. Indeed some metals (e.g. antimony) do not expand and contract. At normal outdoor temperatures, the rate of expansion is fairly consistent and is referred to as the 'Coefficient of linear expansion'. The coefficient of linear expansion for aluminium is 0.000023 for every degree Celsius. This means that a piece of aluminium 10 metres long expands 0.23 of a millimetre for each degree Celsius that its temperature rises. This may seem a small and insignificant amount, but where there are large metal structures that may have to be exposed to a considerable range of rise and fall in temperature, this fraction of a millimetre will soon magnify to many millimetres difference in length. This factor has to be accepted and allowed for in the design of a structure.

You may have noticed that telegraph wires are never stretched taught. If they were taught in summer, they would contract in winter and snap. Again, in situations where pipes carry very hot liquids or steam for long distances, an 'expansion bend' has to be created or fitted in the system to allow the pipes to expand or contract without causing any damage. Before there were improvements in the alloying of steel for the production of railway lines, a gap of approximately 25 mm - 40 mm had to be left between each rail so that in the summer the rails could expand and remain perfectly flat. The familiar rhythm of the train travelling along the railway lines was caused by the wheels as they rolled over the gap.

COGS

Cogs are projections on a wheel or shaft that engage with a similar wheel or shaft to transmit a *rotating* motion. They are the early forms of what we know today as *gear wheels* i.e. wheels with teeth (Fig C.42)

It is known that the Chinese discovered the earliest forms of gears in the third millenium B.C. The evolution of the gear has resulted in some very high precision engineering. The principle of putting cogs in a material to make the 'teeth' is a way of transmitting energy. Where facilities are not always available for the manufacture of metal or plastic materials, gears can be made by using wood and fixing pegs in wheels. Although cogs are capable of transmitting energy, they do so at a low level of **efficiency**.

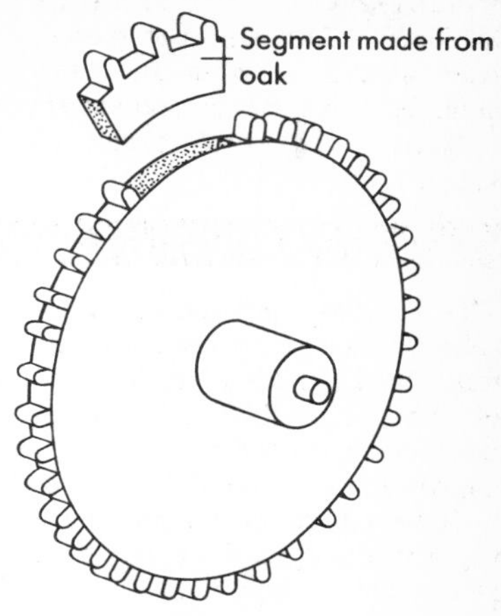

Fig C.42 Cogs

COLD WORKING OF MATERIALS

Metals can be moulded, shaped, deformed, etc. either when cold or hot. Where the operation has the prefix 'cold', then this means that heat was *not* applied, e.g. *cold bending* means that the metal was not heated. This must be stated because some bending, cutting, moulding operations of some metals *do* require heating to red heat before the operation can be successfully performed.

COLOUR

Colour to the scientist is a wavelength of visible light. In nature this wavelength of light can be seen in a rainbow. The colours range from red, through orange, yellow, green, blue, indigo to violet. Colour can be created by passing light through a glass prism.

Colour to the artist is a range of pigments that can be used to produce a painting. Starting with the *primary colours* of red, yellow and blue, other colours of the *spectrum* (the range that can be seen in the rainbow) can be achieved by adding and mixing in varying quantities. When two primary colours are mixed, they form a range of colours known as *secondary colours.* Red and yellow gives orange; yellow and blue gives green; blue and red gives violet. Orange, green and violet are secondary colours. If the primary and secondary colours are mixed, then a third range of colours is achieved, called *tertiary colours.*

The *hue* of a colour is the type of colour from which a variety of similar colours is possible, e.g. red is the hue, while crimson is the colour. The *chroma* of a colour refers to its brightness, while *tone* refers to the amount of black or white that has been added.

While there is a lot to be learnt about colour and its application, you would be wise to begin by using either the tones of a single colour or colours that 'harmonise'. Colours that are close to each other in the spectrum are easy on the eye and are said to be *in harmony* with each other. Colours that are at the opposite ends of the spectrum can be used to show *contrast*, but this has to be done with care if the desired effect is to be achieved.

COMMUNICATION

Communication in the context of CDT means the passing on of information through the medium of drawing or writing. The amount of information conveyed depends upon the *detail* given in the drawing or drawings. The writing part is only there to *support* the drawing. A frequent quote is that 'A drawing is worth a thousand words'. Try to pass on information about the solution to a problem using words only! You will soon realise how a few simple sketches can help you convey an idea and save an awful lot of words. Don't forget that if it takes a long time to write, it will take a long time to read.

COMMUTATOR

A device for altering the course of an electric current.

COMPASS CONSTRUCTION OF ANGLES

Where **construction** methods have to be shown, especially in answering problems related to Design and Communication, the *compass method* of constructing angles is an appropriate method (Fig C.43):

Construction of a 60° angle

a) Draw a straight line and label it A B;
b) Using A as a centre, draw an arc cutting the line at B;
c) Keeping the same radius on the compass, use B as a centre and draw an arc to cut the first arc;
d) Where the two arcs intersect (meet), draw a straight line from A. The angle drawn is 60°.

Remember that the **radius** is one sixth of the **circumference**. Therefore if you strike an arc on a circumference without changing the setting of the compass, you will have marked off a distance of one sixth of the circumference. By joining the centre of the circle to two marks on the circumference you will

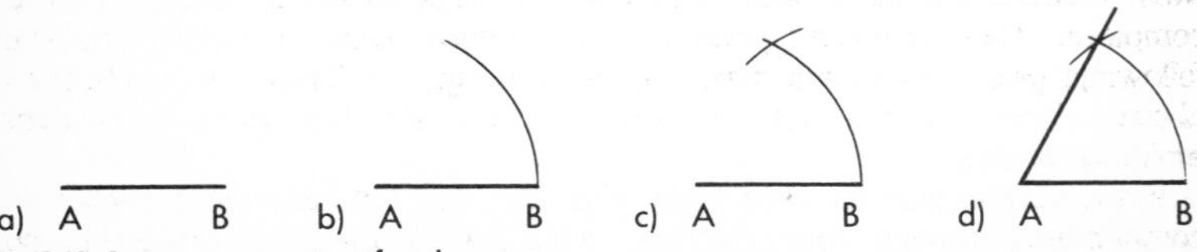

Fig C.43 Compass construction of angles

have divided the circle into sixths. The total degree in a circle is 360° and you have divided the circle into six equal parts (called sectors). Dividing 360° by six gives an answer of 60°, hence you have been constructing angles of 60°. Furthermore you have been constructing angles of 120°, 180°, 240° and 300°.

By *bisecting* an angle you are able to increase the number of angles you are able to construct; e.g. bisecting 60° produces a 30° angle. By bisecting 30° you can obtain an angle of 15° (Fig C.44). To construct an angle of 45° all you have to do is to put a 30° angle and a 15° angle *together*.

Fig C.44
Bisecting angles

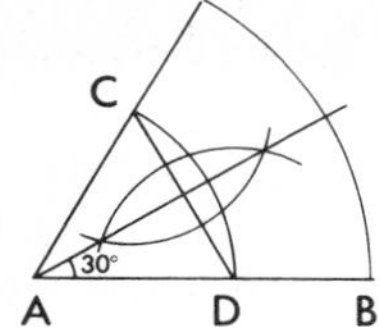

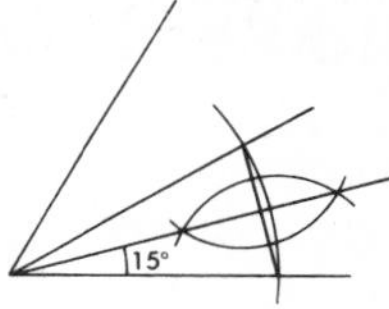

COMPASSES

The choice of compass you require depends mainly upon your needs. Most designs of compasses will draw circles using lead or drawing ink. The range of sizes of circles that can be drawn will vary from a few millimetres to 300 mm. The threaded adjustment allows for a more controlled movement in compasses and greater accuracy in the setting (Fig C.45). For larger diameter circles, extension arms can be fitted and should be able to cope with all your needs. For much larger circles, a *beam compass* is necessary. It is difficult to draw very small circles with a compass and you may find it easier to use a *circle template*.

◀ Template ▶

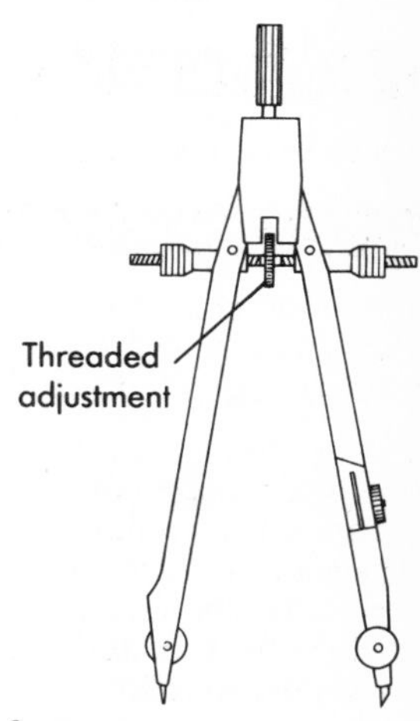

Fig C.45 Compasses

COMPONENT PARTS

Most devices are made from a number of parts which in themselves are complete. The *component parts* of a *mechanical device* could include the following: **gears, levers spindles, wheels bearings,** etc. The components of an *electric circuit* could include; **transistors, relay switches, capacitors, light emitting diodes,** etc.

Items such as screws, clips, nuts, pins, etc., are not generally regarded as components, though they may be essential to the functioning of the components listed above. It would be more accurate to call them *fittings*.

COMPOSITION

The *composition* of a material refers to the ingredients, i.e. the parts or elements that combine together to make that particular material. The composition of High Speed Steel is 4% chromium, 18% tungsten and 1.5% vanadium. A *composite material* is one that is made up of two or more other materials. The composition of concrete is sand, gravel and cement. Therefore the term has a general use and its meaning will have to be considered within the particular context in which it is used.

COMPOUND GEAR TRAIN

Many mechanisms require a *combination* of gears to enable more than one component to be rotating or different components to be rotating at different speeds. The *rotational speed* of the work on a *centre lathe* needs to move at one speed, while the *linear movement* of a *cutting tool* needs to move at another speed. In order to achieve this, a combination of gears are assembled on their respective shafts and adjusted so that they mesh. This means that the rotation of the *driver gear* will cause the other gears to rotate. This combination of gears is called a *gear train*. A compound gear train includes gears that have more than one set of teeth. They are able to be in contact with one gear on one set of teeth and another gear on the other set of teeth (Fig C.46).

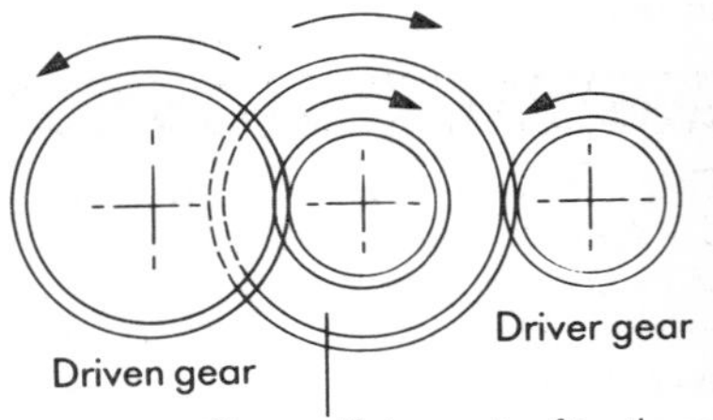

Fig C.46 Compound gear train

COMPRESSED AIR

Air that has been squeezed into a smaller volume is under *compression*. If the container into which the air is compressed has a controlled opening, the air will force its way out of the container until it is balanced with atmospheric air pressure (the pressure of the air around you).

Compressed air has several practical applications. It can be used to run small engines, for spraying varnishes, paints, etc., or for applying a pressure to mould-heated thermoplastic materials. It can also be used for air-brush work in graphic illustration. On a very practical note, it is used for inflating the tyres of most vehicles involved in road transport. Compressed air is also used as a coolant for machine cutting tools such as drills, band saws, etc. It helps keep the tool and the work cool and clear of any loose pieces, without getting wet.

Examples of the use of very high air pressure in industry are found in pneumatic circuits where products are cleaned and abraded. Here a fine abrading dust is introduced into the air flow and the fine particles abrade the surfaces of whatever they contact (sparking plugs are cleaned in this way).

COMPRESSION

Compression is a *pressing force*. Usually a structure that is under pressure is said to be under a load. When you sit on a chair or stool you place its legs under a load, i.e. your weight; the legs are said to be *under compression*. Compression is the opposite of **tension**, where a *pulling force* is applied to an object.

When a beam is under a load its upper surface is being pressed into a smaller space, in which case it is 'in compression', while on the under side the surface is being stretched or pulled and is 'in tension' ◀ **Forces** ▶

COMPRESSION MOULDING

Compression moulding is an industrial process in which a thermosetting plastic in powdered form is placed into the lower half of a metal split mould. The upper half is brought down and, under a **compression** force plus heat, the powdered thermosetting plastic becomes molten and flows to form the shape of the cavity of the mould. Such things as light fittings, switches and door handles are made by this process. The expensive equipment needed for this process puts it outside the range of processes that can be carried out in schools.

COMPRESSION SPRING

There are two types of *coil spring*. *Compression springs* are designed to withstand a pressing force. The coiled springs used to take the load in most forms of land transport, e.g. cars, railway trains, make use of compression springs. On a smaller scale, compression springs are used in the three jaw chuck of a hand drill. Here the springs are used to keep the jaws apart so that a drill bit can be easily fitted. Trigger mechanisms are often spring-loaded, so that when the force applied by the finger is released, the trigger returns to its original position. Figure C.47 shows the sectioned view of a spray gun; here three compression springs are used to make the spray gun function.

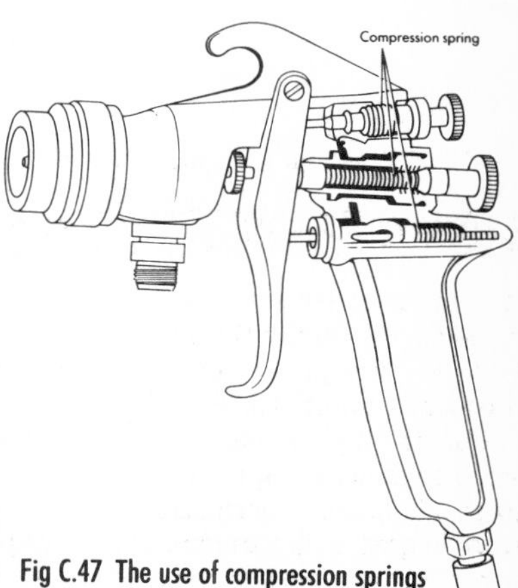

Fig C.47 The use of compression springs

Tension springs are coiled springs which withstand pulling forces.

When using springs in projects it is important that you select a coiled spring according to its type (compression or tension), its length, its diameter and the force it will withstand. A guide to determining the force can be obtained by looking at the gauge of the wire; the heavier the gauge, the greater the force or load that can be taken.

COMPUTER AIDED DESIGN

This term is often abbreviated as CAD and the process is exactly as the term implies. In other words a *computer* is used to *help* solve a *design* problem. By coding a programme into the computer an image can be produced on a screen. Tone values can be selected so that a variation of light and dark areas can be produced. Three important stages are involved in a complete process, i.e. *input, processing* (via a Central Processor Unit – CPU) and *output.*

INPUT	*CENTRAL PROCESSOR UNIT*	*OUTPUT*
Light pen Joystick Digitiser Touch sensitive screen Graphic tablet	All calculations here	Monitor screen Printer Robot Plotter Disk

In this case we are interested in producing a solution to a design problem, which means that the final stage will be a 'printout' of the solution. You must remember that the CPU will only process what it is capable of accepting as input (e.g. an instruction).

COMPUTER GRAPHICS

Computers are able to store and display quite detailed and complex drawings. The drawings can be produced on a screen and can be modified, extended and rearranged. They can also be presented in **isometric** and **perspective** views, and even rotated so that they can be seen from different positions. The application of a graphical image on a screen provides opportunities for engineers, architects and graphic designers to extend their skills of *designing* before decisions are made to *realise* an end product, whether it be a new design for a boat, hair dryer or shopping complex. Computer graphics are relatively new and rapidly developing, and can be seen as a creative tool for designers.

CONCENTRIC CIRCLES

These are circles of different diameters yet sharing the same centre (Fig C.48).

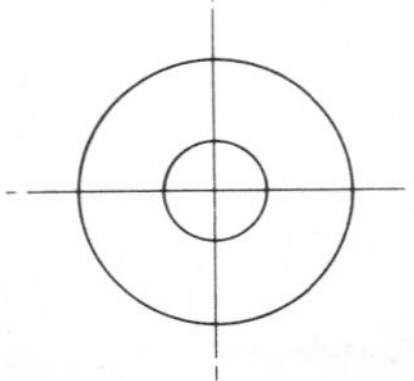

Fig C.48
Concentric circles

CONCRETE

This is a composition of sand, gravel and cement. The three ingredients are usually mixed together while dry to make sure that the mix is even. Then water is added to start the chemical action of the cement. While the concrete mix is wet and easily worked it is put into a mould, or onto an area that has been prepared on the ground, and allowed to set. Tapping the sides of the mould (shuttering) helps to release air that is trapped during mixing, improves the strength of the concrete and avoids small holes appearing in the surface of the casting. Concrete is much used in foundations for buildings because its compressive strength is excellent. But it can also be used for garden benches, park seats, etc.

CONDENSER

◄ Capacitor ►

CONDUCTOR

A *conductor* is a material that will allow the flow of electrons as electricity, or energy in the form of heat. Most metals are excellent conductors. Aluminium and copper are the two most commonly used materials in various kinds of circuits because of their low resistance to a current. Where **thermal** conductivity is required, a nickel steel is used because it must be able to withstand temperatures around 900°C, as in the case of heating elements in an electric oven that can become red hot.

CONE

A *cone* has a circular base and the sides taper to a point. When the point is positioned immediately above the centre of the circular base, the cone is called a *right angle cone* (Fig C.49). The vertical axis from the point of the cone to the centre of the base forms a right angle with the radius of the base.

Cones can be solid or hollow. A solid cone can be sectioned (cut) to show a variety of geometric shapes. These are known as *conic sections* and are described by the *shape* they produce, e.g. ellipse, circle, parabola and hyperbola (Fig C.50). The hollow cones can be produced from a flat sheet of paper, but the paper has to be cut to a certain shape. This shape is called a *development*. If the cone is incomplete it is known as a *truncated cone* (Fig C.51). Knowledge of its construction is useful in the making of lamp shades.

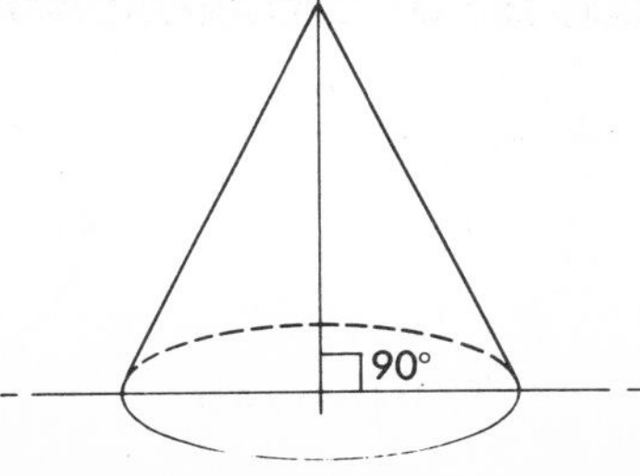

Fig C.49 Right angle cone

Ellipse

Circle

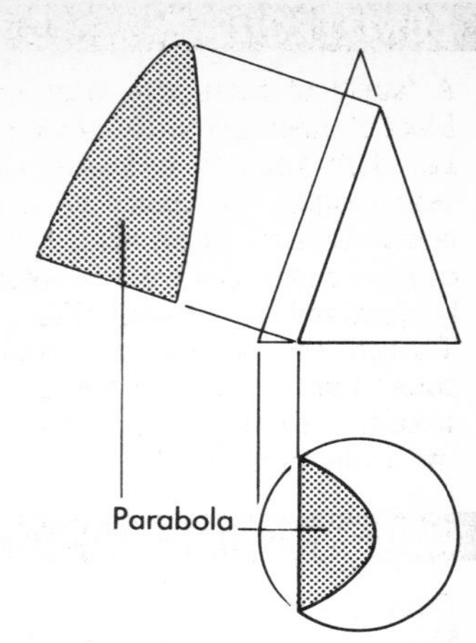

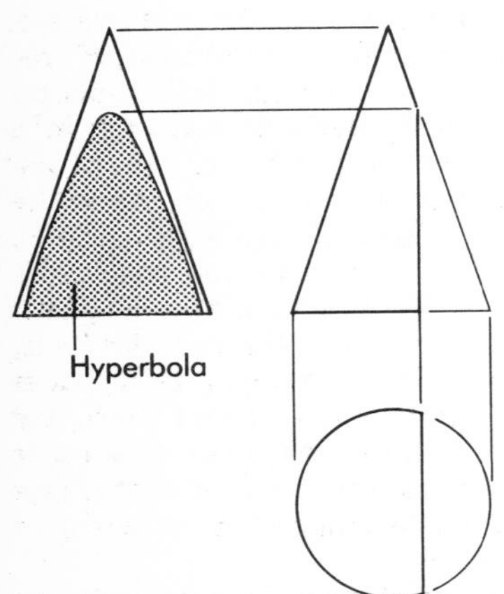

Fig C.50 Conic sections

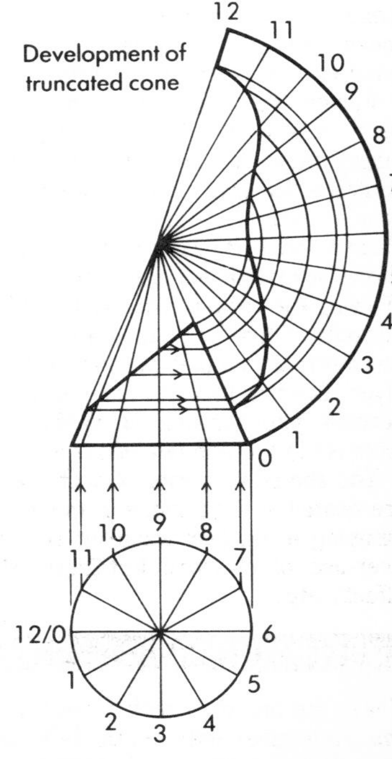

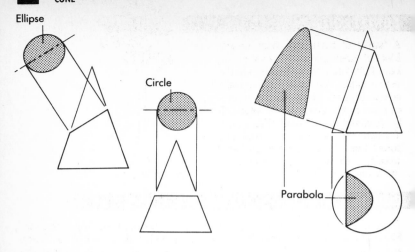

Fig C.51 Truncated cone

CONIFEROUS

A family of trees that bear cones. Most of these trees are 'evergreens', i.e. they keep their leaves all the year round. The leaves are usually needle-shaped. The timber that comes from coniferous trees is botanically classified as *softwood* (Fig C.52). Though the woods *are* generally softer than those classified as hardwoods, there are exceptions.
◀ **Softwoods** ▶

Fig C.52 Coniferous tree

CONSERVATION

To conserve something is to save it from destruction and possibly extinction. Much of plant life and animal life is constantly under the threat of extinction and groups of people have been formed whose main task is to stop the activities that are endangering animal and plant life. The names of groups such as 'Greenpeace' and 'Friends of the Earth' are internationally known and frequently hit the headlines for their activities. Even the Prime Minsters of today are taking measures to ensure that the 'conservation of the environment' is given high priority in the various technological programmes.

Famous people like Dr David Bellamy and Sir David Attenborough have been campaigning for years to encourage us to take better care of our environment. We are now aware of the dangers of using aerosol sprays. The contents that provide the propellant for spray products such as hair lacquer, paints, fresh air sprays and insecticides often contain compounds called chlorofluoro carbons (CFCs), which are harmful to the protective atmospheric ozone layer that encloses the earth. A 'hole' is being created in this layer, allowing the harmful ultra-violet radiation from the sun to reach us in greater strength. Ultra-violet rays are responsible for turning your skin brown, but too much ultra-violet radiation will also cause cancer of the skin. The ozone layer acts as a barrier to the ultra-violet rays and only a safe amount of rays normally pass through. Damaging this layer in the stratosphere is causing an increase in the number of cases of skin cancer.

You should be aware of such happenings and of the national incidents that are related to this topic, e.g. the effects of **acid rain** on plants and animals, the dumping of nuclear waste at sea, the destruction of the rain forests, the over-use of chemical fertilizers, the damage caused by the 'greenhouse effect', etc.

CONSTRAINTS

These are the limits within which you can fulfil a **design brief**. For example a *constraint* given either in the brief or in the **analysis** of the brief could be that the solution must be made from acrylic only. So straight away you are limited to thinking about solutions that could be made in acrylic.

CONSTRUCTION

The method by which all the parts are held together. The construction of a *wooden* box could be such that the sides are held together by dovetails, the bottom rebated and the top tongue and grooved. In the case of a *metal* construction the components could be brazed, silver soldered, rivetted, etc. In the case of a *plastics* material, the parts could be heat-welded or bonded with an adhesive.

In *graphics* there is a need to draw shapes using instruments. The methods by which this may be achieved are through a knowledge of construction *techniques*. Construction *lines* are thin so that they do not interfere with the outline of the shape under construction. All construction lines should be left on the drawing, so it is important that they are thin.

CONTACT BOUNCE

When a switch is operated from 'off' to 'on' or 'on' to 'off', the *change* from one state to the other should be as 'clean' as possible. What really happens is that when the contacts close, they *bounce* many times before the change from one state to the other is complete. Though the bouncing period is very short, i.e. only millionths of a second, in a logic circuit this can mean several changes of logic levels before the system comes to rest. Remember that the cheaper the switch, the more bounces will occur and the longer the period needed for the change to take place.

The bouncing caused by a mechanical switch is not very important in some circuits but in an electronic counting circuit the bouncing may well cause considerable inaccuracy. There are ways of getting rid of the 'bounce' by using a 'debouncing circuit'. ◀ Debouncing, Schmitt trigger ▶

CONTROL SYSTEMS

Most industrial and commercial processes are now computer controlled. With sophisticated sensors, computers can be programmed to control temperature, mechanical operations, counting, sorting, and the storing and retrieving of products or information.

CONVENTIONS

In order to save time and to ensure a clear and accurate presentation of information, a set of rules and symbols have been accepted as a standard means of communication. You will find these in the British Standards Publications. ◀ British Standards Institution ▶

COOLANTS

When a cutting action is taking place heat is generated in the cutting tool and the material being cut. The temperature, if allowed to get too high, may cause damage to the cutting tool and reduce its efficiency. This may result in damage to both the tool and the material. In the case of cutting *metals*, a liquid is used

– a mixture of a soluble oil and water; for cutting *thermoplastic materials*, a jet of cold air is used.

CO-ORDINATES

Co-ordinates are a series of straight, parallel lines that are equally spaced. They are used in graphs and help in determining the areas of irregular shaped polygons. Lines that are drawn mid-way between co-ordinates are called *mid-ordinates*. ◀ Area ▶

COPE AND DRAG

Fig C.53
Cope and drag

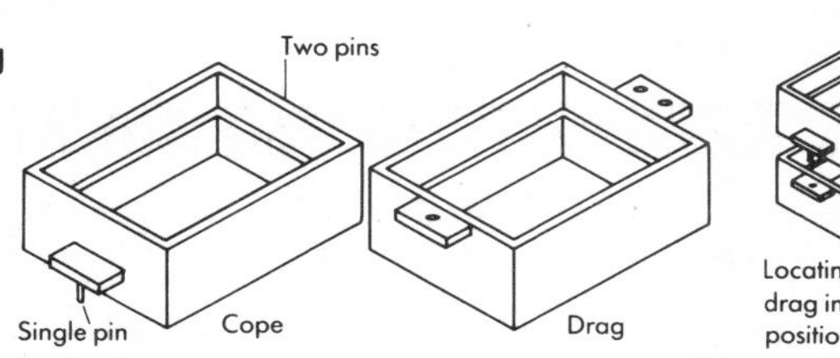

These are the two halves of a flask that are used in casting hot metal. The process involves the use of a casting sand and a pattern to make the cavity for the moulding. The sand is contained by the two halves of the flask. The flasks can be made from wood or metal. Remember that the cope always goes on top of the drag (Fig C.53). ◀ Casting ▶

CORROSION

This takes place with metals. The element iron is particularly noted for its corrosive properties, since it readily combines with oxygen in the air to form an oxide (a thin skin on the surface) called *iron oxide*. This can be seen as a grey skin on the surface when red hot iron is allowed to cool. If, however, the iron is exposed to the air and water, a *hydrated iron oxide* is formed and this is known as *rust*. It forms on iron as an electrolytic process, and has a weakening effect on metals and is a serious cause for concern. Many methods have been developed to protect highly corrosive metals, such as coating with layers of paint, electroplating, anodising and alloying with other elements. Metal alloys, such as stainless steel (an alloy of iron, nickel and chromium) do not corrode and do not need a protective layer. Some metals, like copper, do not rust but they do try to oxidise with the air. Any form of oxidation is a form of corrosion.

COSTING

This is the process of detailing all the factors that determine what an item costs to make. The factors that should be included in the costing are: material; equipment; ancilliary materials such as glues, nails, abrasives, finishes, etc; energy used in heating, lighting, etc; time, including designing, research, and testing; etc.

COUNTERBORE

When a socket screw is used and a flush surface finish is required, the outer surface of the material being prepared is *counterbored.* The first hole drilled is a clearance fit for the *shank* of the screw, and the second drilling in the same hole is a clearance fit for the *head* of the screw. It is drilled with a flat bottom drill called a 'Counterbore', which is specially designed with a detachable pilot. The counterbore hole is drilled to a depth that is equal in size to the length of the head (Fig C.54). Counterboring is done in metals and plastics and is the equivalent to *countersinking* in wood.

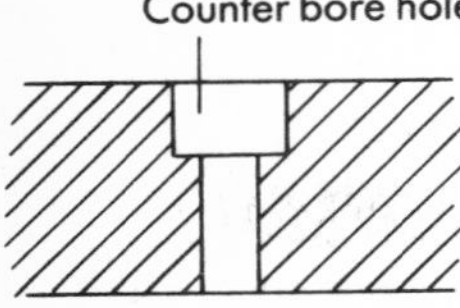

Fig C.54 Counterbore

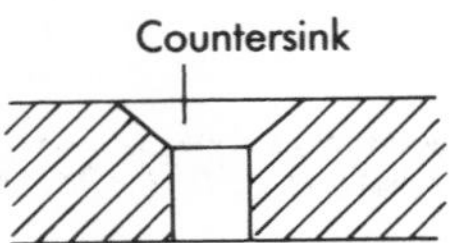

Fig C.55 Countersink

COUNTERSINK

This is a hole drilled with a countersink drill, so that the head of a countersink screw can fit either flush or slightly recessed with the surface of the material being held by the screw (Fig C.55).

COUNTERSINK BITS

These are the drills used to produce the countersink hole. ◄ Centre bit ►

COUPLINGS

Couplings are devices for joining shafts or pipes. The most common is the *flanged coupling* which is used for connecting pipes that are to carry liquids, air, or gases under pressure. Quick release *air couplings* are also available where a change of equipment frequently occurs.

CRAMPS

These are holding devices. Their main purpose is to provide a temporary hold on a component while it is being worked upon, or to hold items while an adhesive is setting (Fig C.56).

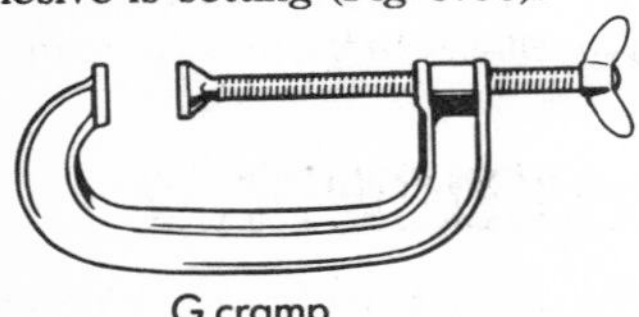

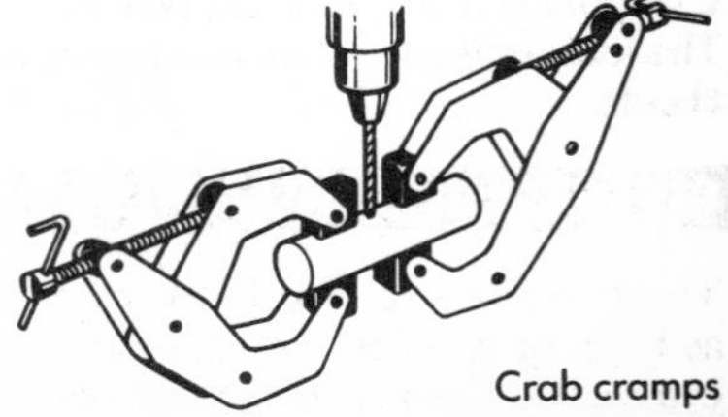

Fig C.56 Types of cramp

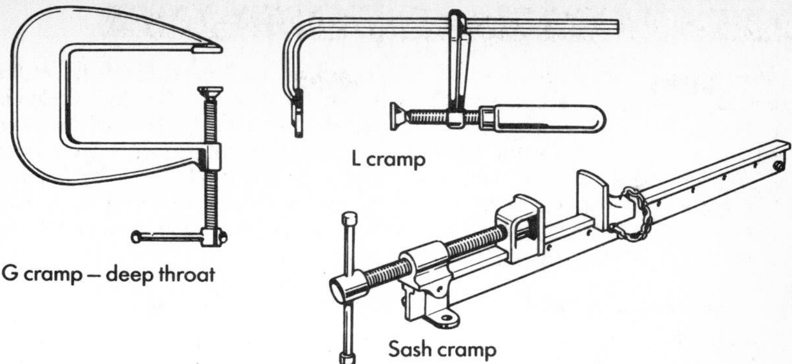

CRANK

Cranks are mechanical devices. They are devices for changing the direction of a force. There are *bell cranks*, single and double. A *single* type changes the direction of a force through 90°. The application of this principle is used in the braking system of a bicycle (Fig C.57).

Fig C.57 Bell crank

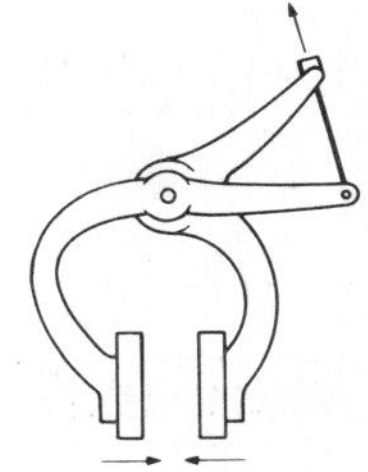

The *double* bell crank is used to produce two directions of movement from a single source. You will find that radio controlled model cars, aeroplanes, and yachts use this mechanism. Cranks and sliders form parts of mechanisms which usually involve you in the construction of **loci** problems.

CREATIVE

This is an activity in which ideas are *developed* from available knowledge. Though the information may be common knowledge an individual may apply that information in a way that is different from other people.

CRIMPING

Crimping is a compressing process in which the material is forced into folds. The folds bring about an increase in strength, similar to the folds in corrugated sheets.

CRITERIA

These are the standards by which you judge or **evaluate** a performance, activity, or product. The standards by which you judge something should be established *before* judging takes place. In fact if you are involved with a design problem that has arisen as the result of a *need,* then the first factor to judge is how well the need is satisfied. To be able to answer this more fully, you would need to go into greater detail, so you would examine the *components* of the solution to see how well they perform their role. If you have analysed a problem and made a *list,* this list could form the basis of your *criteria.* Suppose that in the **analysis** you have written, 'the container must be portable'; the criteria could then be written 'Is the container portable?' For each part of the analysis the same procedure could be carried out. In this way you will have a *set of criteria* which you can use when evaluating your solution.

◄ Analysis, Evaluation ►

CROSS-CUT

This is an arrangement of the teeth of a saw so that you can cut across the grain (Fig C.58).

Fig C.58 Cross-cut

CROSS-LINKING

As a result of a chemical reaction in a **thermosetting** plastic the molecular structure becomes set and cannot be changed by heating.

CRYSTALS

Most pure solid substances are made up of *crystals.* Though there are only a few basic shapes of crystals, the shape of a substance can vary substantially because the crystals are small and the substance is a clump of many hundred or thousands of crystals. Crystals are very regular in form and have an axis about which they are symmetrical (Fig C.59).

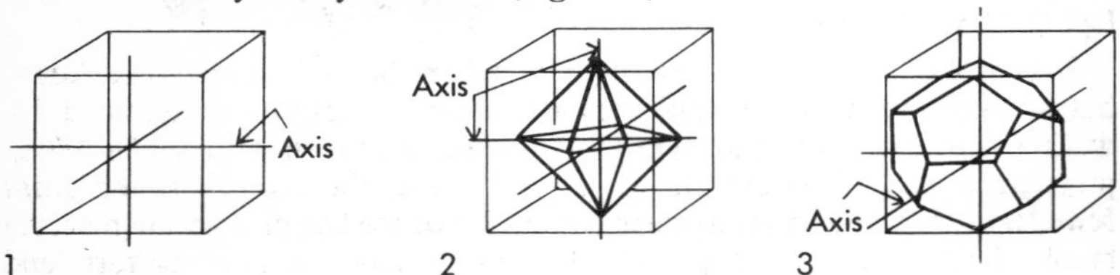

Fig C.59 Crystals

CRYSTALLINITY IN METALS

With the exception of mercury, all metals are in a solid state at normal atmospheric temperatures. However, all metals can be made to *flow* like a liquid when heated to melting point. While the metal is molten, its atoms are vibrating and do not follow a particular pattern. When the metal cools, very small crystals made up of millions of atoms begin to form. With continued cooling, more and more crystals grow on the previously formed crystals. If you watch ice (water becoming solid) forming on a window, you notice how the crystalline patterns grow the colder the window gets. This is what is happening in metals when they cool.

The beginnings of the formation of a crystal is referred to as a nucleus and as the growth continues the atoms take on a regular pattern. The arrangement is very precise and the cells are called *dendrites* (Fig C.60). The dendrites form metallic crystals. There are three structures, the *face-centred cube,* the *body centred cube,* and the *close packed hexagonal* which is similar to the crystalline form of water (Fig C.61).

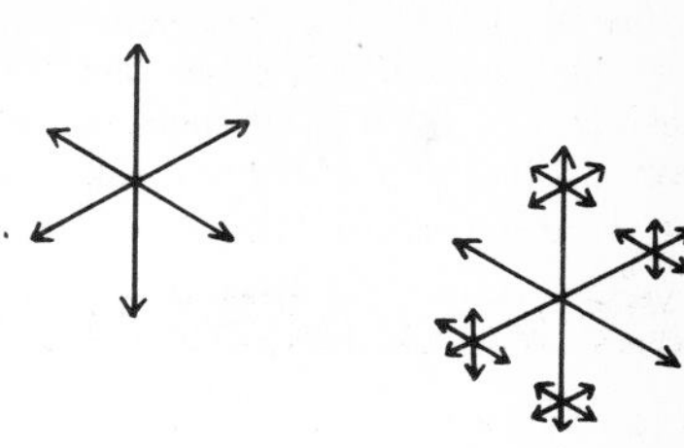

Fig C.60 Dendrites

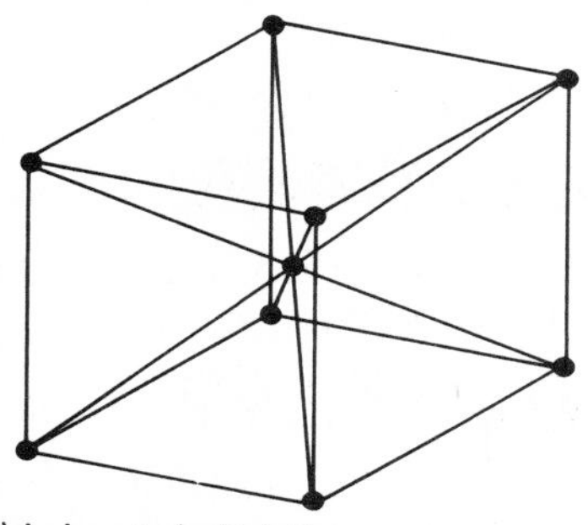

a) body centred cubic lattice

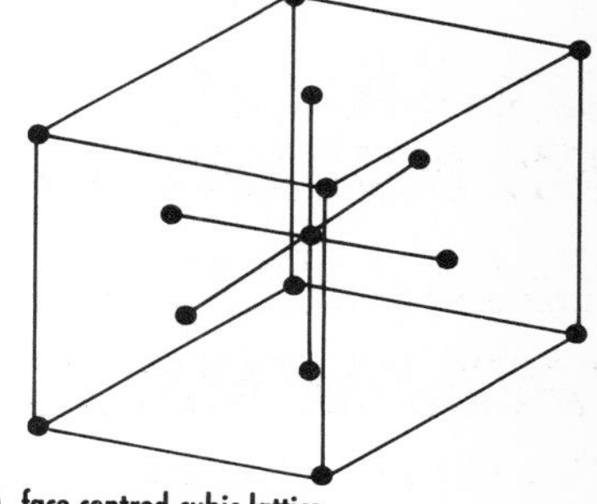

b) face centred cubic lattice

c) water crystallises in a hexagonal form

Fig C.61 Crystallinity in metals

The structures are known as a *lattice,* and are bonded by an atomic force, but in their growth a dislocation in the lattice structure can occur and a weakness or flaw may be present along the line of growth in the metal. When pressure is applied during the working of metal, the crystals at the *grain boundary* (where the crystal grains either side of the line of dislocation occur) break their atomic bonding and slip into a more regular pattern and re-establish their bonding more securely. The weakness no longer exists and the metal is now stronger.

CURING

When a liquid synthetic resin is going 'hard', or 'setting', it is said to be curing. Polyester resins, such as those used in Glass Reinforced Plastics (GRP), are made to cure by adding a chemical. This starts a chemical reaction which will make the liquid state of the resin change to a solid state.

CURRENT

The flow of electrons (electricity) in a conductor is called a current. The term used to describe the movement of electrons, e.g. *flow current*, is used because electricity was originally thought of as an invisible liquid. If you wish to make sure that you spell the word that applies to electricity and not a fruit, remember that this word has an 'e' for electricity, so the correct spelling is with an 'e' not an 'a'.

CURRENT MEASUREMENT

Current is measured in **amperes**. The force that makes it flow, *electromotive force* (e.m.f.), is measured in units called **volts**. Whenever a **conductor** (e.g. a piece of copper wire) is connected to the terminals of an electrical source, the e.m.f. will make a current flow in the circuit. The strength of the current depends on the strength of the e.m.f. and on the *resistance* (the opposition to the flow). ◀ **Ohm's Law, Resistor** ▶

CURVES

Lines are either straight or not straight. The *not straight* lines fit into a very large family of curves in which only a few have names, e.g. *circular, elliptical, hyperbolic, parabolic,* etc. These all conform to regular patterns and you are advised to read about them under the heading of their names if you wish to know more about them.

To assist in the drawing of curves, **templates** have been designed to help you. Circular and elliptical templates are available for drawing complete circles, ellipses, or parts of them. **French curves** are available to assist with more complex curves. When using curves, remember that in 'good quality' curves one edge is bevelled and that this edge should be next to the paper when drawing with an ink pen. The bevel reduces the chances of spoiling your work by the ink running under the template.

CUT SURFACE

This refers to the surface that is created by taking a *section* of a component or geometric solid. ◀ **Cutting plane, Cone** ▶

CUTTING LIST

This is a list of the materials and sizes needed so that you get the materials in the quantity and size you require. Think of it as a shopping list, i.e. a document that has the appropriate details for you to get exactly what you need.

A *cutting list* can only be made once a detailed **working drawing** has been produced. It can be written on the same sheet of paper as the working drawing and should include the following:– name of the part; material from which it is made; sizes of length, width and thickness, in that order; the quantity required and the surface finish if appropriate (e.g. for wood the surface can be sawn or planed). Remember that the sawn sizes are given for natural timber and that when planed, even though the dimensions are now smaller, the wood will still be referred to in terms of the size it was *before* planing.

CUTTING PLANE

The *cutting plane* is the position from which a *section view* is going to be projected. In **orthographic projection** the section view replaces one of the outside views. The convention for a cutting plane in an *engineering* drawing is shown in Fig C.62. The usual convention is for the cutting plane to be given in one view only, but a second view can be helpful in establishing an exact position. ◀ **Hatching, Sectioning** ▶

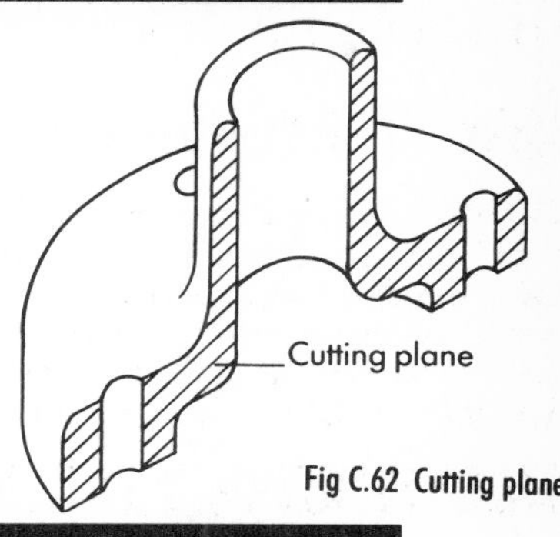

Fig C.62 Cutting plane

CYCLOID

A *cycloid* is a **locus** (the path of a moving point) of a point on the **circumference** of a circle which rolls, without slipping, along a straight line or flat surface (Fig C.63).

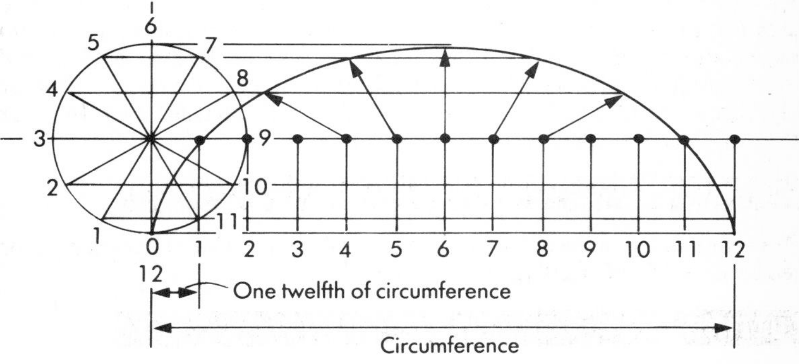

Fig C.63 Cycloid

CYLINDER

A *cylinder* is a **prism**. It has a *circular* cross-sectional shape, taken at *right angles*, at any position along its central axis; it has a *parallelogram* cross-sectional shape when taken *parallel* to the central axis; it has an *ellipse*

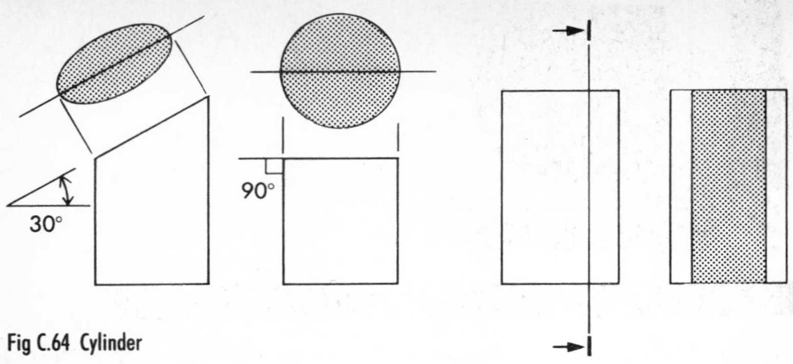

Fig C.64 Cylinder

cross-sectional shape (or part-ellipse shape) when taken at any angle *other than 90°* to the central axis (Fig C.64).

CYLINDER TRUNCATED

Truncate means to cut off the top. If the top is cut at an angle to the central axis (normally 30°, 45°, 60°, or 90°), then the cylinder is said to be *truncated*.

In pneumatics the cylinder is the device for producing the force and the linear motion. There are two types of cylinder, single acting and double acting.

◀ Single acting cylinder, Double acting cylinder ▶

DANUM TRENT

A system for mounting electronic and electrical circuits was developed at Danum Grammar School in Doncaster. The quickness and ease with which circuits could be mounted and modified made them ideally suitable for use by students working out circuitry in a practical way. The components are fitted on a plastic extrusion, which can be easily clipped to additional lengths should further development be necessary (Fig D.1).

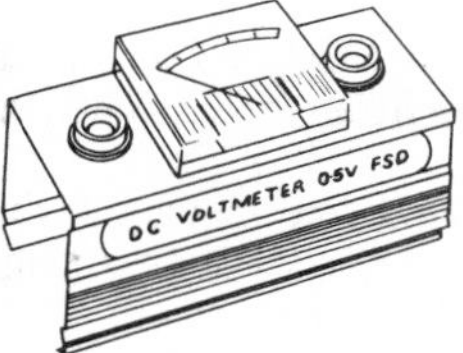

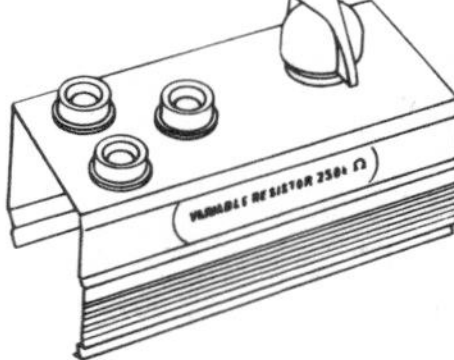

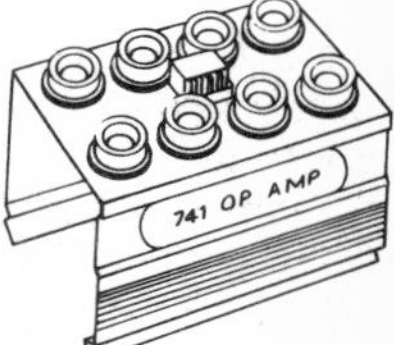

Fig D.1 Danum trent

DARLINGTON PAIR AMPLIFIER

This is the compound connection of two transistors to operate as a *single* transistor. The first transistor receives a small current at its base (input signal) and passes on an amplified current (emitter current) to the base of the second transistor which emits an even larger current. The increase of the current is the *square value* of a single transistor; e.g. if the value of the first transistor is 100, then the value of the current emitted from the second transistor is 100 × 100, which is 10,000. Figure D.2 shows the coupling of the two transistors.

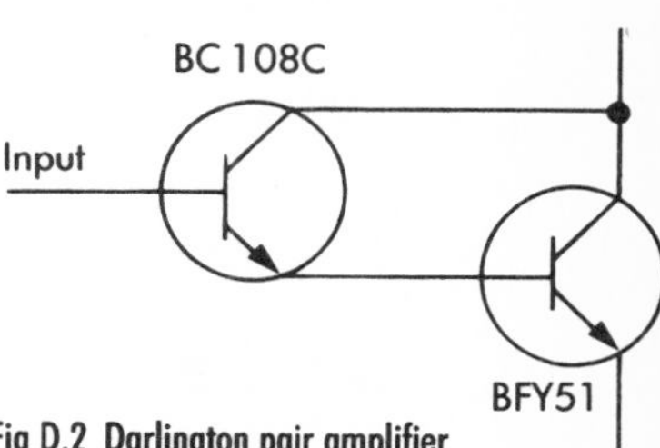

Fig D.2 Darlington pair amplifier

DATA

In general use the term *data* is often taken to mean 'acceptable or reliable information' which can be used to perform other functions.

DATA PROCESSING

This is the automatic or semi-automatic arrangement and processing of numerical information input into the system. The Analogue and Digital computer are examples of data processing equipment. You may have used a digital counter to interpret pulse signals received from an active *anemometer head* (a device used to measure wind speed). The data can be processed by the counter and displayed as wind speed in miles per hour.

DATA PROCESSING FLOW CHART SYMBOLS

These are the symbols used to represent an activity. *Arrows* represent a particular activity while *nodes* (crossing point of the lines) indicate time. For detailed information refer to BS4058 *Data processing flow chart symbols, rules and conventions*, or BSI PP7307 for more limited information.

DATUM

The singular of data. One piece or unit of information.

DATUM LINE OR SURFACE

These are the *lines* or *surfaces* from which other measurements are taken. On an engineering drawing, dimensions can be taken from a datum line (Fig D.3).

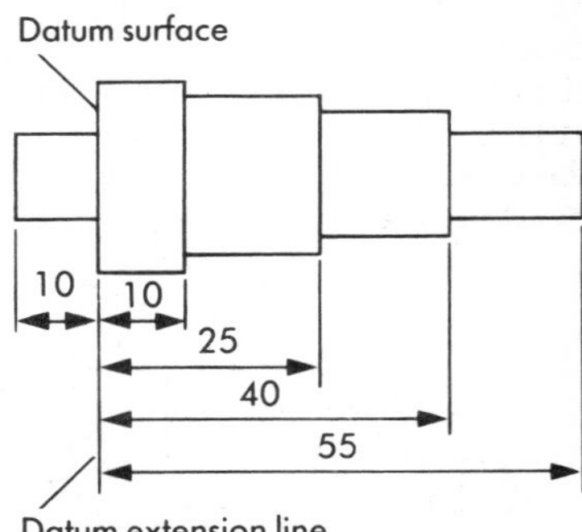

Fig D.3 Datum line or surface

DEBOUNCING

This is a method of eliminating *bouncing* in a circuit, where changes from logic level 0 to logic level 1 must be as 'clean' as possible. There are two circuits that can be used when using TTL logic chips. The first circuit uses a 2K2 pull up **resistor** and a 10μ **capacitor** as shown in Fig D.4a). The second circuit is developed further by including a 100R resistor to form a **potential divider** with the 2K2 resistor. This will have the effect of holding a **Schmitt** inverter at 0.22V so that it will remain on logic 0 (Fig D.4b)). This type of circuit is only suitable for manually operated mechanical switches that are not rapidly switched on and off. Remember that the capacitor needs time for recharging.

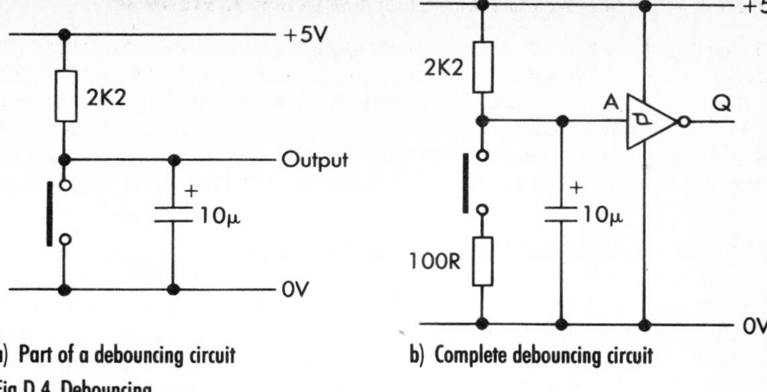

a) Part of a debouncing circuit
b) Complete debouncing circuit

Fig D.4 Debouncing

DECIDUOUS

This is a botanical classification of trees covering two types, deciduous and coniferous. Deciduous trees are recognised by their flat leaves and the fact that the leaves fall in the autumn of each year. There are, however, exceptions to this rule, perhaps the best known example being Holly. The timber obtained from deciduous trees is called a hardwood. Again the classification (hardwood) is established botanically rather than in terms of its characteristics. Indeed, one of the most commonly used timbers in model making is *Balsa*, which is a very soft and light wood for working. Quite often the deciduous tree is shaped in outline in the manner of its leaves (Fig D.5).

◀ Hardwood, Softwood ▶

Fig D.5 Deciduous trees

DECISION MAKING

Whenever you are involved in problem solving, designing, planning, etc., you will inevitably reach a stage where decisions will have to be made. You will have to *choose* the appropriate material, process of manufacture, order in which things have to be done, and so on. *Decision making* is all about gathering relevant *information* from which you will choose, select, plan and decide how to proceed. You only make decisions after careful thought has been given to alternative possibilities.

DECODER

A *decoder* is a pulse detector. It receives a pattern of pulses which have been transmitted by means of a code from a pulse coder. A suitable decoder must be used to pick up the signals of the pulse train and turn it back into the original information that was being transmitted. Morse code, where each letter of the alphabet can be identified by a series of dots and dashes, is a well known example of a decoder being used.

DECODER DRIVER CHIP

These are integrated circuits which send a certain pattern of pulses that can be used to control movement with the aid of stepper motors. Projects involving buggies, cranes, robots, computer controlled lathes, etc., use decoder driver chips in their circuitry.

DEFORMING

Deforming a material means to change its shape, by bending. Though a trimming process may be required to put the finishing touches, the main shaping process involves deforming the material.

Most metals, thermoplastics and wood can be deformed when they are in the appropriate condition. Metals have to be **annealed** or heated to a temperature where they can be deformed by beating (beaten metalwork) or **forging.**

Thermoplastics have to be heated so that they can be either bent along a straight line or formed into complex shapes by such processes as **vacuum forming** or by using a **plug** and yoke mould (Fig D.6).

Wood can be deformed using a *laminating process* where thin slices of wood are bonded together with an adhesive while in a **former**. Such items as a salad serving spoon and forks, wooden jewellery, etc., use this process. When larger thicknesses of wood are used, the wood is *steamed* to make it more pliable, before putting it in a former. Such items as curved roof beams, furniture, tennis racquets, squash racquets, etc., can be made using this process. Wood can also be deformed after it has been steam heated, put in a former and allowed to cool and without the need of an adhesive to help it retain its curved form. Wood has its own *natural adhesives* which soften when steam heated and set when cooled. So when a piece of wood is thoroughly steamed it will faithfully reproduce the curved shape of the formers used. Such products

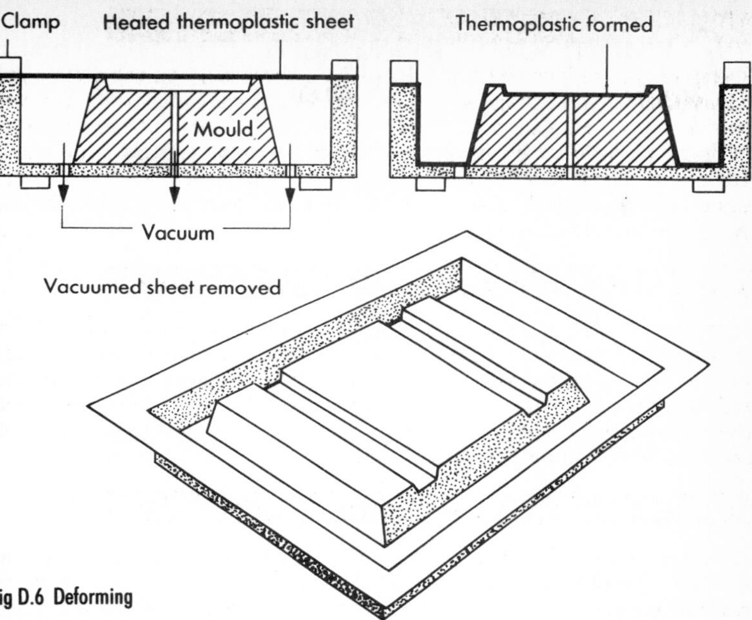

Fig D.6 Deforming

as walking sticks, parts of chairs, hockey sticks, etc., are produced by *steam bending* techniques.

Remember not to confuse deforming processes with **reforming** processes. Reforming process include **casting** and **enamelling**. ◀ Form, Laminate ▶

DEGASSING

The process of *degassing* a molten metal that is being prepared for **casting** is necessary if the gasses in the metal are to be released before being poured into a **mould**. If the gasses are *not* encouraged to escape, by plunging a degassing tablet into the melt, the finished casting will have blow holes which will be unsightly and cause a weakness. Degassing should be done in a well-ventilated area. The action is quite vigorous; when all activity stops, the process is complete.

DELAMINATION

Laminated boards are made from layers of wood called **lamina** which are bonded together by an adhesive. When the adhesive breaks down, its bonding power no longer holds the lamina together and the lamina start separating – a process known as *delamination*. Delamination can be caused by the use of a poor quality glue or by soaking the laminate in water. Many types of manufactured board have a top layer known as a **laminate** and are widely used in kitchen furniture. Delamination occurs when the laminate begins to part from the board.

DESIGN/DESIGNING

The activity to produce an end product or solution to a problem is known as *designing*. The end product may be referred to as the *design*.

DESIGN BRIEF

All problem solving activities need to be given a *statement* outlining what is required. This can be given in two or three words or in a short sentence, such as 'Design a product that could be sold at a summer fete to raise money for a charity', or 'Design a security system for a bicycle', or 'Design a means of conveying graphical information about a building layout'. For further information you would then read a **specification** and/or an **analysis**.

Think of the design brief as a heading of a newspaper article. It tells you just enough for you to know what the topic is aobut.

DESIGN FOLIO

This is a folder or *folio* containing all the evidence of the work that has led to the problem being solved. It is usually presented in the form of a book. The cover bears a title and the name of the author. It shows the work in the same order as that outlined in a Design Process, and in a well organised folio the pages are numbered and a contents list is prepared so that the 'looking up' of particular information is made quick and easy.

DESIGN LOOP

This is a graphical presentation of the activities to be completed in a design activity. It is referred to as a *loop* because the complete process brings you back to the beginning. The evaluation, which is the final stage, involves you referring to the 'design brief' which is where you began.

DESIGN PROCESS

This is a sequence of activities which result in an artefact being designed (Fig D.7). It includes; identification of a need, writing a design brief, analysing the problem, research/investigation, developing ideas, testing and evaluating, developing a chosen idea, producing a detailed working drawing, making the solution, testing and evaluating the product to see how well it fulfils the design brief and analysis. ◀ **Design loop** ▶

DETAIL DRAWING

As the name suggests the drawing must be fully detailed so that hidden detail, constructional detail, sizes, name of the material to be used etc., is given. The question to answer is 'Could the item in question be made from the given information?' A detailed drawing can also be called a '**working drawing**', but this usually implies that the drawing is to be done in **orthographic projection**

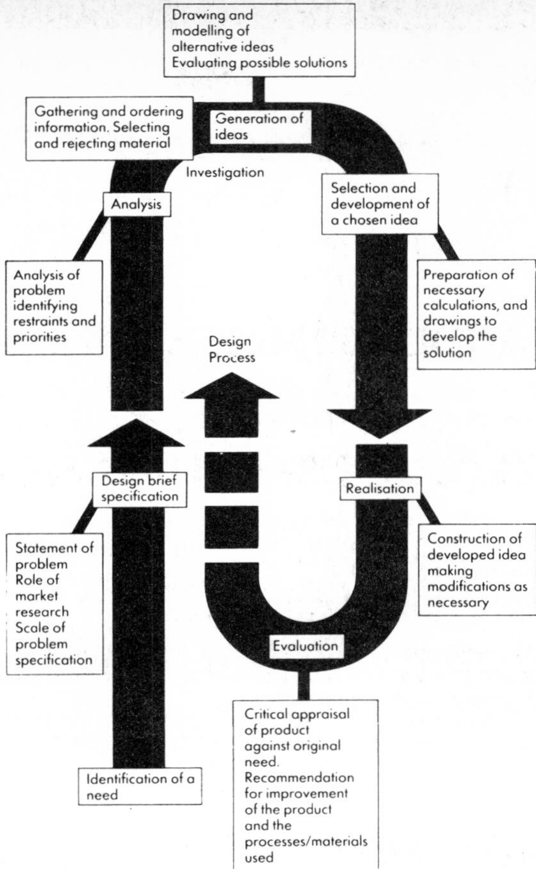

Fig D.7 The design process loop

and with the aid of instruments. Not all detailed drawings have to be drawn with instruments and they can be done in **exploded views** as well as assembled views.

DEVELOPMENT

The word development has two different uses. The first is in the development of ideas and the second is in the development of geometric forms from a two dimensional plane. Where you hear or see the word on its own it usually means a geometric method of constructing a development of a geometric figure e.g. cube, cone, cylinder (Fig D.8), or more complex forms such as the intersection of cones and cylinders etc (Fig D.9).

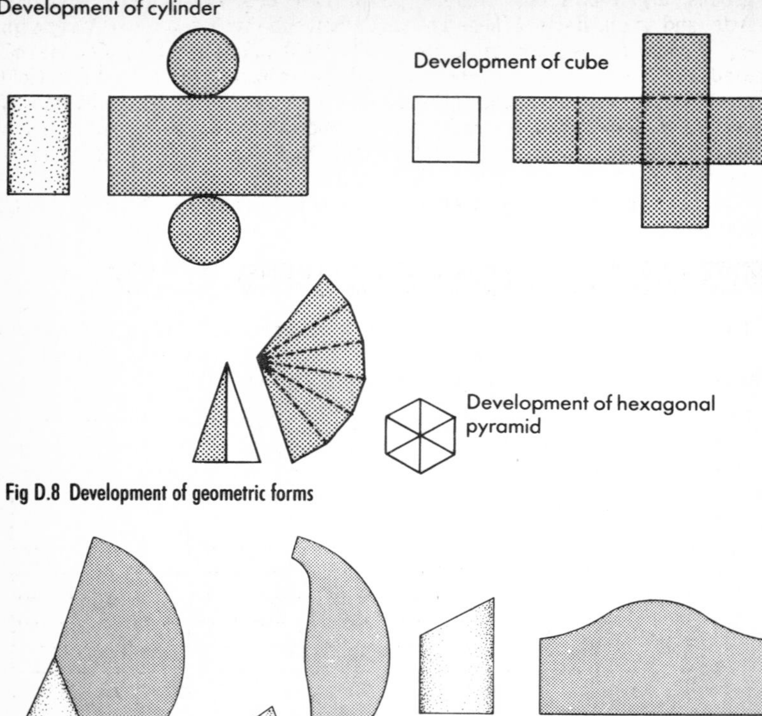

Fig D.8 Development of geometric forms

Fig D.9 Development of more complex forms

DEVICE

This is a general term for an object, system, jig, tool, etc., that will perform a particular function. Quite often the word device is deliberately used in **design briefs** so that a pre-conceived idea is not hinted at in the wording, e.g. 'Design a device for opening a bottle', or 'Design a device for displaying wind speed and direction'.

A device in *electronics* can mean a part that contains one or more active elements, such as a **transistor**, **integrated circuit** or a **diode** etc.

DEWEY DECIMAL SYSTEM

This is the system of classifying books in libraries. It was devised by Melvil Dewey in 1870. All books are given a number and are put into one of ten major groups, e.g. Philosophy, Religion, Social Sciences, Language, Technology, Arts, and so on. Each of these groups is then sub-divided into smaller groups, e.g. Technology is given the group number 600 and then sub-divided into 610 Medical Science, 620 Engineering, 630 Agriculture, etc. The sub-dividing goes further into still smaller groups. The two groups that do *not* fall into this system of classification are fiction and biography. *Fiction* is put on the shelf by alphabetical order of the name of the author, and *biography* by the last name of the subject.

Most books that you will need to refer to in the library for CDT will be in the 600 group.

DIAGONAL SCALES

These are constructed to provide a reliable means of taking very precise measurements. The *diagonal scale* gets its name from the diagonal lines drawn to obtain the precise measurements (Fig D.10).

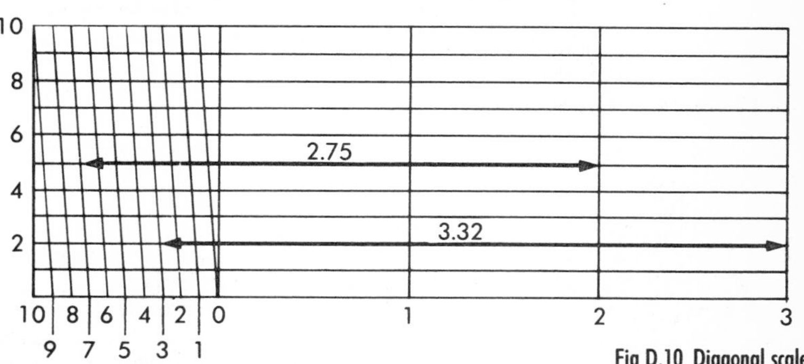

Fig D.10 Diagonal scale

DIAGRAM

This is a lined drawing that is concerned mainly with communicating information clearly. The quality of a diagram can be assessed by the ease with which it is understood. The plan of the London Underground railway system is an excellent example of how quite complex information can be presented in a diagram so that it can be easily understood.

DIAL GAUGE

These are the precision instruments used to determine the sizes of material being processed on a lathe by a skilled operator. Such *dial gauges* have been superceded by more sensitive electronic devices and are not necessary for work produced on a Computer Numerically Controlled lathe.

DIAMETER

A straight line that passes through the centre of a circle and meets on the circumference. ◀ Circle ▶

DIES

When referring to casting processes the *dies* are metal moulds. They are usually expensive to make but they have the advantage of producing high quality castings, i.e. the surface finish is smooth and the fine detail clearly reproduced. They can be used many hundred thousands of times, thereby making the high initial cost of the dies worthwhile.

Dies are also used in *press forming*. Though simple punch dies can be used in schools, press forming is essentially an industrial process. Car bodies, metal sinks, basins, baths, etc., are press formed using highly polished dies. Metal dies are also used in *plastic injection moulding* processes. These can be used to produce wheels for buggies, toys, etc., and can be found in use in many schools.

Dies are also used to *cut threads* on a bar of metal (Fig D.11). They are held in a die holder and rotated clockwise and then partially anti-clockwise on a bar of metal, so that an *external thread* is produced. The opposite partner to the die is a **tap** which cuts *internal threads*.

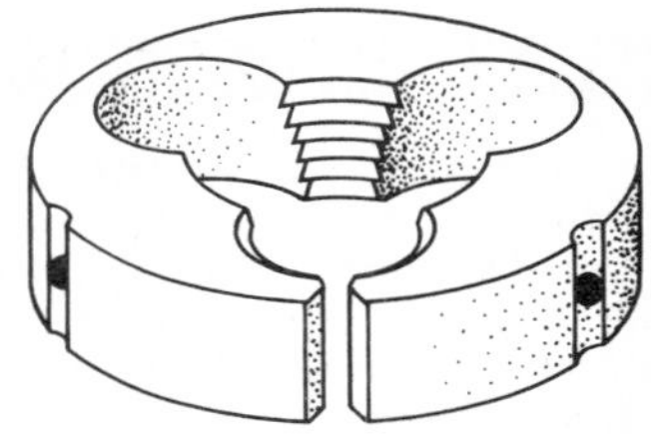

Fig D.11 Dies

DIGITAL CIRCUITS

A *digital circuit* is based upon a series of electronic switches. The switch is either 'on' or 'off'. The system is extremely reliable and the two state or binary systems form the basis of all control and computing devices.

Modern industry depends very much upon automation. It takes out many of the mundane repetitive tasks that were at one time done by people. Still more important, these tasks can now be done with greater speed, accuracy and reliability. The tasks of precision drilling, of turning and shaping material, and automatic sorting, counting and checking, etc., could not be done at the speed required without the help of digital circuits.

DIGITAL COMPUTERS

The *digital computer* enables a number of operations to be put in *sequence* so that a calculation, or display of information, can take place efficiently and quickly.

The logic circuits that sequence so many functions are now to be found in the home, e.g. digital clocks, electronic musical instruments, stereo equipment, etc. The commercial world of banks and other organisations dealing with money depends to a great extent upon digital computers. Even police records are now kept in store in digital computers for quick and reliable retrieval of information. ◀ **Logic gates** ▶

DIGITAL DISPLAYS

◀ Displays ▶

DIHEDRAL ANGLES

These are the four right-angles between the planes used in orthographic projection. ◀ Orthographic projection ▶

DIMENSION

This is a measurement that is given on a drawing. The most commonly used unit today is the *millimetre*, even on scaled drawings of large objects such as buildings.

DIMENSIONING

Certain standards have been laid down so that all drawings are set out in a similar pattern, e.g. all dimensions must be written above the horizontal lines and all dimensions must be written on the left-hand side of vertical *dimension lines* (Fig D.12). One way of helping you check whether the figures are the correct way round is to see if all the horizontal and vertical figures can be read from the bottom right hand corner of the sheet of paper on which the drawing is presented. The only other thing to check is whether the horizontal figures are written *above* the line (Note: this means above and not on the line.)

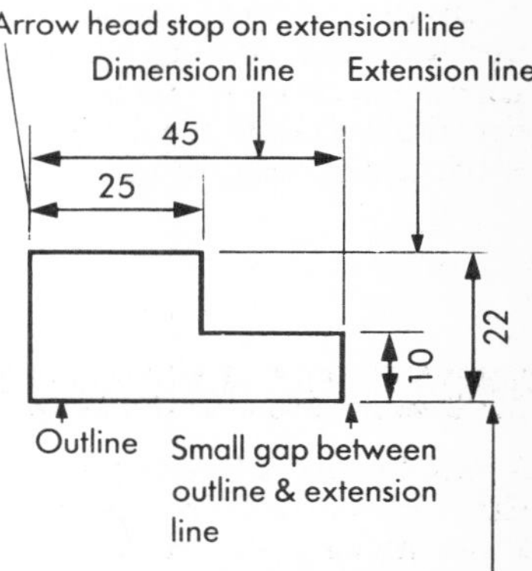

Fig D.12 Dimensioning and dimension lines

DIMENSION LINES

Dimension lines are drawn *parallel to* the edges of straight outlines and *between* projection lines that are at 90° to the edge being dimensioned. The thickness of the dimension line is thinner than the outline so that the outline stands out more obviously than any other line.

Dimension lines are terminated as shown in Fig D.12, but only one method must be used on a drawing or series of drawings belonging to a project. See British Standards PP7320.

DIODES

A *diode* is able to receive electrical pulses and to allow a current to flow in one direction only; it is known as a *forward biased diode*.

The diode (two electrodes) was introduced by Sir John Ambrose Flemming in 1904. At this stage the diode was a **valve** and not a **semiconductor** as it is better known today. A diode is capable of detecting radio waves and it was not until a major advance in electronics which came in 1948 with the development of the **transistor** by Shockly, Bardeen and Brattain that the diode valve could be replaced with a *solid state* device. The advantages of using transistors was enormous. Far less energy was required to make them respond; they did not require heating before they functioned; they were made from solid materials,(e.g. Germanium (Ge) and silicon (Si) were two important semiconducting materials) which were considerably more robust than valves. But perhaps the major feature of progress in electronics was the considerable reduction in size of transistors and other components.

PROPERTIES OF DIODES

An important property of a diode is that it will allow a current to flow in *one direction only.* When the polarity of the supply voltage is reversed, practically no current flows and it is then termed a *Rectifier.*

Point contact diodes

'Point contact diodes' were first used in the 1920s, when amateur radio enthusiasts built their own receivers. In order to demodulate the radio waves, a metal to semiconductor rectifying diode was used. This was a crystal of impure galena, with the metal as a spring made of brass wire. The sharp point of the wire made the contact with the crystal, and it was the appearance of this that gave the name 'cat's whisker' to such radio enthusiasts. The modern version still requires a metal point contact, but it now presses into a piece of germanium or silicon. The *point contact diode* is now used only in low current circuits where it can be used as a signal diode.

Junction diodes

Junction diodes appear very similar to point contact diodes, but the word junction refers to the fact that the different types of germanium or silicon are *diffused* into each other to produce a junction. This diffusion brings about a build-up of a negative charge in the p-type material and a positive charge in the n-type material. These charges produce a low voltage of about 0.1V across the junction. This is called a '*junction voltage*'. When the flow of electrons stops, the junction becomes neutralised and this narrow layer is known as the 'depletion region'. This depletion region has a high resistivity, similar to that of pure silicon or germanium.

DIP COATING

This is a process where a layer of a plastics material is fused onto the surface of a metal. The major problem for many years was not in fusing a plastics material to a metal but in obtaining a coat of *even* thickness. It was not until it was discovered that a solid material could be made to behave like a liquid, that success was achieved. When a *powder* of a solid state material is placed in a tank and air is blown through it from below, the fine particles of powder rise and vibrate. To test whether or not the powder *behaves* like a liquid, it is possible to place a piece of *wood* on the surface to see if it floats. To take this test one stage further, it is possible to place a piece of *metal* on the surface and to observe what happens. The powder can be said to behave like a liquid if the *wood floats* and the *metal sinks*, exactly as you would expect them to in a tank of water. Such a process is called **fluidisation** and the container is known as a **fluidising tank**.

The process of *dip coating* involves a piece of clean metal being heated to approximately 300°C. It is then suspended on a thin wire and dipped into the fluidising tank until submerged (Fig D.13). A few seconds are allowed for the heat from the metal to melt the powder near the surface and to allow some unmelted powder to stick to the wet surface of the melted powder. It is then removed and returned to the electric oven.

Here the top layer of not-quite-melted powder is given time to melt before being removed from the oven. The metal is then allowed to cool while still suspended from the thin wire. When cool, the thin wire can be carefully removed and the small hole sealed over by smoothly passing a hot iron (approximately 300°C) over the hole.

This method of applying a *surface treatment* to metal is useful for protecting the metal from corrosion and for giving some colour, e.g. metal draining racks, bottle holders, refrigerator shelves, etc.

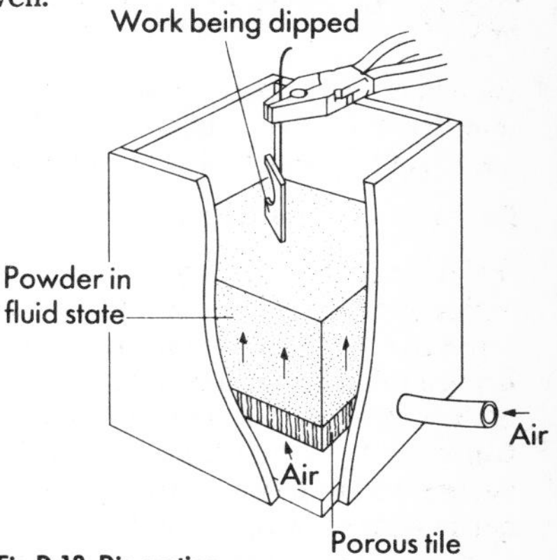

Fig D.13 Dip coating

DIRECT CURRENT

The flowing of an electric current in a circuit in *one direction only*. This is achieved nowadays by attaching a *conducting wire* to the terminals of a battery. A current will then flow at an even rate from the negative terminal to the positive terminal.

It was the ability to produce a current that led the Italian physicists Luigi Galvani and Alessandro Volta in the late 18th century to develop the first practical electric cell, then known as the *Volta pile* (battery).

Batteries have a wide range of applications, from supplying an energy source to start a car engine to supplying an energy source to an integrated circuit in a watch, hearing aid, calculator, etc.

DIRECT CURRENT MOTOR

Direct current motors can only run from a DC supply. The supply can come from either a **battery** or from an AC supply that is then fed into a **transformer** set at the appropriate voltage, i.e. the same as the electric motor.

In 1834 Hermann de Jacobi built an electric DC motor-propelled craft for the Tsar of Russia. Though this was believed to be the first electrically powered device, Thomas Davenport, an American engineer, used an electric motor to drive a small locomotive around a circular track at about the same time. By the 1850s, considerable improvements in the design of the electric motor had taken place and the motor had become a commercial success.

In a simple DC motor, a coil of wire is wound on a soft iron core. This in turn is mounted on pivots which are free to rotate between two permanent magnets. A DC supply to the coil is made via two fixed carbon blocks, called *brushes*. The brushes rub on a split cylinder, called the *commutator*, each half of which is connected to one end of the coil. When a current passes through the coil, it becomes magnetised and turns to align itself with the north-south poles of the permanent magnets. Once moving it cannot stop, and the *rotational* movement is maintained as long as there is an electrical supply (Fig D.14).

DC electric motors usually require a low level voltage, i.e. 12V and below; therefore their application is mainly in systems that require a low level energy output, e.g. drive systems in model aircraft, in buggies, etc. Remember to check that the motor you use has the correct electrical supply, i.e. DC, and that it is set at the correct voltage.

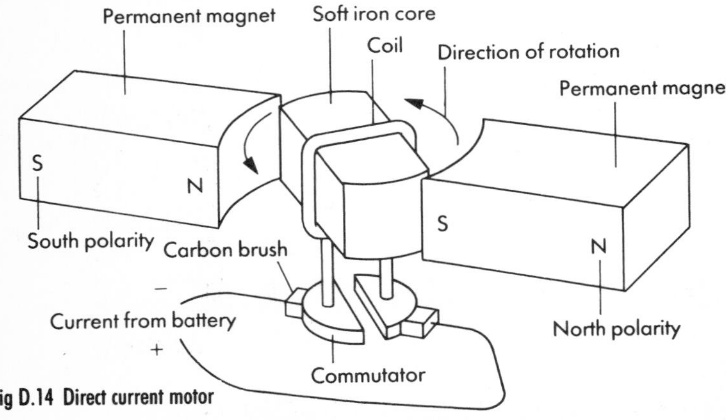

Fig D.14 Direct current motor

DIRECTRIX

A *directrix* is a straight line that is at a given ratio from the focal point of curves obtained in a conic section i.e. **ellipse, parabola**, and **hyperbola**. The ratios are 2 : 3 for an ellipse, 1 : 1 for a parabola, and 3 : 2 for a hyperbola (Fig D.15).

DISPLAYS

Moving coil meters, like electric motors, make use of the principle that if a current is passed through a wire in a magnetic field, it will tend to move. This *motor effect* which causes a *rotational movement* is used in a *galvanometer*.

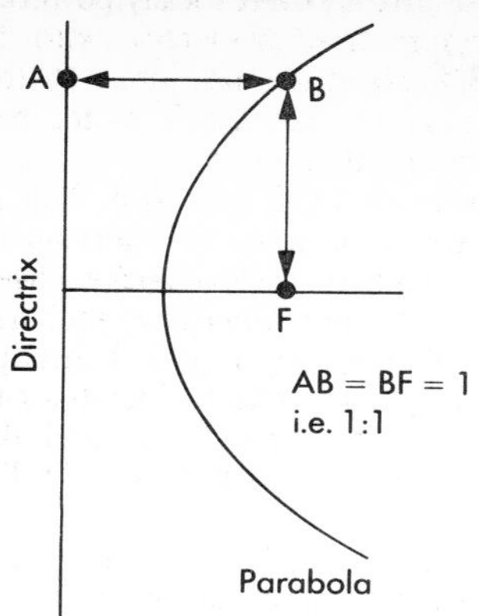

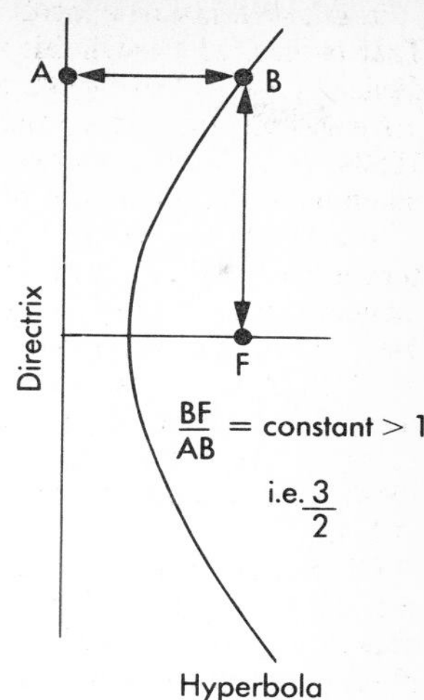

Fig D.15 Directrix

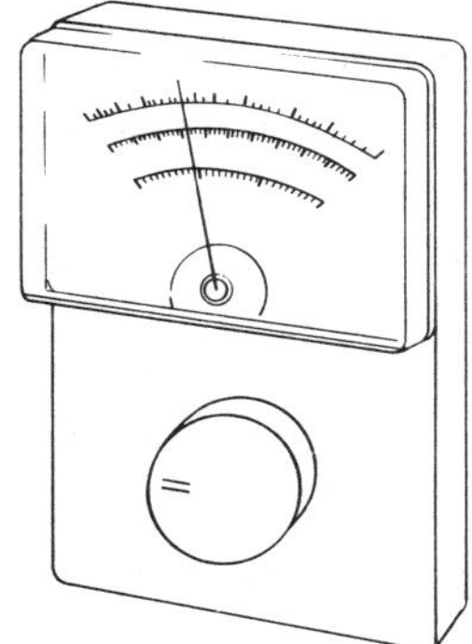

Fig D.16 Multimeter display

Fig D.17 Seven-segment display

Here the deflection of a needle is proportional to the strength of the electric current in the coil.

There are many other types of meter, e.g. Avometer, Multimeter, DC Voltmeter, Microvoltmeter, etc., all of which use the moving coil principle, and where the reading is taken by noting the position of the needle when it comes to rest over a scale (Fig D.16).

Digital displays present numbers only, and each number is created from a seven-segment display (Fig D.17). These are simple to read and extremely accurate. This form of display is used in digital watches, calculators, etc.

Light Emitting Diodes (LEDs) are also useful as low-voltage display devices. They can only be used one way round in a circuit. The colours that are available are red, green and amber. ◀ **Light Emitting Diodes** ▶

DIVIDING A LINE

This **construction** is useful for dividing a length of line that cannot be easily divided mathematically into a given number of equal parts. For example, the length may be 73 mm and the number of divisions 5 (Fig D.18a)). A practical application of this method can be used when dividing a piece of material into a given number of even widths. Just turn the ruler at an angle to the two edges until you arrive at a measurement that is easily divisible by the number of equal widths that you require. Say you require *three* equal widths, and the material you have has a total width of 55mm. Move the ruler at an angle to the two edges until you get the 10 on one edge and 16 on the other, as in Fig D.18 b). Mark off the positions 12 and 14. Repeat this further along the length of material and then join the first pair of marks with the second pair of marks. These lines will be parallel to the edges and exactly one third of the total width apart.

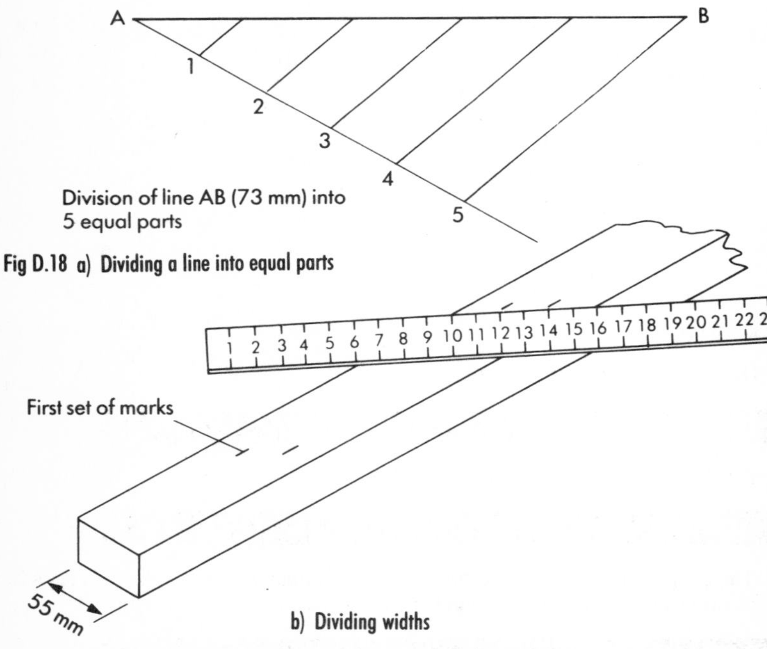

Fig D.18 a) Dividing a line into equal parts

b) Dividing widths

DIVIDING AREAS

The area of a plane figure can be divided into smaller areas to represent proportions of the whole. To divide it in half is easy, but to divide it into many parts that are *not equal* is more difficult. **Pie charts** are commonly used to display facts and figures visually.

◀ Pie charts, Construction of angles ▶

DIVIDING LINES IN PERSPECTIVE

In order to create the feeling of distance, lines representing identical acutal measurements get smaller the further away they move. An approximate method can be used to achieve this effect.

All the telegraph poles in Fig D.19a) are in *reality* an equal distance apart, but on the *drawing* they are not. This effect of perspective is achieved by drawing the first telegraph pole and then two thin 'perspective' lines to a *vanishing point* (VP). Next, estimate the distance apart of the first two poles and draw a thin diagonal line from the top of one pole to the bottom of the other. To find the position of the *third* pole, draw a line *parallel* to the diagonal line, starting from the top of the second pole. Where this diagonal line cuts the perspective line indicates the position of the third pole. This can be repeated as many times as there are poles to draw. Figure D.19b) illustrates how to draw horizontally in perspective. ◀ Perspective ▶

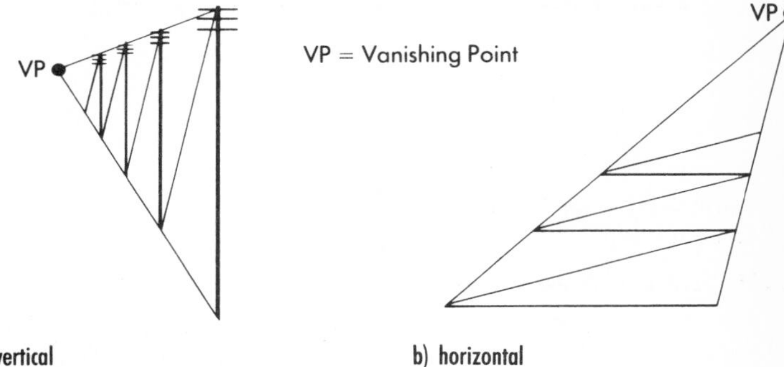

a) vertical

b) horizontal

Fig D.19 Dividing lines in perspective

DODECAGON

A twelve-sided **plane figure**.

DOPING

The process of adding impurities to provide negative and positive charges to a piece of pure silicon or pure germanium.

DOT SHADING

This is a technique of using *dots* made by a pen or sharp pencil on an area to be shaded. The closer the dots are together, the darker or more dense the tone value will be. This technique can be done using one size of dot. The graphic technical pens with interchangeable drawing tips are most commonly used. Fibre tip pens can be used, but you must avoid applying too much pressure, otherwise the tip will be damaged. ◀ Rendering ▶

DOUBLE-ACTING CYLINDERS

These are used in connection with **pneumatic** circuits. There are a variety of types, including non-cushioned, buffered, cushioned etc. (Fig D.20).

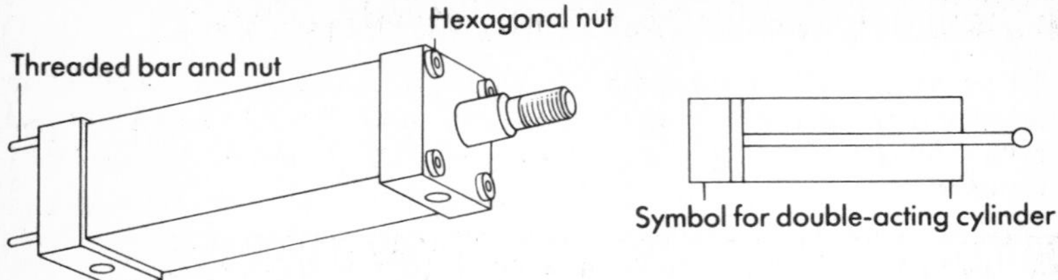

Fig D.20 Double-acting cylinder

DOWEL ROD

Lengths of round section wood have evolved over many hundreds of years as a device for joining other pieces of wood together. The Egyptian, in their construction of the 'mushrabiahs', lattice-work or grills, used hundreds or thousands of dowels to join hundreds of thousands of turned balls. The joining was done without the use of glue or nails, so the wood sometimes became distorted with the changes of weather (Fig D.21a).

Today, the dowel is used much more as a construction device to hold together, with the aid of an adhesive, solid timber and manufactured board (Fig 21.b)). For accurate alignment of the dowel and the hole into which they will fit, a *dowelling jig* is available.

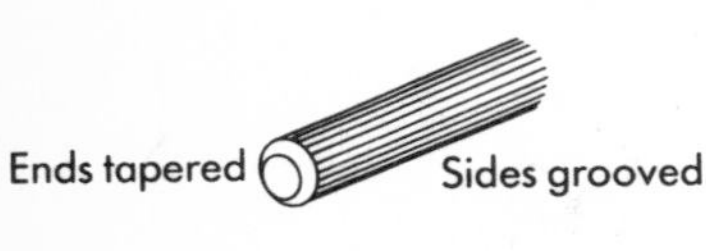

a) Modern dowel

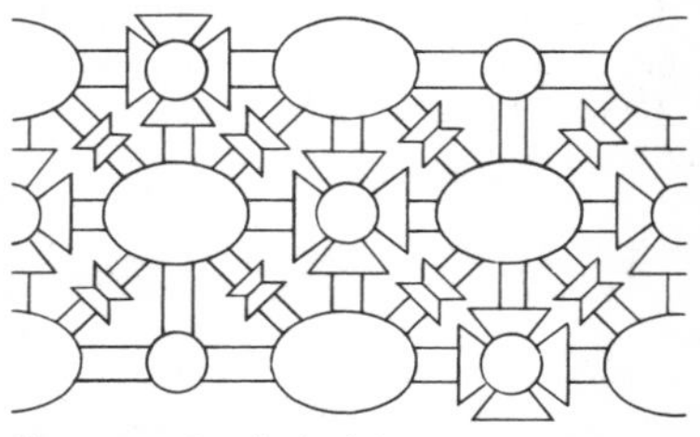

Fig D.21 Dowel

b) Egyptian 'mushrabiahs'

DRAFT

When designing a component that is to be made by a **casting** process, allowance must be made for the pattern or casting to be removed from the mould. This is done by slightly *tapering* the sides, so that the narrower end passes freely from the mould as it is withdrawn. The taper is known as the *draft* (Fig D.22).

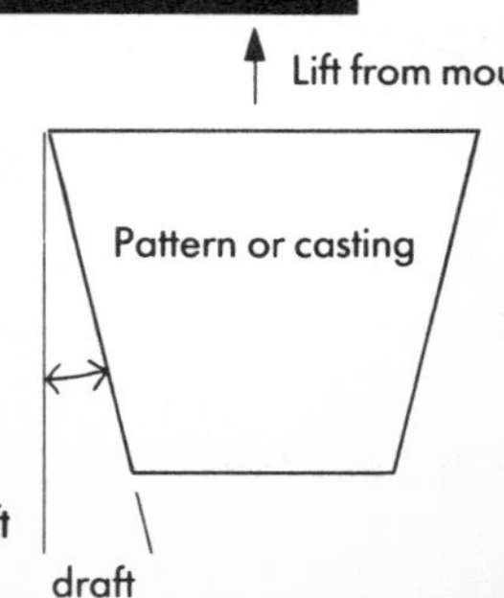

Fig D.22 Draft

DRAG

This is the *lower half* of a flask that is used in sand casting processes. The *top half* of the flask is called the cope. ◀ Casting, Cope and drag ▶

DRAUGHTING SKILLS

These are the skills you require when drawing. A draughtsman is skilled in drawing **plans** and **orthographic** views, and using draughting equipment or even a draughting machine. Much of the equipment has now been replaced by computers.

DRAWING ASSEMBLIES

When a product is made of several components it can be drawn with all the components put together, i.e. *assembled.* A detailed drawing of the parts as *individual* components is helpful when making the component. But for checking that the sizes are correct and that the parts do actually fit together, it is useful to draw all the components assembled.

DRAWING BOARD

There are many designs of drawing board, ranging from very plain pieces of manufactured board used in conjunction with a tee square, to quite elaborate boards with draughting machine heads. In mid-range is the drawing board with a *fitted parallel motion* which is often used in schools today (Fig D.23a). Also available are *portable plastic* drawing boards, which come complete with a device for clipping the paper, a parallel arm with scales, and an adjustable protractor. Board sizes are governed by the standard sizes of paper, such as A3 or A4 (Fig D.23b).

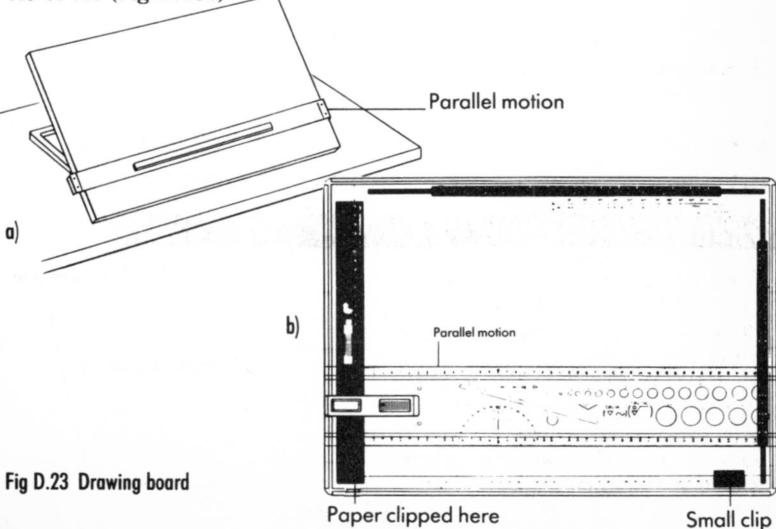

Fig D.23 Drawing board

DRIVER AND DRIVEN

In most mechanical systems where there is a need to *transfer motion* from one source to another, it is helpful to know which is the *driving* source. This particularly applies when there is to be both a transfer of motion and a *change of pace*, i.e. slower or faster. If a pulley wheel is fitted to the shaft of an electric motor, then this pulley will be referred to as the *driver pulley*. The corresponding pulley on the component that has to be driven, is called the *driven pulley*. When the transfering of motion is done through a train of cog wheels the classification of driver and driven cog applies.

◀ Gear trains, Pulley wheels, Speed ratio ▶

DROSS

This is the waste material that floats on the surface of molten metal just after it has been degassed. The dross is removed with a long-handled metal spoon until the clean molten metal is revealed. The melt can then be used for casting by being poured into a mould. **Note**: these operations are dangerous and are normally performed by a teacher.

DRY TRANSFER LETTERING

This is a process of transferring a chosen letter onto a surface of paper by rubbing the protective sheet on which the letter is supplied. The finished result often looks very professional. There is a wide range of *styles* of lettering in both *lower case* (small letters) and *upper case* (capitals). The letters are also available in a range of *sizes*. The letter forms are not all the same height, so a 'point size' is often given, e.g. 72pt (20.3 mm), 48pt (14.5 mm), 16pt (4.3 mm), etc.

The dry transfer technique also includes drawings of transport, trees, people, etc., so that features can be *added* to an existing drawing to give it more interest or appeal.

Remember: In dry transfer lettering, although the letter forms are of a professional quality, care must still be taken with alignment and spacing. Poor spacing can spoil the finished result.

DUCTILE

A ductile material is one that can be drawn or stretched without becoming weak. Metal rod that is pulled through a die to reduce its diameter must be ductile in order for it not to break. A *malleable* material, i.e. one that will extend permanently in any direction without breaking apart, is capable of being drawn. The production of metal wire is dependent upon the metal being malleable.

Plastic materials can be *made* to be ductile, in order for it to be drawn into threads.

DURABILITY

In general terms durability means to last. For example, a durable *metal* or *plastic*, is one that will resist wear by friction. A durable *wood* is one that will resist decay. Teak is noted for its durability and was mainly used for building ships and supporting railway lines as sleepers long before it became popular for making furniture. Its resistance to moisture and to insect attack make it a popular wood for both outdoor and indoor furniture.

Glass reinforced plastic is also a very durable material. It is water-resistant and able to withstand considerable wear.

DURALUMIN

This is a trade name for a metal alloy of aluminium and copper. It is extremely light and hard and is used in the production of aircraft.

EARTH

In alternating current (AC) electric circuits there are three colour-coded wires. The colours are brown for live, blue for neutral and yellow and green for earth. The *earth wire* is a safety device. If the live wire accidentally touches a metal casing to which an earth wire is attached, the electric current flows down the earth wire to the ground. If a person was in contact with the metal, the current would still flow in the earth wire and prevent the current from harming the person. Like the river that follows the line of least resistance, so electricity will choose to flow through the wire and *not* the person. Where there is *no* earth wire connection, the electricity will try to flow to earth by whatever means available, which might be through a person, who would then receive a 'shock'. Once the flow of current has reached earth, the **fuse** (another safety device) would be blown and the supply of electricity stopped. More sensitive devices such as 'contact breakers' will cut the supply of electricity as soon as a fault is detected, thereby reducing the chance of a person receiving a shock.

EBONISING

Ebony means black. A hardwood which is very dark in colour (almost black) also has the name ebony. Because of its hardness and its ability to acquire an excellent finish, it has been a popular hardwood for centuries. It was particularly popular in the ancient courts of Asia, India and Egypt as a material for making furniture and carvings. Though it is still used today in musical instruments, jewellery, and small sculptures, it is now a rare wood with few supplies available. However, the black sheen of ebony is still popular, so more readily available hardwoods are treated with a black polish that gives an *ebony appearance*. This process is called *ebonising*.

ECOLOGY

Ecology is the study of living things in their environment. In order to know more about the way plants, animals, fish, insects and birds survive you need to see and observe them in the fields, hedgerows, rivers, seas, cliffs and forests.

Concern about the survival of plants and animals has grown in recent years because man is changing the face of the earth so rapidly and using technological processes that are harmful to the environment. Large areas of forests are being felled, toxic chemicals are being released into the air, waste is being dumped into the oceans, chemical fertilizers and insecticides are being used to increase the yield of crops, and so on. All this is being done to such an extent that many species of plants, animals and birds are dying out, never to be replaced. **Acid rain**, the depletion of the **ozone layer**, water pollution and other consequences of a deteriorating environment are forcing ecology and environmental protection to the top of the political agenda.

ECONOMY

Economy is often thought of as money and the spending of money, but, this is only one aspect. The term economy also includes how sensibly *materials*, *energy*, and *time* are being used. 'Economy' is really concerned with avoiding unnecessary waste.

Good planning, care in selecting an appropriate material and process can result in a product being produced not only with very little waste of energy and time, but also most important today, with no harmful effects on lives or any living organism.

EFFICIENCY

Efficiency is about doing things well. Being skilful at drawing or solving problems is to do with human efficiency. But computers and machines can also be assessed according to their ability to perform functions. The qualities of 'efficiency' include reliability, durability, the ability to perform functions independent of support from other sources, and so on. There is no such thing as 100% efficiency. If this were possible, then in mechanical terms man would have discovered how to achieve perpetual motion.

◀ **Mechanical efficiency, Mechanical advantage** ▶

EFFORT

The energy required to move a load is called the effort. ◀ **Levers** ▶

EIGHT BIT BUFFER

Also known as an *Octal* Buffer. This is an integrated circuit that contains eight **Darlington pairs** or drivers. The ULN 2803A circuit in Fig E.1 has an eight bit memory. This type of driver can be connected to a device that needs a 5V power supply. However, it can also control devices working on high loads, providing that the power source is separate.

◀ **Darlington pair amplifier** ▶

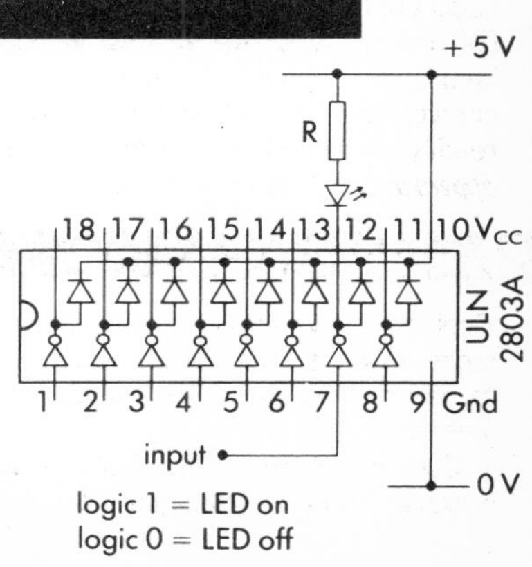

Fig E.1 Eight bit buffer

ELASTICITY

The ability of a material to *stretch* and then return to its original size is known as elasticity. Similarly, if an elastic material is *compressed* it will reduce in size, but immediately the pressure is released it will seek to return to its former shape and size.

Rubber is not the only material that is elastic. All materials are elastic. If they were not elastic, even to a small degree, materials would not be able to withstand forces. Bridges and buildings move or 'give' in a strong wind, but return to their original form when the wind stops. When they do not, the **elastic limit** of the materials has been *exceeded*. Even rubber bands break when stretched too far!

MEASURING ELASTICITY

The elasticity of a material can be *measured*. When a material is subjected to a pulling, twisting or a pushing force, it will change size. These forces are known as **'Strain'**. The *'Stress'* on a material is the force acting on the material divided by the original size; in the case of a material being twisted, stress is the angle through which it twists.

Hooke's Law states that the stress divided by the strain is *constant* for any material and is called the **modulus of elasticity**.

In practical terms the elasticity of a material is important. The suspension system of a vehicle depends upon the components being able to withstand vibration. Even the strings of a guitar or piano depend on a form of elasticity in order to produce a note. ◀ **Debounce, Hooke's Law** ▶

ELASTIC LIMIT

This is the point up to which the extension and load applied to the material remains constant. *Beyond* this point, the material rapidly stretches until it finally fractures. ◀ **Yield point, Modulus of elasticity** ▶

ELASTOMERS

Synthetic elastomers are a group of plastics that have similar properties to the natural elastomer, rubber. Synthetic rubber was invented in Germany in 1909. It is produced chemically by **polymerisation** of either isoprene, which is a product of the distillation of natural rubber, or polymerisation of a mixture of substances such as butadiene and styrene.

The molecules form a loose structure with only a small number of cross links and chains. The resulting material is similar to natural rubber. Because the *chemical mix* can be controlled, the *properties of the material* can also be controlled and improved. For example, the mix of *isoprene and iso-butaline* produces a synthetic rubber that is far better than natural rubber in resistance to weathering, so this is used in the making of rain coats. It is also resistant to gases, and so is used to make inner tubes and air cushions. Neoprene is a type of rubber derived from a mix of *acetylene gas* and *hydrochloric acid.* It is resistant to high temperatures, to oil and to other chemicals and so is used to make hose pipes, conveyer belts, etc; which are subjected to such conditions or substances.

ELECTRICAL RESISTANCE

Resistance is a measure of how difficult it is to make an electric current flow in a material. Copper has a very low level of resistance and electricity can flow easily through it. Iron has rather more resistance. The *shape* of the material also has an effect. A long thin wire has greater resistance than a short fat one.

The degree of resistance (R) is measured in ohms (Ω).

If a coil of copper wire has a resistance (R) of 3Ω and a DC voltage supply (V) of 12 volts, then the rate of flow of current (I) will equal 12/3, i.e. 4 amperes (Fig E.2a)). Note that $I = V \div R$.

If however, the 12 volt supply is AC, then other factors have to be considered. The continuously changing current through a coil sets up a changing magnetic field. The production of an electromagnetic force in the coil is said to be 'self-induction'. The property that causes this is called 'inductance' and is measured in units called **Henrys**. *Lenz's Law* states that the induced electromagnetic force opposes the current causing it (i.e. the current in the coil). This opposition force is called '*impedance*', symbol Z, and the opposition force to the alternating current is called '*reactance*', symbol X.

In Fig E.2b), the impedance Z is equal to $\sqrt{R^3 + X^2}$: e.g. when the resistance (R) equals 3 Ω and the reactance (X) equals 4 Ω, the 'impedance' will be $\sqrt{9 + 16} = \sqrt{25} = 5\Omega$.

Remember: Direct current (DC) has resistance R and alternating current (AC) has impedance Z. ◀ **Ohm's law** ▶

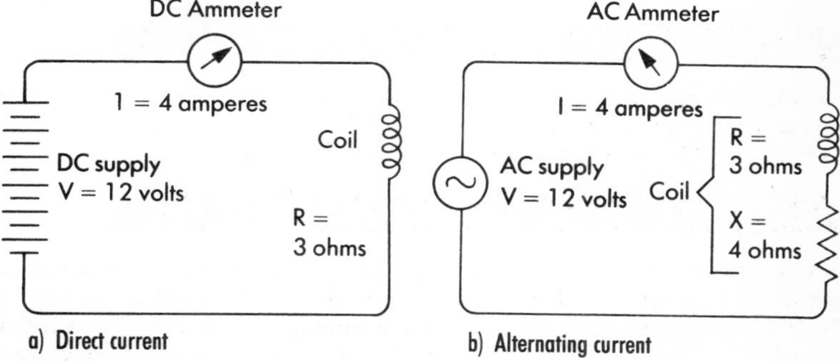

a) Direct current

b) Alternating current

Fig E.2 Electrical resistance

ELECTRICAL RESISTORS

These are devices of known resistance that are built into a circuit to prevent other components being damaged by too high a current. If connected in *series*, the resistance is calculated by *adding* the individual resistors, e.g. a 3Ω resistor and a 6Ω resistor produces a 9Ω resistance (Fig E.3a)). If the same value resistors are connected in *parallel* (Fig E.3b)), then the following formula must be used:

$$\frac{1}{R} = \frac{1}{R_1} + \frac{1}{R_2}$$

$$\text{ie } \frac{1}{R} = \frac{1}{3} + \frac{1}{6} = \frac{1}{2} \quad \text{ie } R = 2\,\Omega$$

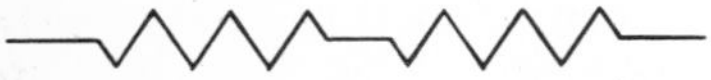

a) Resistors in series

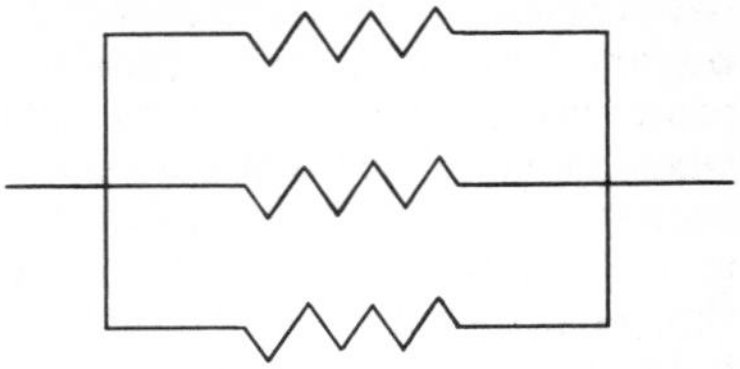

Fig E.3 Electrical resistors

b) Resistors in parallel

Resistors can also be used to change the value of resistance. Remembering that the resistance of a material is proportional to its length, then a change of length will bring about a change of resistance. ◀ **Resistors** ▶

ELECTRICAL AND ELECTRONIC SYMBOLS

Symbols are a quick and easy way of presenting information and are particularly useful in designing circuits. Electrical and electronic symbols are standard, and you are recommended to follow the symbols given in British Standard publications. e.g. PP7303, Table 1.

Some of the symbols you can expect to find are shown in Figure E.4.

Description	Symbol
Fuse	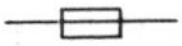
Resistor, general symbol	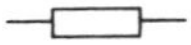
Variable resistor	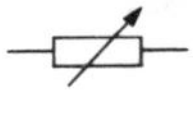
Resistor with sliding contact	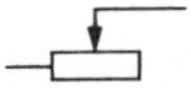
Potentiometer with moving contact	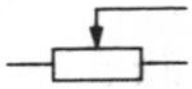
Heating element	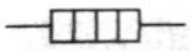

Fig E.4 Electrical and electronic symbols

ELECTRICITY

Electricity is the movement of electrons and protons. When the movement is in a circuit, the electricity is said to *flow*. This movement of **electrons** and

protons supplies an energy that provides lighting, heating, and power for machines.

Electricity has been known about for more than two-and-a-half thousand years; the word comes from 'elektron', the Greek for amber. It was not until the 1800s that man learnt how to control it and to make it a useful form of energy.

There are two main sources of electricity. The first was via the development of the *electric cell* by Volta, from which has developed the **battery**. The energy from such a source is, however, limited. The second source is mechanical energy via an electro-magnetic force (magnetism formed when an electric current passes through a wire). This came from a chance happening to Professor Hans Christian Oersted during a lecture in 1819. He noticed that when an electric current passed through a wire, a compass needle situated nearby moved. Though not a prepared part of his lecture, he went on to discover that the needle moved back to point North again when he disconnected the wire, i.e. he stopped the electrical flow in the wire. He had discovered **Electromagnetism**. It was this chance discovery that led to the development of electric motors and generators.

Remember: Electricity from batteries is **direct current** (DC), but from generators it is **alternating current** (AC).

ELECTRICAL CIRCUITS

Electricity can only flow in a *complete circuit*. It either has to flow *directly* (DC) from the negative terminal of a battery to the positive terminal, or it *alternates* (AC) between a live and neutral connection. Both become inactive if the circuit is *broken* by a switch.

ELECTRICAL CONDUCTORS AND INSULATORS

Metals are known to allow the flow of electricity *more readily* than most other materials. These materials became known as **conductors**. Copper is perhaps the best known metal conductor.

Glass, amber, ebonite, and other materials, known to *resist* the flow of electricity became known as **insulators**. Of synthetic plastics, Polyvinyl Chloride (PVC) is possibly the best known insulator.

Electrical cables consist of an inner core, usually copper, surrounded by an insulator, usually PVC.

ELECTROLYSIS

An example of electrolysis is the process of chemically depositing a coat of one metal on another by using electrical energy. When an electric current is passed through an electrolyte, the flow of electrons carries with it the ions of the metal being deposited.

An example of electrolysis is when copper electrodes are placed in a solution of copper sulphate. The copper sulphate is completely ionized into positive copper ions (Cu^{2+}) and negative Sulphate ions (SO_4^{2-}). In addition, the water in the solution is slightly ionized into hydrogen ions (H^+) and hydroxyl ions (OH^-). The copper and the hydrogen ions move towards the cathode, but *only* the copper is accepted because copper has a greater tendency to accept electrons and become an atom than has hydrogen. The result is that the copper anode slowly dissolves, while fresh copper is deposited on the cathode.

Coating one metal with another provides a protective and more attractive finish to a metal that would otherwise corrode. The chromium plating of mild steel is a well-known example and was much used for car bumpers, fittings etc.

ELECTROLYTE

An electrolyte is a liquid through which an electric current may be passed. When a cathode and an anode are connected to a DC supply and placed in an electrolyte, a current will flow from the cathode to the anode. An electrolyte is used in **electroplating, anodising,** etc. For different metals and different processes, the appropriate pure chemicals are used. For example, to *anodise aluminium*, the electrolyte is made from water, sulphuric acid and sodium sulphate. To *electroplate copper*, the electrolyte is made from copper sulphate crystals, sulphuric acid, sodium sulphocarbonate and water.

The solution used in an electric battery or cell is an electrolyte. Pure water cannot be used because it is a good electrical insulator. Chemicals such as acids (e.g. sulphuric acid) and bases or alkalis (e.g. caustic soda) are used to break up the molecules so that they become electrically charged ions.

Note: Since the preparation of electrolytes requires carefully measured portions and the acids and other chemicals used can be dangerous, it is advisable that only qualified people make the preparations. ◄ **Anodising** ►

ELECTROMAGNETISM

◄ **Electricity** ►

ELECTRON

This is an elementary particle that has a negative charge. All atoms have electrons. They move in an orbit round a nucleus. Electrons moving in one direction form an electric current.

Electrons were first discovered by Sir J.J. Thomson in 1897; they were then known as *cathode rays*. Such rays in a tube are what is meant by a 'Cathode ray tube'. The continuous stream of electrons that pass through an anode or positive electrode onto a phosphor-coated surface form the images that you see on television.

ELECTRONICS

Electronics started in the 1800s when scientists studied the effects produced by electricity in the air at low pressure, i.e. partial vacuum. The effects were often impressive. When an electric current was produced with a **potential difference** of several thousand volts in a glass tube, it was the glass that glowed a light green colour, not the remaining air. When, in 1895, Röntgen investigated the effects of putting thin metal in the tube, he discovered that new rays were being formed. These rays became known as X-rays, and have played an important part in the detection of broken bones, dislocations and the presence of many forms of disease.

In 1904, Ambrose Flemming's **diode valve** passed current in one direction only, enabling radio signals to be detected. This opened the way to developments which brought in radio, television, radar, electronic computers, etc.

In 1948, the **transistor** was born. Like the valve, the transistor can amplify signals, but has the advantage of being sturdy, very much smaller and requiring much less energy to function. Because transistors are made from solid material, they are known as 'solid-state' devices.

The development of electronics has dramatically affected our lives. Not only in the hospitals, where highly sensitive monitoring and control devices help to keep us alive when we are ill, but in the everyday experiences of using calculators, credit cards, computers, traffic light signals, etc.

ELECTROPLATE

To coat with silver. ◀ Electrolysis ▶

ELEMENTS

These are the simplest substances of which all matter is formed. They are distinguished from each other by the number of electrons in their atoms outside the nucleus. There are over 100 elements and for a complete list you can refer to the 'Periodic Table of the Elements'. You will find them grouped into light metals, heavy metals, non-metals, sub-metals, and rare gases. Each element has an Atomic weight, a Chemical symbol and an Atomic number.

Unless you are studying a science subject, for CDT you need only be aware of the elements and the way they are classified into groups.

ELEVATION

This is the view of an object. In **orthographic projection**, three or more views of a single object may be drawn, e.g. Front view, Side view, Plan view, Section view etc. The term elevation, though technically correct, is rarely used today and the term **view** is preferred. All recent publications by BS use the term view. ◀ Orthographic projection ▶

ELLIPSES

An ellipse is the view of a circle when seen at an angle. The diameter remains constant and is known as the *major axis*. At right angles to the major axis the diameter of the circle gets smaller as the viewing angle changes, and this is known as the *minor axis*. If the circle is rotated through 90°, all that will be seen is a straight line. The ellipse is formed between the circle and the straight line.

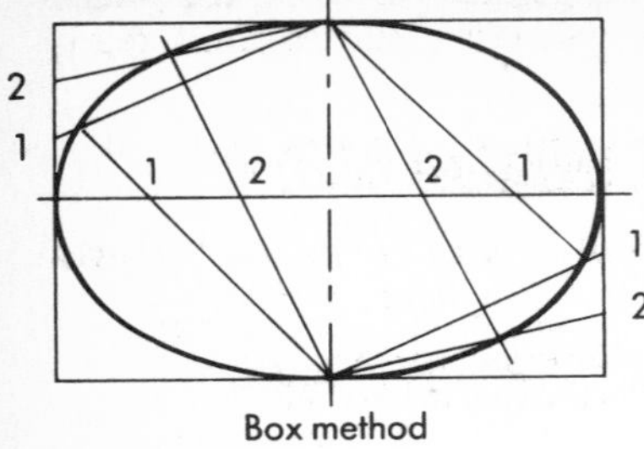

There are several ways of drawing an ellipse. One is to *construct* an ellipse (Fig E.5) and the other is to use a *template*. Templates are quick and easy to use, but mistakes are easily made by not getting the major axis at the correct angle in three dimensional drawing. Figure E.6 should help you to get the correct angle.

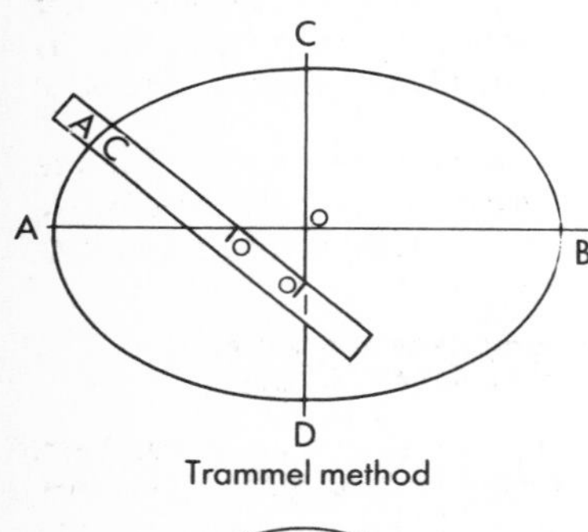

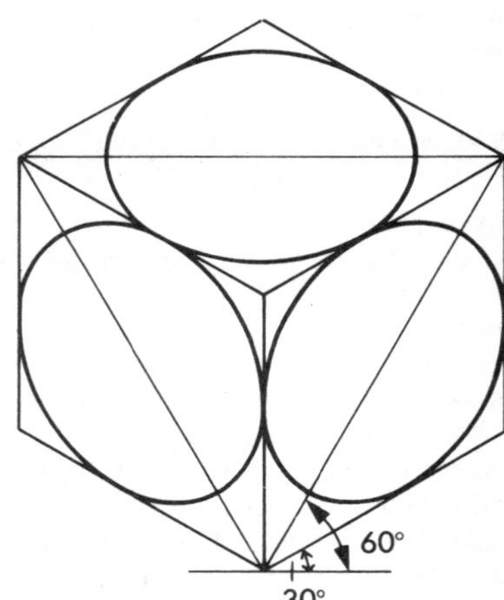

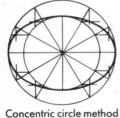

Concentric circle method

Fig E.5 Constructing ellipses

Fig E.6 Drawing ellipses with a template

EMBEDDING

This is the technique or process of placing an object in a resin while it is in a liquid state, and allowing the resin to set hard so that the object is completely 'embedded' in the resin.

A natural *embedding* process really started millions of years ago when insects were trapped on the sticky resin that ran down the bark of Baltic pine trees. Eventually, after many years, the insects would be completely covered and preserved in the resin which had become hard. The particular resin is better known as *amber*. When the samples of amber were discovered (long after the trees had gone) they were shaped and polished, revealing what had been trapped inside. To this day amber is a popular material for jewellery and if it contains an insect, leaf, etc., it is often regarded as having still greater interest and value. Today, embedding is done using clear polyester resins. ◀ Encapsulation Potting ▶

EMITTER

This term is widely used and is short for *emitter region*. It refers to the region of a bipolar junction transistor. ◀ Transistor Semi-conductor ▶

EMPIRICAL RESEARCH

This type of research relies mainly upon what you *see and experience*, rather than upon theoretical knowledge. It is a method of finding things out by handling materials and working with them, to see what can be done and what cannot be done.

When using the empirical approach to solving a problem you are recommended to make notes and drawings of what you see so that you have a *record* of what you have done. This can then be available for assessment. Photographic evidence is another way of recording empirical research.

ENAMELLING

Enamelling is a process of fusing glass onto a metal surface. It has been done for thousands of years and examples of Egyptian work done 3500 years ago can be seen in museums. Enamelling in Britain did not start until about the sixth century AD. Since that time the art of enamelling has grown and has become a commercial and practical process for coating domestic articles, such as saucepans, teapots, insides of cookers, etc.

Enamel is a colourless glass, called a **flux** and is made up of silica, red lead, and potash. It is ground to small pieces, mixed with coloured metallic oxides and smelted. The product is a lump, or lumps, of enamel which, for general application, are ground into a fine powder. Enamel beads or threads can also be formed for producing special designs in jewellery.

The process of enamelling is done by first sprinkling finely powdered enamel onto a chemically clean metal surface, then placing the work in an oven that is heated to approximately 800°C. The powdered enamel is allowed to melt, before removing the work from the oven and allowing it to cool. The enamel solidifies and forms a coloured coat of glass that has fused to the surface of the metal. Many different enamelling techniques have evolved over the years. Such names as 'Cloisonné', 'Champlevé' etc., are well-known techniques used in jewellery making.

ENCAPSULATION

As described under **Embedding** this is a process of embedding an object in resin. Today, crystal-clear resins are available for such purposes, together with appropriate catalysts and activators so that curing takes place within hours.

The process involves several stages. Since some objects float and others sink, to encapsulate an object in the *middle* of the resin it is necessary first to pour some prepared resin (activator and catalyst added) into a rigid polythene container. Allow the resin to cure, then place the object on the cured resin, where it will remain in position. If the object is light and will readily float, you need only prepare a small quantity of resin and pour sufficient on to help it bond to the already cured resin. Allow this second layer of resin to cure before adding a final layer, to completely encapsulate the object (Fig E.7). If the object is sufficiently heavy *not* to float, then the second preparation of resin should be enough to cover the object completely. Complete curing can take several weeks, after which the resin can be removed from the container, trimmed and polished.

a) Stages in encapsulating an object that will float

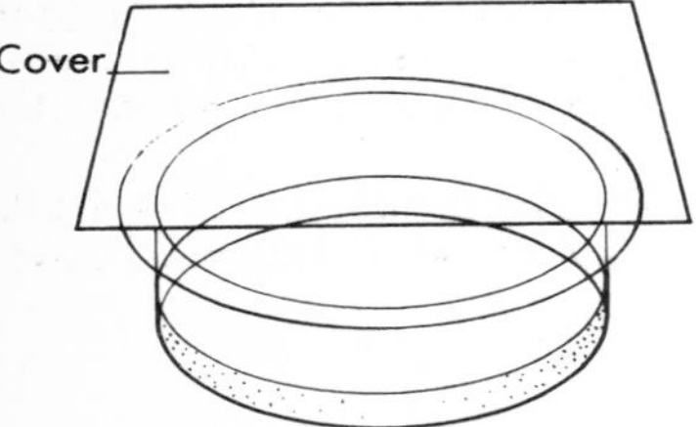

1. Pour first layer of resin, cover and allow to cure

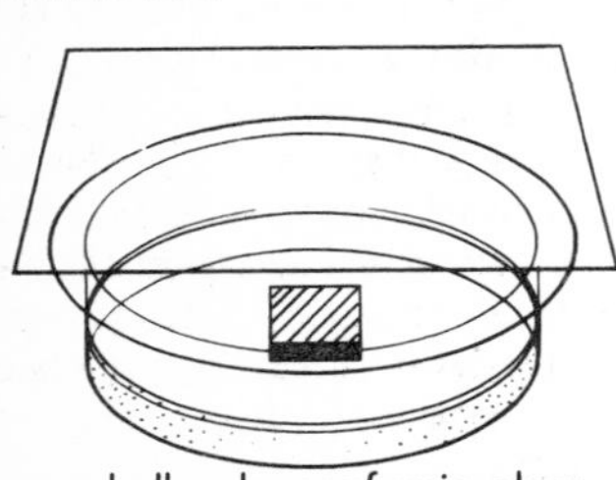

2. Pour a shallow layer of resin, place object in position and allow resin to cure

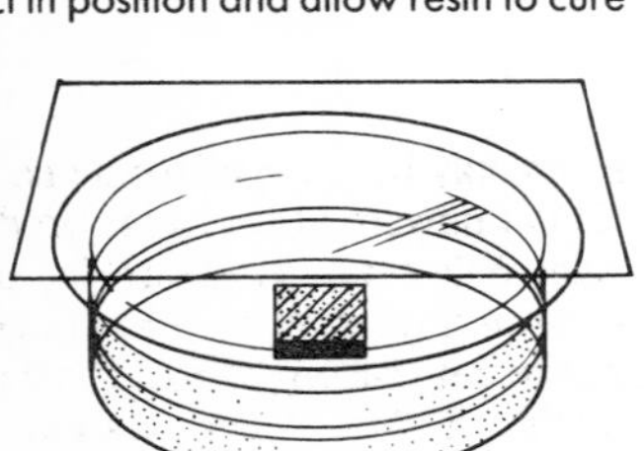

3. Pour a third layer of resin, cover and allow to cure

b) Stages in encapsulating an object that will *not* float

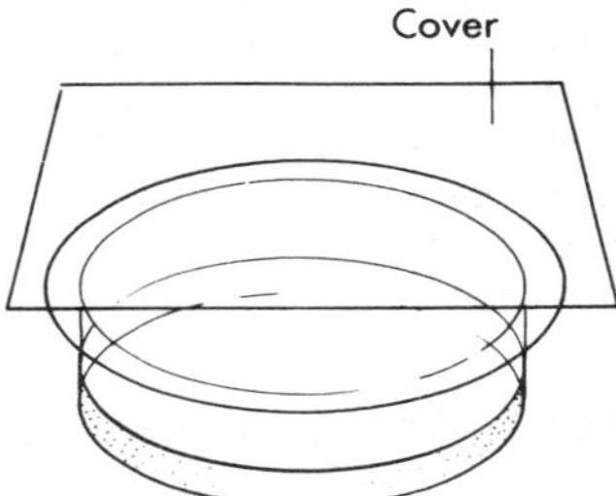

1. Pour first layer of resin and cover and allow to cure

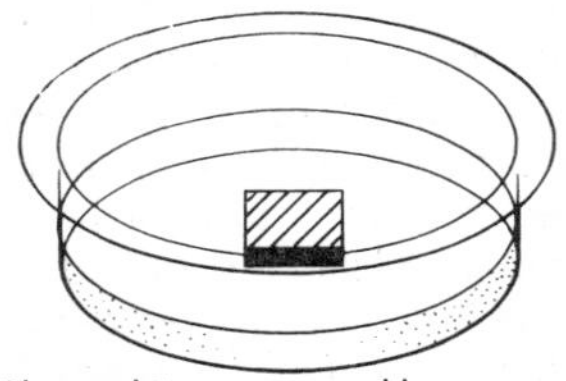

2. Place object on cured layer

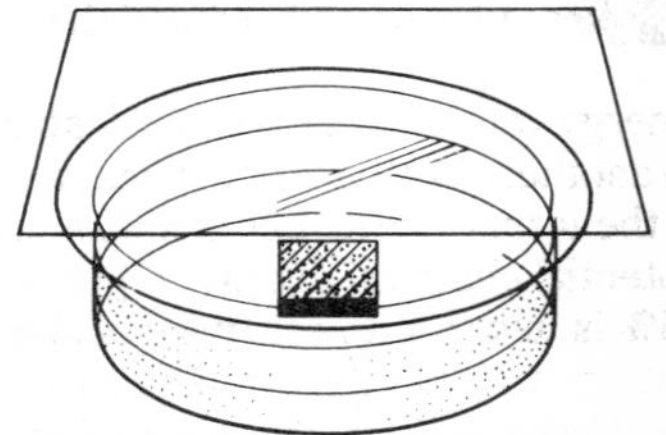

3. Pour second layer and cover

Fig E.7 Encapsulation

For good results, certain steps must be taken:

- add only the correct quantities of activator and catalyst;
- use a container with a highly polished internal surface;
- cover the work after each stage, avoiding dust in the air falling on the curing resin;
- prepare only small quantities of resin to avoid crazing (small cracks) appearing, caused by the exothermic heat given off during polymerisation.

ENERGY

Energy is concerned with movement and activity. If something is moving, a **force** of some kind has been applied to make it move. Examples of energy are all around you. When you walk you use energy to move, a car uses mechanical and chemical energy to move. An electric light bulb uses electrical energy to light a room. A fire is a release of energy that has been stored. Plants depend upon energy from the sun to take in carbon dioxide and release oxygen (the process called photosynthesis).

There are many forms of energy but you should concern yourself with mechanical, electrical, kinetic, potential, and stored forms. Remember also to consider the conservation of energy.

ENERGY CONSERVATION

Conserving energy is concerned with avoiding wasteful uses. When a building is heated, a constant source of heat is required to keep it warm. This is because the materials from which the building was made cannot prevent the heat escaping. When a building uses *less* energy than one of similar size in order to keep it warm, it is because the materials used in the first building provide better **insulation**. With a greater use of insulating materials (air trapped in spaces, i.e. bubble plastics sheets, expanded polystyrene) and sealed units (double glazing, double- and triple-layer polycarbonate sheeting, etc.), far less heat will be lost to the air. In these ways, less energy will be required to provide a comfortable temperature.

ENERGY CONVERSION

Energy can never be lost or destroyed, it can only be *changed* from one form to another. With every change, a proportion of unwanted energy is produced in the form of heat. For example, a car engine only converts about 25% of the potential chemical energy of petrol into a useful driving force. The remaining 75% is unwanted heat, which in turn is kept under control by using still more energy to operate the fan and water pump in the cooling system. The remainder is list in the form of exhaust gases. A 25% level of 'efficiency' is really very poor; although 100% efficiency is not possible, engineering designers are striving to reach a degree of efficiency that gets nearer to this figure. ◄ Mechanical efficiency ►

ENERGY SOURCES

The major source of energy is the *sun*. The sun plays an important role in the growth of plant and animal life. The *nuclear energy* in the heart of the sun is converted into heat and radiated to earth. The *light* from the sun falls on the leaves of plants where it is converted into a chemical energy. The plants die, become fossilised and form coal. Of course some animals feed on plants; and even those that feed on other animals, eat animals that *have* fed on plants. These plants and animals, if buried for more than 300 million years, become the main source of fossil fuels, coal, petroleum or crude oil, and natural gas.

The *natural* sources of energy, such as wind, tides and running water in rivers, all contribute a source of energy that can be converted into electricity.

ENERGY STORAGE

Energy storage in the form of electricity can only be achieved by using a dry cell or **battery**, and then the level of power can only be small and in a DC supply. In a hydro-electric power station the problem is overcome by 'Pumped Storage'. The turbo generators are converted into pumps at night, when energy demands are low, and pump the water used during the day back up to the high reservoir. The water can then be used again the following day, turning the turbo generators to produce electricity when the energy demands are high again. This system can only work where there are two lakes or reservoirs at different levels.

ENERGY TRANSMISSION

Electrical energy can be transferred to a mechanical rotating motion. This is done by bringing an electrical supply to an electric motor. To make use of that motion, **pulleys**, **gears** and **shafts** etc., are linked together to provide a mechanism that will perform a function. The electric motor in a portable drill, or toy robot, brings about a rotating motion which has to be *transmitted* to the functioning or working component, i.e. the drill bit or the moving arm of the robot. Rotary motion can be converted into **reciprocating** motion, rotational speeds can be increased, decreased, or changed in direction by the use of gears. In these ways energy can be transmitted through mechanisms to the working part.

ENLARGEMENT AND REDUCTION

In basic terms this means making a drawing of something either larger or smaller than the original.

Where detailed and irregular shapes are concerned, such as an aerial photograph of a town, a practical method of enlarging or reducing the details is to use a *grid* (Fig E.8a)). A grid is drawn on translucent (see-through) paper which is then laid over the photograph. A grid with the same number of squares is drawn on a *second* sheet of paper. The size of the squares can be smaller for a reduction, or larger for an enlargement. The individual squares are located by a number and a letter. Any particular detail from the overlay on the photograph can be drawn in the corresponding square on the sheet of paper. A gradual build up of the information in each square will result in the ratio of enlargement or reduction being consistent.

Geometric methods of enlarging and reducing figures can be used in a number of different ways; these are shown in Figure E.8b).

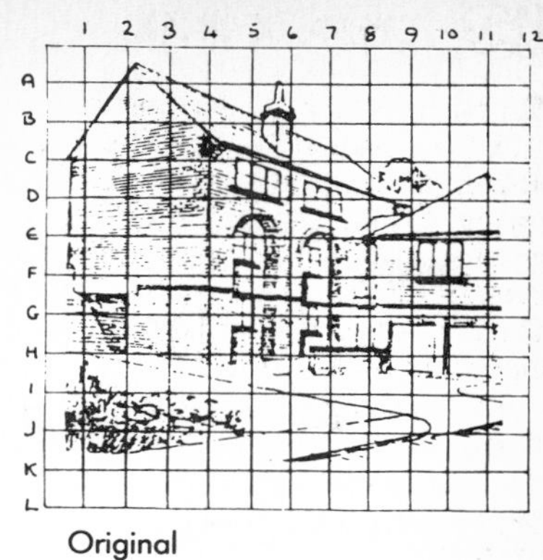

Original

a) Grid method

Fig E.8 Enlargement and reduction

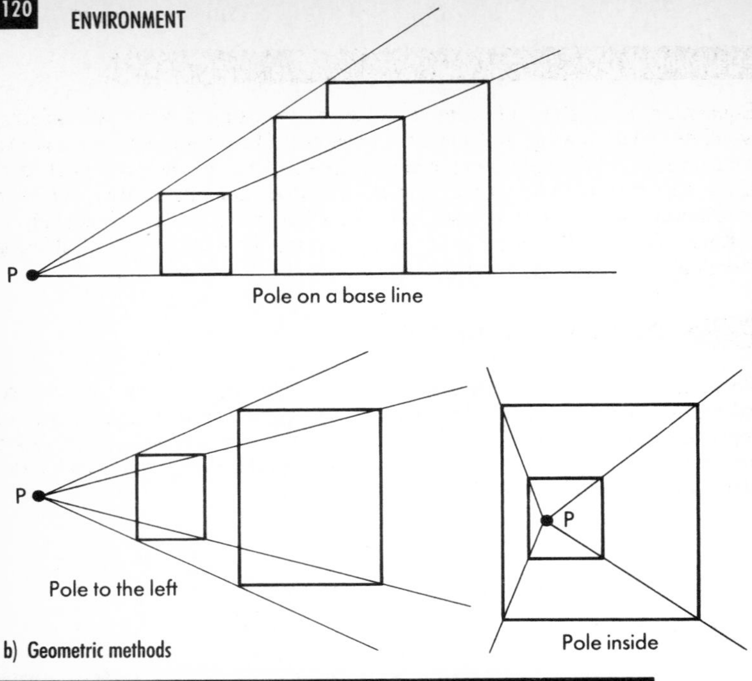

b) Geometric methods

ENVIRONMENT

The environment is your immediate surroundings. The boundaries are set by the particular situation, i.e. if you are concerned with designing a piece of furniture for a particular room, then the environment is the space within that room.

EPROM

EPROM is an abbreviation for Erasable Programmable Read Only Memory. This is a memory device that is not only capable of storing information when the electrical power is off, but is also capable of being altered by the user. Information stored can be removed (erased) and programs can be introduced.

EQUILATERAL TRIANGLE

An equilateral triangle has all sides of equal length and all angles equal, i.e. 60° (Fig E.9).

60°
60°
60°

Fig E.9 Equilateral triangle

EQUILIBRIUM

Equlibrium is a state of balance between opposing forces. All objects, whether still or moving, are subjected to **forces**. The weight of every part of a structure, e.g. bridge, building, chair, imposes a force on the parts next to it. If the structure is to be sound, then all the forces in all the parts must be in equilibrium. When the forces are *not* in equilibrium, the structure is likely to collapse. Because these forces are *still*, they are classified as 'static'. *Moving* forces are classified as 'dynamic'.

EQUILIBRIUM DIAGRAMS

These are diagrams or *vectors* from which the forces in a structure can be calculated. Frameworks are drawn in one **plane**. The parts of a structure are represented by a *single line* and the connection of one part with another by a *pin joint*. The forces are labelled using **Bow's notation**. Figure E.10 shows a structure and a scaled equilibrium diagram.

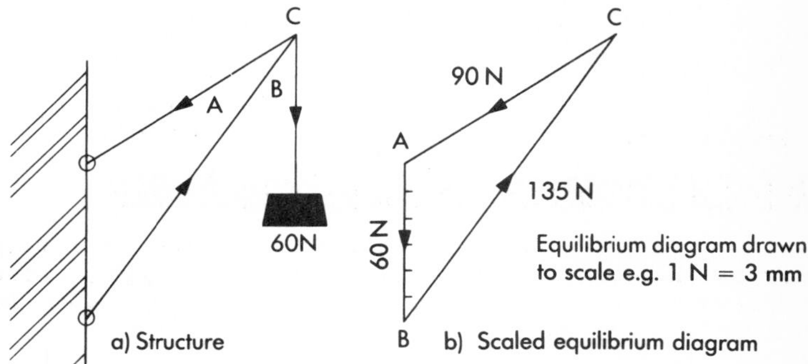

Fig E.10 Equilibrium diagrams

ERECT

To erect something is to put parts together and to build a product. When using assembly kits you can erect a crane, bridge, support, etc.

ERGONOMICS

Ergonomics is a study of finding ways to help human beings perform specific functions efficiently. It is an area of study that has brought a number of previously separate areas of study together, because they all affect one another. A full understanding of how a human being responds in a given situation needs the help of the engineer, doctor, artist, and designer. Take for instance the design of the controls of an aeroplane. These controls are crucial to the safety of the crew and passengers; the pilot has to be efficient and correct in all his responses. The *instrument systems* must therefore be clear and easy to read; the *controls* must be easy to operate and easily identified; their shape, form, colour, texture all need to be carefully considered; the *positioning of the pilot* must be considered in relation to the tasks that have to be performed. To design even a small household product, like a tin opener, needs the application of a similar variety of areas of knowledge to ensure that the instrument is used efficiently.

Ergonomics is often confused with **anthropometrics**, which is only concerned with measurement and is a *part of* ergonomics. In the example of the aeroplane, it is important to know the *position* of the controls, etc., and this would be considered as the *anthropometric* contribution to the design of the aeroplane cabin.

ESCRIBED CIRCLE

A circle that touches one side of a triangle and the extension of the two remaining sides (Fig E.11).

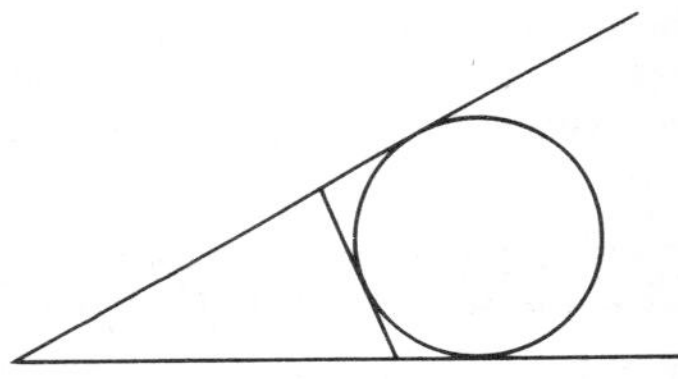

Fig E.11 Escribed circle

ESTIMATED PERSPECTIVE

As the name suggests the length of lines are *estimated* rather than measured. When drawing in **perspective**, lines and spaces can be drawn in a way which involves measurement. *Measured perspective* is a more advanced form of perspective drawing and not essential for anyone studying GCSE. Estimated perspective can be used to produce some excellent quality graphical representations. ◀ Perspective ▶

EUTECTIC POINT

◀ Heat treatment ▶

EUTECTICS

Most alloys go through three stages when changing from a solid state to a liquid state, i.e. solid, semi-solid (*pasty*) and liquid. Some alloys do *not* however go through the middle stage. There is a metal alloy which goes from solid to liquid when heated and, when cooling, from liquid to solid. A mixture ratio of 65 parts tin to 35 parts lead will cause such a two stage change and is known as the *eutectic* alloy for tin and lead.

Many soft solders used for soldering electrical contacts also have this quick change from one stage to another, reducing the time needed for the connections to be held until the solder has solidified.

EVALUATION

Evaluation is the process of assessing the merit of an object, solution, idea, material, etc. At the end of a project you are expected to write an evaluation. It is formally presented under a heading of that name and judgements are listed a), b), c), etc. The **analysis** of the problem provides the criteria on which the evaluation is made. For example, it may have been stated in the analysis that the design of the instrumentation must be easily read and understood. The evaluation should then contain your objective opinion as to how easily the instruments could in fact be read.

EXHAUST AIR

The air trapped behind a piston in a single-acting cylinder has to be released to the atmosphere before the return spring can function. This is done by using a **Three port valve.** Here, port one is connected to receive the compressed air, port two is connected to the cylinder, and port three is controlled to release the exhaust air to the atmosphere. Port three is also known as the **exhaust port.**

EXHAUST PORT

◀ **Three port valve, Five port valve** ▶

EXOTHERMIC HEAT

This is the heat generated during the chemical process of **polymerisation.** The rise in temperature of a resin during the **curing** period is hardly noticeable on large thin layers that may occur in Glass Reinforced Plastics. However, if a quantity of the resin (with catalyst and activator added) is left over, its temperature may rise to a point where combustable materials (such as paper) left in contact with it may actually ignite.

Although exothermic heat will cause crazing during the curing process, the effect may be desirable in sculpture or jewellery; it would not be so where strength is an important feature.

Remember: Do not pour unwanted resin into a waste paper basket. You could cause a fire.

EXPANSION

Most materials get larger when heated. The *rate* of expansion varies with the material. ◀ **Coefficient of linear expansion** ▶

EXPLODED DRAWING OR VIEW

These are drawings which are drawn in *three dimensions*, where the component parts are drawn as separate pieces. They are, however, drawn along an axis to show how the parts can be assembled. This type of drawing is often used to show how kits can be assembled (Fig E.12).

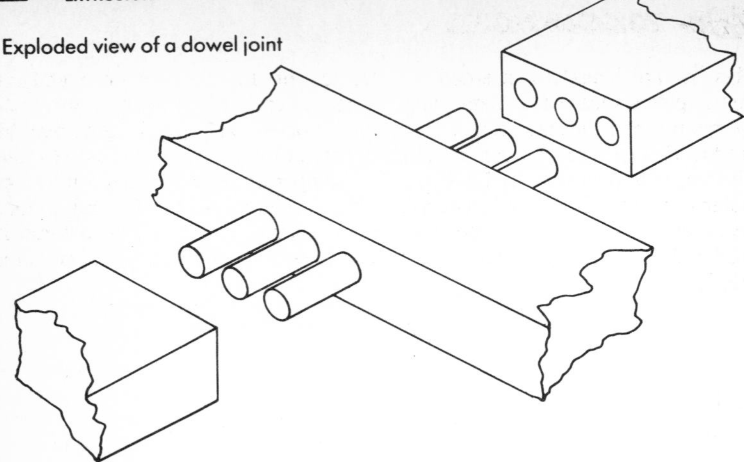

Fig E.12 Exploded drawing

You can also make good use of this type of drawing in your projects. If they are drawn well, you will be able to communicate your knowledge and understanding of how components fit together, as well as demonstrating your drawing skill.

EXTRUSION

When a metal or plastic material is forced through a die it will adopt the shape of the die. Therefore, a die with a square hole will produce a length of *extruded material* that will have a square cross-sectional shape. Dies can be made to a wide range of specifications according to the form of extruded material required. Figure E.13 shows some examples of extrusions.

Uses for extruded aluminium or plastics are evident in many construction kits which contain parts made from extruded aluminium or plastic. For example, kits, produced by Fischertechnik, or the Danum Electronic assemblies, which use PVC extrusion.

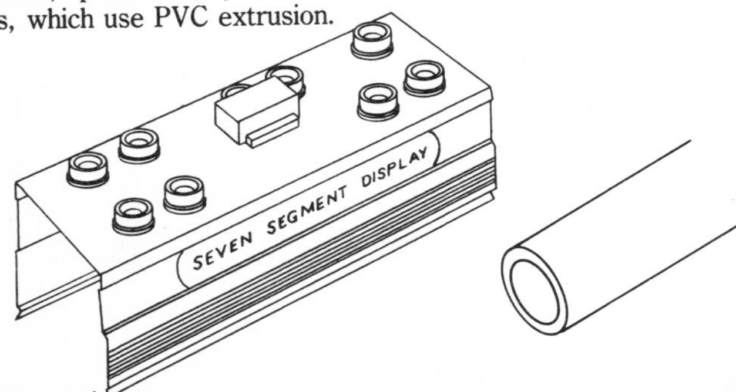

Fig E.13 Examples of extrusion

EXTRUSION PROCESS

This is an industrial method or *process* of forming either metal or thermoplastics material. Many types of pipe to carry water or gas, are made by this method, because it is a continuous process, and long lengths may be produced. Pipes can be cut to suitable lengths for transporting and storing. The material to be extruded is heated to a temperature that will allow it to flow under pressure. The 'soft' material is then forced through a die and, where necessary, cooled as it leaves the die. It is important that the material is solidified as soon as possible, so that the cross sectional shape is maintained (Fig E.14).

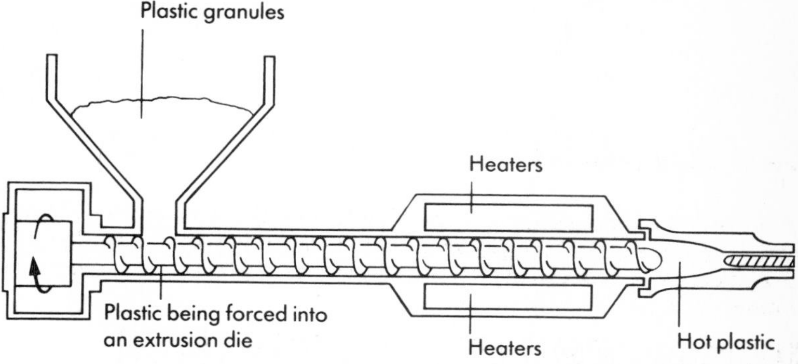

Fig E.14 Extrusion of piping

FABRICATE

This is the term used for putting metal components together by welding or brazing etc., and for making or constructing forms *without* casting or moulding.

FACE EDGE

This is the edge of a piece of wood which has been planed smooth and is true and from which marking out measurements are taken. The symbol ∧ is used to identify this edge from the others (Fig F.1).

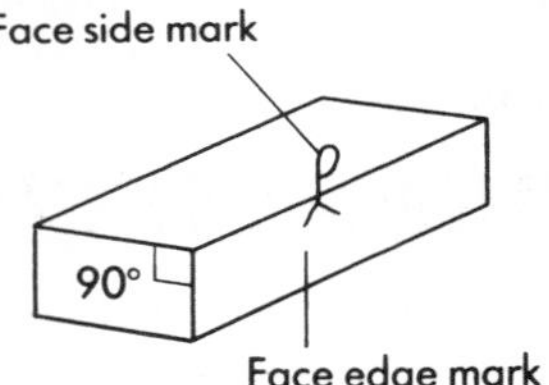

Fig F.1 Face edge and face side

FACE PLATE

When work is set up in a centre lathe, it can either be held in a chuck or fixed to a face plate. Large work, like a wooden bowl or the base of a lamp, needs to be securely held and the best method is to screw the work to a face plate.

Be careful not to use screws that are too long, because in the process of removing wood you do not want to damage the cutting tool or to have holes in your bowl, lamp base, etc., that will show.

FACE SIDE

This is the first side that is planed true and is at right angles to the face edge. The face side is identified by a loop symbol. All marking out is done from this side and the face edge. The face side always faces inwards on cabinets and frame construction (Fig F.1).

FARAD

A farad is a unit of capacitance. A **capacitor** has a capacitance of one farad when a charge of one coulomb increases the *potential difference* between the capacitor's plates by one volt. The farad is a large unit and is subdivided into one millionth of a farad, 'microfarad' (μF), a thousand millionth of a farad, 'nanofarad' (nF), and a billionth of a farad 'picofarad' (pF). If a capacitor is marked 470 pF you could call it a 47 picofarad or a '47 puff' capacitor.

FASHION

To fashion a piece of wood is to shape it by using cutting tools. Fashion also refers to style. Fashion is not something that is expected to last, so there is always a constant change of interests, tastes, styles, etc. Fashion can be most readily recognised by the clothes that are worn, the styles of hair, and the most popular types of music that are played. Fashion also affects the type of furniture, wall paper, fabrics and pictures, etc. Less obvious examples of fashion that are still important include the style of lettering and graphical imagery.

FASTENINGS

These are devices that are used to hold or fasten components together. For *temporary* holding, screws, nuts and bolts are used. For *permanent* fitting, rivets are used.

FEATHER

A thin piece of wood used to strengthen a mitred joint (Fig F.2). The feather is often used in picture frame construction.

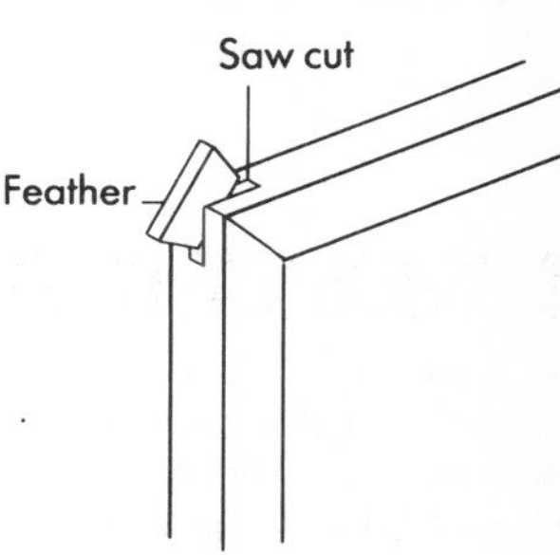

Fig F.2 Feather

FELT-TIP PENS

These are colouring pens which, although available in a variety of widths and shaped tips, are *not* suitable for very fine line work. However the instant application of colour which also dries very quickly makes them useful for most graphic work. Some pens are refillable with ink and have replaceable tips, but most felt-tip pens are disposable.

The inks fall into two main groups – *water-soluble*, i.e. the marks can be washed in water to remove them, or *permanent*, i.e. they cannot be removed by water. Therefore, in selecting a medium for a poster that is to be placed outside, where it is likely to get wet, it is important to use the pens with the appropriate type of ink.

FEMALE MOULD

There are two types of mould, *female* and *male*. The female mould can also be called a *negative* mould; the male mould can be called a *positive* mould. The difference between the two is clear; the female mould has a hollow, and the male mould has a raised portion (Fig F.3).

The type of mould to use depends upon the type of finish required, remembering that the casting taken from a female mould will have the smooth side on the outside. This is important in the production of Glass Reinforced Plastic hulls for boats. ◀ Male mould ▶

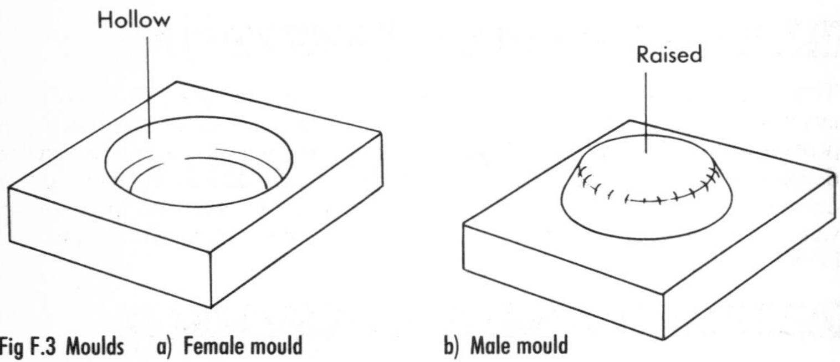

Fig F.3 Moulds a) Female mould b) Male mould

FENCE

Many machines that are designed to remove material, such as a circular saw, band saw, etc., have an adjustable fence. The fence is set at the chosen distance away from the cutting blade, so that when the work is kept firmly against the fence and moved gradually forward, the cut will always be a constant distance from one edge of the work.

FERROUS METALS

These are metals containing *iron*. Ferrous metals include steel and the various types of steels, e.g. tool steel, carbon steel, stainless steel, etc.

Iron has been used by man as the main material for making tools and weapons since 1200 BC. It is still a major material even though other materials, such as aluminium, now play a still more important role in our lives. Most alloys of iron will *rust*, which is a characteristic of iron itself. Iron can also be *magnetised* or attracted by a magnetic field, something that is not true for other metals. Therefore a magnet can be used to separate the ferrous metals from the non-ferrous metals.

FERRULE

This is a collar, usually made from brass, that fits around the neck of the wooden handle of a chisel to stop the handle from splitting (Fig F.4). Chisels with plastic handles do not require a ferrule because the material is tough and will resist splitting.

Fig F.4 Ferrule

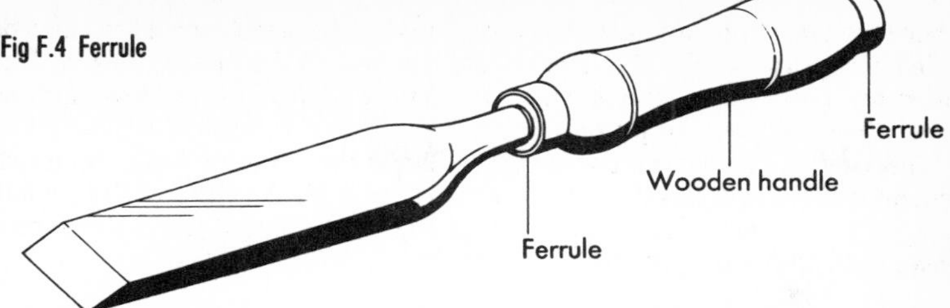

FIBRE BOARD

This is a manufactured board that is made from the fibres of wood. It is available in sheet form, and is often laminated with a plastics material top to provide a clean and attractive surface. Fibre boards are available in varying degrees of hardness, and are referred to as low density (soft), medium density, and high density (hard). Because of their stability, i.e. they will not warp, they can be used in wide sizes and long lengths and are frequently used in making furniture.

FIBRE GLASS

Glass can be drawn into fine threads or fibres when melted. These fine fibres can be woven together to form a fabric, mat or roving. The main use of such material is in the reinforcement of synthetic resins, commonly known as **Glass Reinforced Plastics** or G.R.P. (Fig F.5).

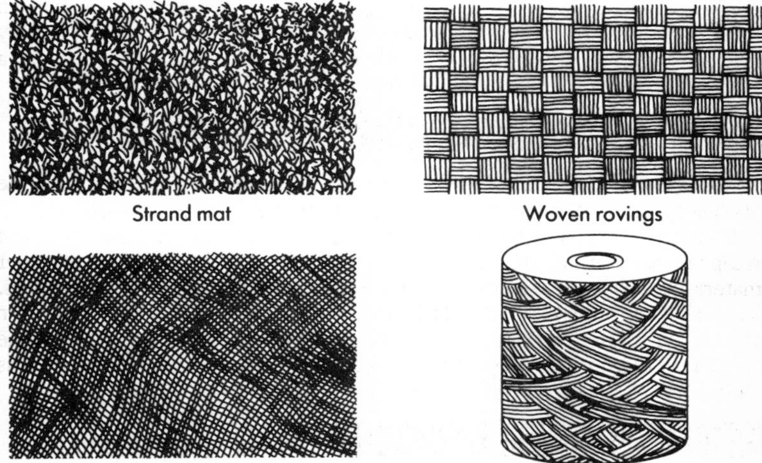

Fig F.5 Fibre glass

FIBRE-TIP PENS

These are pens that have a tip made from long synthetic fibres. The fibres are hard wearing and are available in narrow widths, i.e. 0.5 mm and smaller. The fibres are enclosed in a metal sleeve and enable you to draw fine, accurate lines. The black pens are particularly useful for lined working drawings and as an alternative to the more expensive technical pens. The pens contain a water soluble ink in a variety of colours.

FIFTY FIVE TIMER CHIP

This is an electronic device that generates a regular signal that is used to synchronize operations in a computer. The timer chip can be used as a clock pulse generator. The regular pulses sent out to the elements of a logic circuit are called *clock pulses*. The interval between each pulse is known as the *clock frequency*.

FILLET

This is the small narrow part between two adjacent surfaces on a moulding. It is used to provide a clean break from a flowing curve in one direction to a flowing curve of different size or direction of flow (Fig F.6a)).

The term *fillet* also applies to the radiused parts of patterns used in the casting process. The purpose here is more functional than aesthetic. It is important in sand casting processes *not* to have any sharp corners on the pattern, because where sharp corners *are* formed in the sand there is a danger that grains of sand will be removed and caught up in the flow of molten metal. This will not only spoil the appearance of the casting, but will also cause a weakness where the sand is trapped in the metal. So all external corners are rounded and internal corners are hollowed by putting in a fillet. Various lengths of a fillet are available (Fig F.6b)). The fillet shapes are most commonly formed with a filler paste and rubbed down when hardened with an abrasive paper held on to a rounded piece of wood.

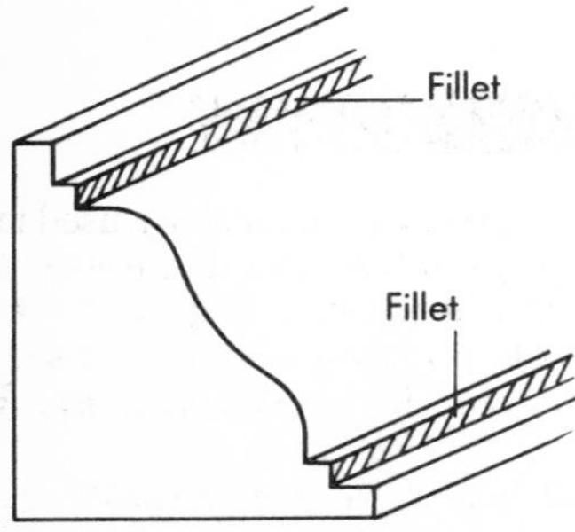

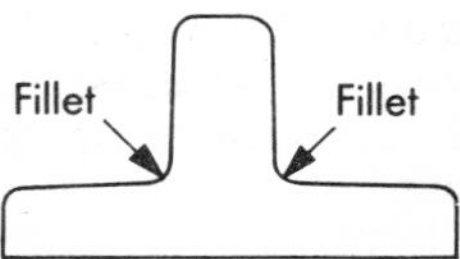

Fig F.6 Fillet a) Moulding b) Wooden pattern from which a metal casting is to be made

FINAL DRAWINGS

These are the drawings that have *all* the details of what is to be made.
◀ Working drawings ▶

FINISH

This is sometimes referred to as the surface treatment of a material. To complete an article a treatment is often needed. For example, polish, varnish and stain are *finishes* that could be used on woods; oiling, blueing and planishing are finishes that could be used on metals; edge-buffing and lightly applying an antistatic fluid could be used for plastic materials such as acrylic. Some materials such as plastic laminated boards need *no* surface treatment, since the surface appearance cannot be improved or made more durable by applying a paint, lacquer, etc.

FIRE RESISTANT MATERIAL

Most materials that are manufactured from natural sources, such as trees, plants and animals, are inflammable. But so too are many of the synthetic materials such as cellulose foam.

Plastics materials can be produced to be *fire resistant*. This does *not* mean that they will not burn at all, but rather that they can resist bursting into flames for a period of time, e.g. 30 minutes, 50 minutes, etc. There are standards laid down for materials to have varying *levels* of fire resistance in given situations, and these are published in British Standards publication B.S. 476. The levels are governed by the time that is thought reasonable for people to get to safety and the degree of fire risk. The door from a garage that is built-in as part of the house has to have a fire resistant door.

FISCHERTECHNIK

A construction kit that allows easy assembly and easy dismantling so that the development of solutions to problems can be built and modified as ideas emerge.

FITTINGS

This is a general term used to include a wide range of devices that are used in the assembling and making of objects. For projects that involve the use of *wood* and *metal*, *fittings* such as nails, screws, hinges, rivets, nuts and bolts would be among a long list of items. In technology projects involving *electronic circuits*, such things as clips, plugs, leads, etc., would be included on a long list of fittings.

The items that you require for the production of an artefact should be included in the *parts list*, giving the number required and any specific detail related to type and size. Often these details are left out of projects and yet they play an important role in the production process.

FIVE PORT VALVE

There are five ports (five threaded holes) to this valve. These valves are mainly used in circuits that have a double acting cylinder i.e. a cylinder where the piston must return to its starting position. Such a movement of a piston can be considered as two distinct movements. The *outward stroke* (positive) and the *inward stroke* (negative). Such movements are necessary in stamping, in pressing, in opening and closing doors, etc.

The five ports have the following functions:

a) *port one* receives compressed air;
b) *port two* releases the compressed air to the cylinder, which goes positive;
c) *port four* receives the exhaust air from the cylinder which passes through the valve and is exhausted through *port five* to the atmosphere.

At the same time exhaust air is received by port two as the piston goes negative, and this is released to the atmosphere through *port three.* A five port valve, with circuit diagrams, is shown in Fig F.7.

These five port valves can be operated by finger push button, foot pedal plunger, rotating cam roller-trip, or a plunger. the double pressure type can be operated by air signals coming from a pilot valve.

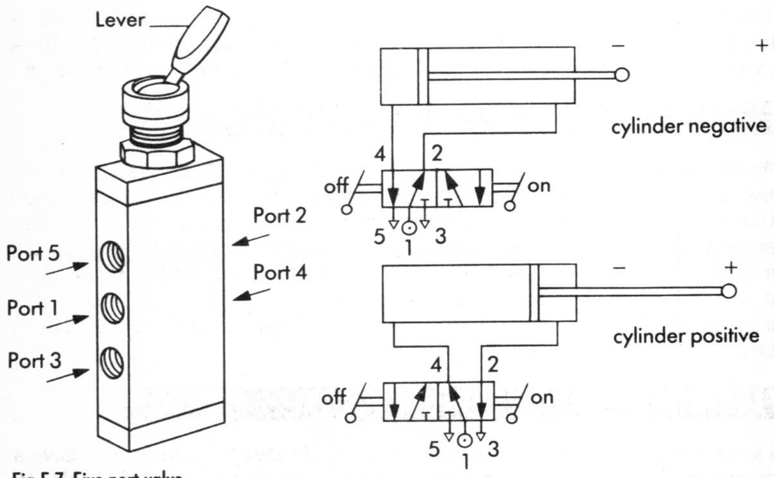

Fig F.7 Five port valve

FLANGED COUPLING

This is a device for joining shafts (Fig F.8).

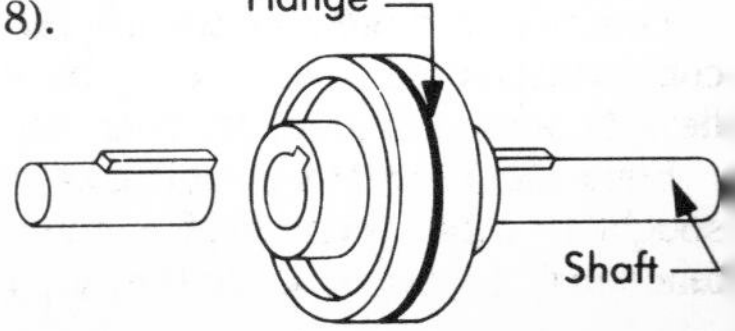

Flange

Shaft

Fig F.8 Flanged coupling

FLASHING

When metals or plastics are forced into split moulds under pressure, some of the material finds its way *between* the two halves of the mould. The result is that when the moulding is ejected, a thin fin of material remains on the moulding. It is this excess material that is called flashing.

Flashing on a moulding is produced because either the two halves of the mould were not fitting properly together, or the mating surfaces are damaged. Although flashing can normally be easily removed and the moulding is perfectly acceptable, you should aim to *avoid* flashing occurring by making sure that the mould is correctly assembled *before* injecting a material, and that the mating surfaces are perfectly flat and undamaged.

FLASHOVER

A flashover refers to an electrical discharge in the form of an arc or a spark between two electrical conductors, or between a conductor and earth. The terms *arcover* or *sparkover* are more specific descriptions of a flashover.

FLASK

This is a device used in making a sand mould for a metal casting. The parts of the flask are called **cope** and **drag**. When these are assembled ready for a casting process, they are considered to be a flask. ◀ **Cope and drag** ▶

FLATPACK FURNITURE

As the name suggests, this furniture can be packed flat. This means that it is *not* assembled when bought and can be assembled by the customer after being transported to its destination. Such furniture can be standardized using large scale production techniques, making it less costly. It is also easier to transport in bulk and to store when not required for use. It has two disadvantages; first, if a surface becomes damaged it is not easy to repair; and second, the assembled furniture does not have the same level of rigid construction as factory-assembled furniture.

FLEXIBILITY

This is the ability to change according to need. If a *design solution* must have a degree of inbuilt flexibility, this means that it may have to be adaptable, to cope with a variety of needs. Many of the demands placed upon a *power tool* will mean that it has to be flexible enough to cope with the attachments for drilling, hedgetrimming, sanding a surface, etc.

Flexibility can often be associated with *human beings*. The ability to adapt to cope with situations can mean the difference between success and failure. A flexible person is more likely to succeed than someone rigid and inflexible.

Flexibility in *materials* can be of some advantage, but many ways have been sought to make them *rigid*, since it is in this state that they become more functional, especially when they have to withstand forces. Thin sheet material which, in a flat condition, is quite flexible is made rigid by introducing curves and folded edges. Look at a plastic beaker and see how the rim is rounded; look down the sides of the beaker at the curved loops or corrugations. These may add to the appearance but their main function is to counteract the flexibility of the material without adding extra material and weight.

FLEXIBLE CURVE

The need to draw lines that are *not* straight, circular, elliptical, etc., can present a problem. A 'Flexi-Curve' is a flexible length of material that can be bent into a variety of curved, flowing shapes, and yet remain in the position set, so that with careful handling a curved line can be drawn. The advantage of this device is that it can be bent to follow a variety and combination of curves so that only *one* movement of a pen or pencil is necessary to draw a curved line. The similar process using **french curves** often means moving from one part of the curve to another and drawing the line in several stages. The line produced is usually less 'flowing'.

FLEXIBLE JOINTS

When a mechanism has to slightly adjust its alignment with another it is often resolved with a flexible joint. A very simple example is where the shaft of an electric motor of a model boat must be aligned with the shaft of a propeller. The transmission between the motor and the propeller is achieved by using a small rubber tube. It will grip the two shafts but is also flexible enough to accept the difference in alignment.

FLIP FLOP

This is a bistable multivibrator circuit that has two inputs corresponding to two stable states. The name flip flop describes the action when an input pulse received causes the device to 'flip' into a corresponding state and remain in that state until a pulse from the other input causes it to 'flop' into the other state (Fig F.9).

Flip flops are commonly used in computers as counting and storage elements:

a) A *D-type flip flop* is a clocked flip flop with a delay. The D stands for delay. One clock pulse input will delay the output by one clock pulse.
b) An *SR flip flop* (Set and Reset) whose inputs are designated S and R have logic inputs 0 and 1. Logic 1 should not be allowed to appear on both inputs together, as the output will not be accepted.
c) A *JK flip flop* has inputs designated J and K. These devices are normally clocked and avoid the simultaneous states of 1 appearing on both inputs, as in S and R.

Data can be transferred along a chain of flip flops and can be used as a shift register.

Clock input

R Q

S $\bar{Q}$

Input		Output	
R	S	Q	$\bar{Q}$
0	0	no change	
1	0	1	0
0	1	0	1
1	1	indeterminate	

Fig F.9 Flip Flop

FLOW

The term flow can be used to describe the movement of a metal in a liquid state. It can also be used to describe how the elements of a graphic illustration hold together, or it can be used to indicate the movement of electrons in a circuit.

FLOW CHARTS

Presenting information or a set of instructions in sequence using symbols is commonly used today in schools, industry, commerce, etc. The advantage of using such *flow charts* to describe operations and processes is that they are easy to follow. The symbols are standard and British Standards publication PP7307 Table 14 shows you the most commonly used symbols. A few examples are shown in Figure F.10. You will find it easier to draw these symbols quickly and neatly if you use a flow chart template.

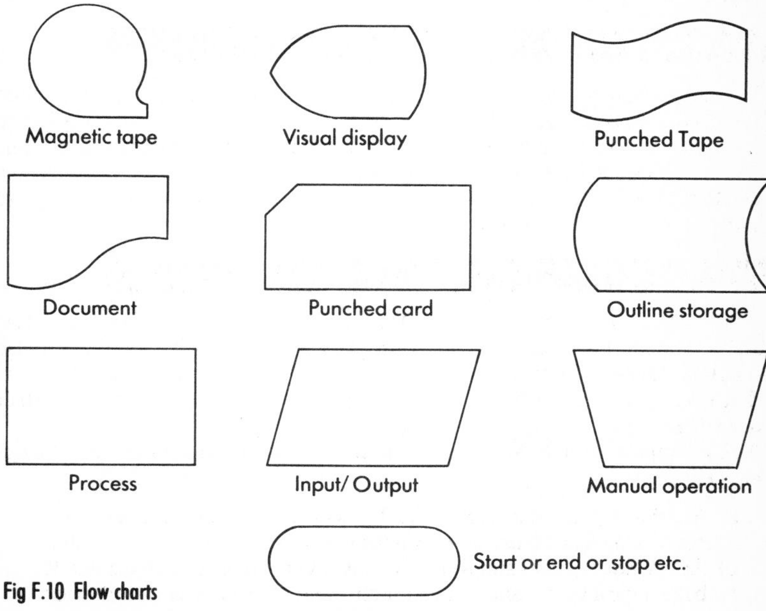

Fig F.10 Flow charts

FLOW DIAGRAMS

These are the same as **Flow Charts**.

FLUIDISATION/FLUIDISER

This is a device for making a powdered plastics material behave like a fluid.
◄ **Dip coating** ►

FLUIDISING TANK

◀ Dip coating ▶

FLUID POWER SYMBOLS

These are used to present fluid circuits in a more simple form. See British Standards publication PP7307 Table 7 for further details.

FLUSH FINISH

To bring two or more surfaces to the same level. When components are fitted together, to avoid some parts, such as screws, being 'proud' (sticking out), the holes are countersunk or counterbored. The screw can then be fitted so that its head is level with the surrounding surface.

FLUX

This is a substance used in soldering. It stops the metal absorbing oxygen from the air and forming an oxide layer, and also 'wets' the surface to help the solder flow. It is applied to the surface *before* heating begins so that it can melt before oxidation takes place.

There are two main groups of flux. *Active*, which is corrosive, and *passive*, which is non-corrosive.

Resin flux is used when soft soldering joints in intricate electrical wiring, where it would be impossible to wash away surplus flux after the soldering process is completed. When soft soldering joints in tinplate sheet, zinc chloride is a commonly used flux. Being an 'active' flux, it also cleans the metal, so ensuring that a good join is possible. Surplus flux must be washed away with water after the soldering process is completed. Multi-core soft solders have a core of flux included in the solder so separate applications of flux and solder are not needed.

FOCAL POINT

A focal point is a fixed position from which other constant distances are measured or constructed. The focal point of a **circle** is the centre. The circumference is a constant distance from the centre. An **ellipse** has two focal points, in a fixed position on the major axis. The distance between the ellipse and the two focal points is based upon the length of the major axis and the length of the minor axis.

Such loci as the parabola, ellipse and hyperbola have a focal point that is a fixed distance from a **directrix**. ◀ Parabola, Ellipse, Hyperbola ▶

FOCUS

The focus is the meeting point of lines, or the point from which lines radiate. To *focus* attention is to concentrate on a particular detail, just as a camera lens will *focus* on detail so that it stands out clearly from less important material.

FOLIO

The folio is a document that contains all the details of a project that has been involved with a design activity. ◀ **Design folio** ▶

FOLLOWER

This is the part of a mechanism that remains in contact with a **cam** and follows the cam as it rotates. There are several types of follower, each designed to suit different shaped cams (Fig F.11). The main function of a follower is to ride smoothly over the cam, helping to change the rotary motion of the cam to the reciprocating motion (rise and fall) of the follower.

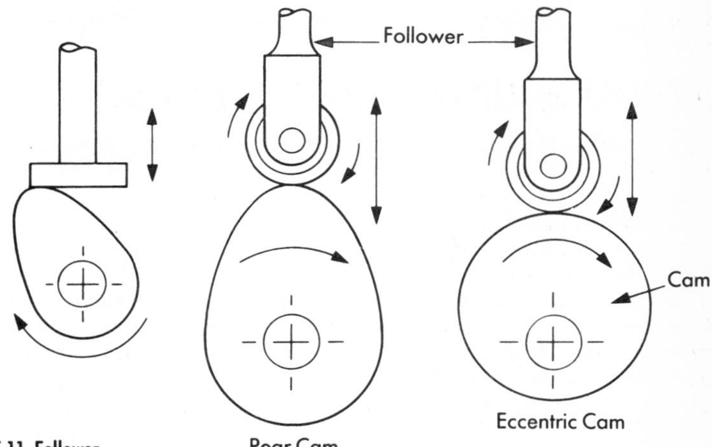

Fig F.11 Follower

FORCES

A force is a load. A load can act upon a structure in four different ways:

a) **compression** (squeezing);
b) **tension** (pulling);
c) **torque** or tortion (twisting);
d) **shear** (cutting).

FORESHORTENING

This is how the eye sees things as they get further and further away from you. The further away they are, the smaller they get (Fig F.12).

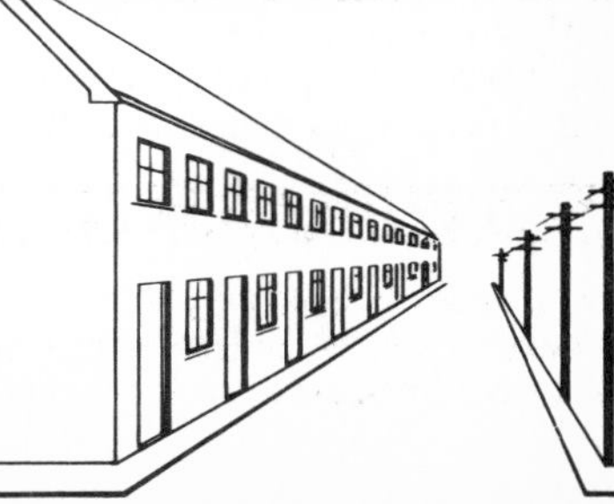

Fig F.12 Foreshortening

FORGING PROCESS

Some metals can be reshaped, when red hot, by hitting with a hammer. This reshaping process is called forging. The advantage of forging metals is that the grain structure is not weakened, in fact it is strengthened by the crystal grains becoming more compact from the compression blows of the hammer (Fig F.13).

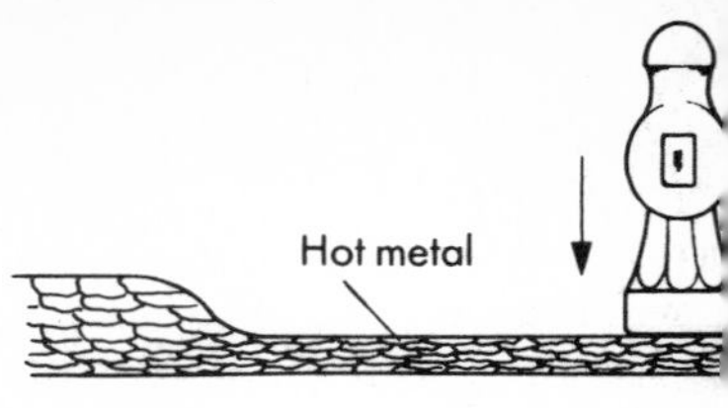

Fig F.13 Forging process

FORM

The form of something usually relates to its three-dimensional shape. *Sculptures* are a three-dimensional form.

FORMER

These are devices that are used to make something. They are not, however, tools. A *former* is used to *support* the material being worked so that it can take on a new form. A common example where formers are used is in **laminated** work where the laminations are going to take on a curved form. Most violins, cellos, guitars, etc., require formers when being made. On a simpler level formers are used to hold wood laminates in place while forming the curved back of a chair or the curved form of salad servers. Acrylic can be easily formed when heated (Fig F.14).

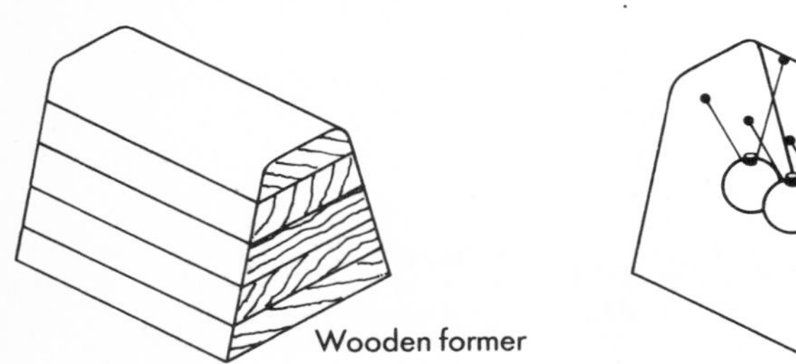

Fig F.14 Former

FRENCH CURVES

These are a set of templates that have a wide range of slow and quick curved edges. The user selects the part of the curve which is near to the curved line that is to be drawn, and then draws using the **template** to steady the movement (Fig F.15).

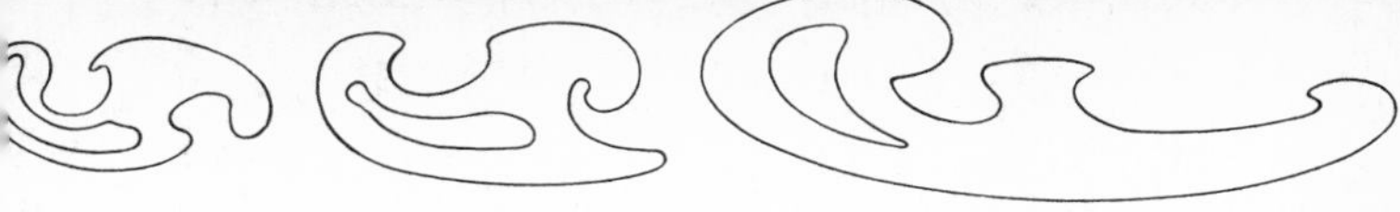

g F.15 French curves

REQUENCY

equency is concerned with how often something happens in a given time. n example is the number of times the heart beats every minute. A vibration n be measured by the number of complete movements that are made in a ven time. Frequency is measured in **hertz**. This unit of measurement is ncerned with how many times the vibration, pulse, wave, etc., happens in e second.

FREQUENCY BANDS

iese are *ranges* of sound waves that are internationally agreed. Some amples are as follows:

Low Frequency (LF)	30 – 300kHz
Medium Frequency (MF)	3000kHz – 3MHz
Very High Frequency (VHF)	30 – 300MHz

FREQUENCY VOLTAGE

n Alternating Current is constantly changing from negative to positive and sitive to negative. The change however is smooth and as you can see on a nusoidal graph (see Fig A.3; **Amplitude**) the current changes from a aximum in one direction to zero, then on to a maximum in the other rection, before returning to zero again. The number of times this is repeated r second is known as the **frequency**; the AC mains supply is set at 50Hz.

RICTION

◀ Newton's first law of motion ▶

RIENDS OF THE EARTH

his is an organisation concerned with the way in which the environment and e resources of the world are treated. They are concerned about such issues topics as 'Acid rain', 'Dumping of toxic waste materials', 'Nuclear warfare', well as other issues related to the environment. Their aim is to draw tention to such issues so that governments and people take appropriate tion.

FRUSTUM

This is the portion of a solid after its top has been removed. The frustum of cone or pyramid is one that has had its top removed (Fig F.16).

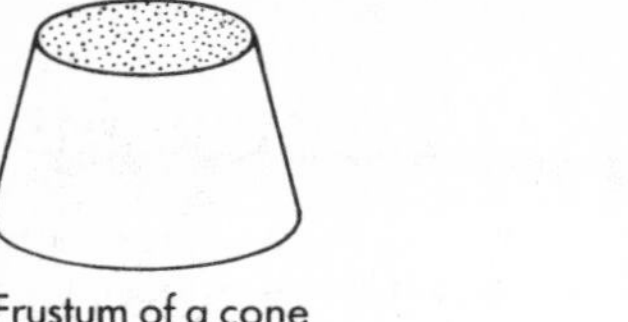

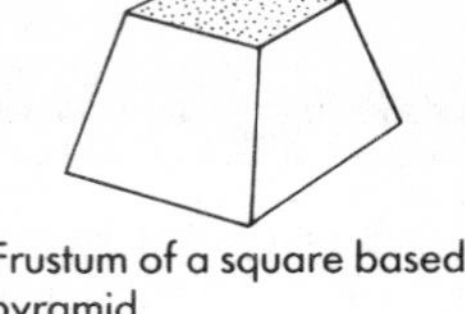

Fig F.16 Frustum

FULCRUM

The fulcrum is the point of balance or the point about which rotation occur when there is an uneven balance. It is also the point where pressure can b most effectively exerted to move a load with a lever. The position of a fulcrui is important when wanting to achieve a **mechanical advantage**, i.e. using th least effort to move a load (Fig F.17).

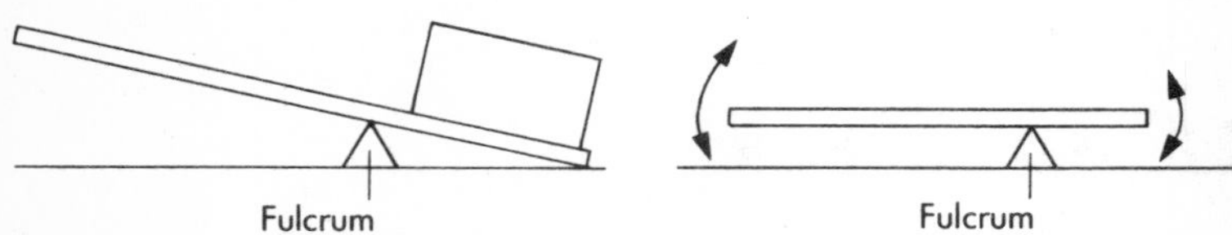

Fig F.17 Fulcrum

FULL SIZE

A drawing that is the same size as the object. When a drawing is the same siz as an object it is termed full size and is stated as scale 1:1. Usually you nee only draw to scale 1:1 when a **working drawing** is being prepared.

FUNCTION

Almost everything that is made has a function. A bridge has the function allowing people to cross over an obstacle such as a river, a road or a railwa Buildings have the function of protecting people from the rain and cold. painting has the function of communicating the artist's impression. It has ofte been said that the *form* of an object is governed by its *function*. The boat th has to float looks very different from an aeroplane that has to fly. Th statement 'Form follows function' is based upon this observation.

FUNCTIONAL SURFACES

The condition of a surface will determine the efficiency of mechanical devices. Where surfaces have to slide or fit with precision, the dimension is important and is often expressed as a **tolerance**. If this degree of accuracy is *not* kept, the function of the assembly may fail. See British Standards PD7308 for further details.

FUSE

This is an item that is included in all electrical devices to prevent components within that device getting 'over loaded' (too much current), or preventing someone receiving an electric shock. Each fuse has a rating in *amps*. In a standard household, these range between 3 and 30 amps. A 3 amp fuse is suitable for radios, lights, etc., whereas an electric cooker or oven may need a 30 amp fuse.

Remember: The fuse is the weakest part of the circuit; it should 'blow' (break the circuit) before any damage is caused.

GALVANOMETER

◀ Displays ▶

GATE

The term *gate* is short for 'gate electrode'. It is an electronic device for suppressing the flow of electric pulses. The gate is switched on or off by electric signals. The current is controlled by the very much smaller current that enters the control electrode of the field effective transistor.

A *digital gate* is a circuit that has two or more inputs but only one output. The conditions applied to the input affect the voltage level of the output. Digital gates are commonly used in logic circuits.

Analogue gates are a linear circuit device that produce an output signal only during a predetermined interval of an input signal. These gates are used in electronic control systems.

GEARS

Gears are wheels with teeth. The teeth are specially shaped so that they mesh (fit exactly) with the teeth of another gear wheel, even when the gear wheels are of different sizes. Motion can be transmitted through 180° and 90° by using different designs of gears (Fig G.1).

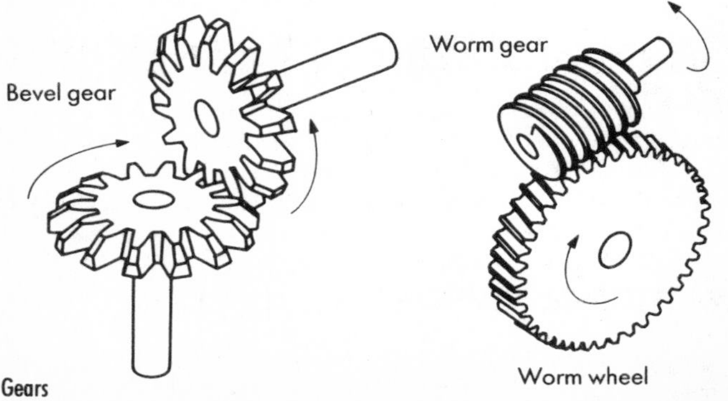

Fig G.1 Gears

Gears are mainly used in mechanisms to transmit *rotary* motion. *Linear* (straight line) motion can be achieved by combining a gear wheel called a *pinion* with a *rack*. ◀ Rack and pinion ▶

GEAR TRAINS

A combination of gears arranged to transmit motion to two or more working mechanisms is known as a gear train. The most common example is the gear train on a lathe, used to transmit a rotary motion to the work and the automatic linear motion to the cutting tool. The sizes of the gears used determine the **speed ratio** of the moving parts i.e. the work and the cutting tool (Fig G.2).

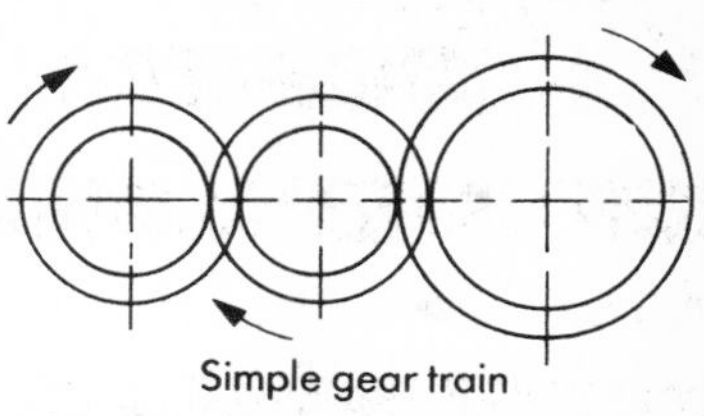

Fig G.2 Gear train

Gear trains are used for automatic feed, and thread cutting, on a centre lathe. The ratio needed in order to make the final gear go faster or slower is worked out by choosing a gear with the appropriate number of teeth. The in-between gears called 'idlers' do not affect the *speed* of the final gear, only the *direction* in which it rotates.

GEL COAT

This is often the *first* coat of a synthetic resin that is applied to a mould in **Glass Reinforced Plastics** (GRP) work. It is a thicker resin than the general purpose resin and will cling better to vertical sides while uncured. This property means that the first coat will be of an *even* thickness, even on the vertical sides. The gel coat can also have a pigment mixed in with the resin to give the artefact a colour. Remember that the *first* coat will be the *surface* finish in the artefact.

A *thixotropic resin* is another name for a gel-resin that you may use in connection with GRP work.

GENERATE

To generate is to make something happen. In *graphical terms* it is to produce moving lines (generators) in the construction of the surface of solids. In *electrical terms* it is to convert mechanical energy into electrical energy using a device called a *generator*. In designing, the term means 'generate ideas', to bring about new ideas.

ELECTRICAL GENERATOR

This is a mechanical device that converts one form of energy such as that obtained from fossil fuels, or water etc., into electricity.

Fig G.3 Generator

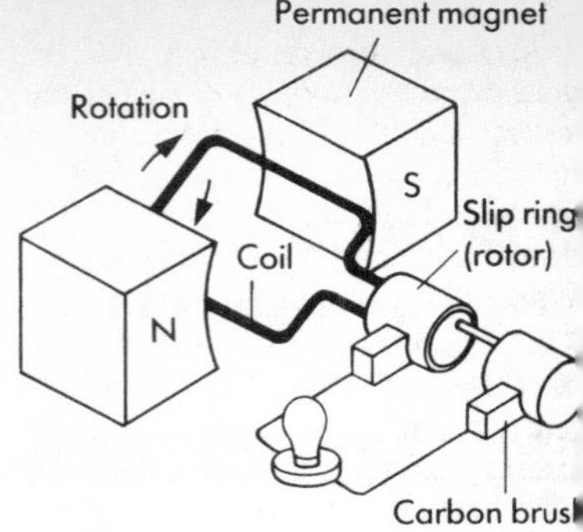

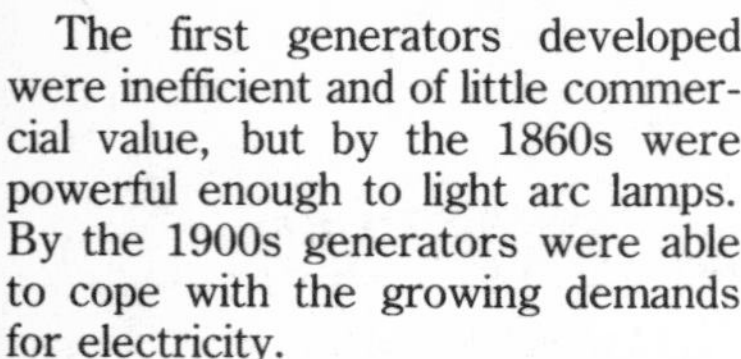

The first generators developed were inefficient and of little commercial value, but by the 1860s were powerful enough to light arc lamps. By the 1900s generators were able to cope with the growing demands for electricity.

A simple generator is similar to a simple electric motor (Fig G.3). A coi wound on an iron core, is mounted so that it can rotate between the poles of permanent magnet. As it rotates, an *electro magnetic force* (e.m.f.) is induce in the coil. The rotating coil cuts through the magnetic field between the pole of the magnet, and as it does so, the induced emf alternates. As a result th emf increases from zero to maximum strength, decreases to zero, increase to maximum strength in the opposite direction, and then decreases again t zero. The emf is transferred from the coil via two slip rings which are mounte on a rotor connected to the coil. The slip rings come into contact with a pair c carbon brushes and the emf now appears in the brushes. The alternating em gives rise to an alternating current in the conductors attached to the tw brushes. This type of generator is known as an *AC generator* or *alternator*.

In a simple direct current (DC) generator the coil is connected to **commutator** instead of **slip rings**. Though the current flowing through the co still alternates, the commutator reverses the connections to the carbo brushes every half turn. This means that the current leaves the coil by on brush and returns by the other one. Unfortunately, the strength of the direc current varies with the rotation of the rotor. This can be overcome b arranging several coils around the rotor and connecting each one to a separat pair of segments of the commutator.

GENERIC

Generic is a term which applies to *all* the members of a group or family. I is the name of the group to which all the members belong, e.g. *wood* is the generic name for all the different types of wood that exist; *metal* is the generi name for all the different metals that exist; *tools* is the generic name for all the tools that exist.

When answering questions, however, do not use the generic term wher you are expected to give the *specific* term; e.g. instead of giving the answe 'wood', name the specific wood, such as beech, oak, mahogany, etc.

GEOMETRIC CONSTRUCTION

Whenever instruments such as a compass, a pair of dividers, etc., are used to draw a geometric shape, the process is called geometric construction.

A triangle can be drawn just by using a ruler, but you would be limited in your degree of accuracy. Using the ruler alone would not be considered as 'construction'. If, however, you use a ruler and a compass, then you would be following a procedure called construction. To construct a triangle you would first of all draw the length of one side, and from the ends of this line you would draw two arcs of given radii, i.e. equal to the lengths of the other two sides. Where the two arcs cross, you use two straight lines to join with the ends of the first line. You have now drawn a triangle by geometric construction. ◀ Developments, Polygons ▶

GEOMETRIC FORM

Forms are divided into two main groups: natural and geometric. Though many natural forms, such as the hexagonal shape cells of a honeycomb, can fit into either group, the majority of forms fit into one or the other. Geometric forms can be drawn using instruments, whereas most natural forms are drawn free hand.

GEOMETRIC GRIDS

These are lined grids that can be used to develop patterns, or *isometric* and *perspective* grids that can be used to assist with three-dimensional drawing. The grids are usually placed underneath detail paper or tracing paper so that the grid can be seen. Once the drawing is complete, the grid paper can be removed, so leaving a three-dimensional drawing with very little or no evidence of construction lines.

GEOMETRIC PATTERN

These are patterns that are usually symmetrical and are made up of a combination of geometric shapes.

GLASS MAT

This is a sheet of chopped strands of glass threads arranged at random in layers, and bonded together with a medium that is compatible with the resin used in GRP work. Mats are made in continuous lengths about 1 metre wide. The thickness of the mat is governed by the weight of glass used per square metre. For lightweight work, $300g/m^2$ is suitable. The most commonly used weight is $450g/m^2$. The texture of a mat is governed by the coarseness of the strands of glass. Tissue mat has very fine strands and is used as a final layer where a reasonably fine finish is desired. ◀ Fibre glass ▶

GLASS REINFORCED PLASTICS (GRP)

Resin on its own is quite brittle when cured, but resin that has a layer (or several layers) of glass fibre mat is very strong. It is this quality, plus its lightness, that makes GRP a popular choice for boats, the front of the highspeed trains, etc.

GOLDEN MEAN

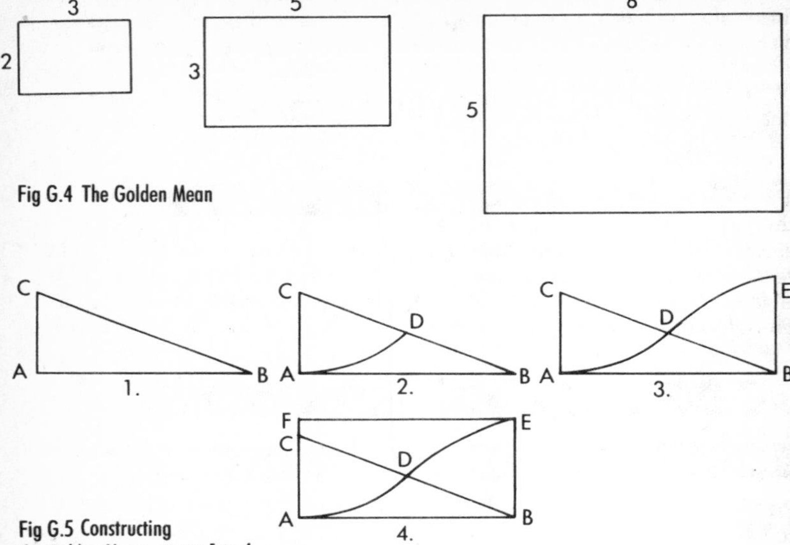

Fig G.4 The Golden Mean

Fig G.5 Constructing the Golden Mean: stages 1 to 4

The '*Golden Mean*' is a proportion that is reputed to have been worked out by Leonardo Fibonacci in the 1200s. He produced a series of numbers in which the addition of the two previous numbers gives the next number., e.g. 1+1=2, 1+2=3, 2+3=5, 3+5=8, 5+8=13, 8+13=21, etc. When this is written as a series, the numbers appear like this: 1, 1, 2, 3, 5, 8, 13, 21 etc. (Fig G.4).

Use any two numbers that are next to one another and you have a proportion that is equal to the 'Golden Mean'. The higher the numbers, the greater the accuracy.

A method of constructing a rectangle to the proportions of the 'Golden Mean' is as follows (Fig G.5):

a) draw a right angle triangle with AB twice the length of AC;
b) from C, draw an arc equal to AC to cut CB and call it D;
c) from B, draw an arc equal to BD and from B draw a line at right angles; where the line meets the arc, call it E;
d) the lines AB and BE are equal to the proportion of the 'Golden Mean' and the two remaining sides of the rectangle can be drawn parallel to AB and BE.

If you are ever in doubt about a 'pleasing' proportion, you can always compare your attempt with one based upon the 'Golden Mean'. The proportion of rectangles based upon the Golden Mean are widely regarded as 'pleasing to the eye'.

GOLDEN SECTION OR RATIO

Dividing a line into the 'Golden Ratio' was well known in ancient Greece. It forms the basic proportions of many of their temples and other classical buildings and sculpture. The proportion is achieved by:

a) drawing a line AB;
b) drawing BC equal in length to half AB and at right angles to AB;
c) with centre C, drawing an arc equal to CB to cut AC at H;
d) with centre A, drawing an arc equal to AH to cut AB at D;

The ratio of AC to AB is the same as the ratio of AD to BC (Fig G.6). By using these lengths to draw a rectangle, the rectangle will have the Golden Section ratio. Again these proportions are 'pleasing to the eye'.

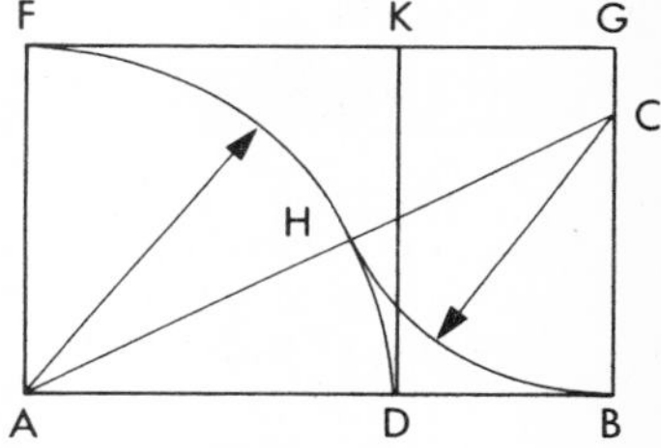

Fig G.6 Golden Section or Ratio

GRAPHICS

Presenting information using pictures, symbols, etc. Using graphics to communicate or present information visually is not new. The Egyptians used Hieroglyphics (Pictograph, ideograph, etc.) to represent a word, symbol or sound over 4000 years ago. Today, the need to communicate with people of different languages and levels of ability has become very important, and this has given rise to a much greater use of graphics as a means of communicating.

GRAPHS

A graph is a means of presenting mathematical information using lines and shapes to depict quantities of varying kinds. The size of a shape is proportional to the quantity it is representing. Suppose two quantities are given, the value of one being equal to half the other; it follows that in a **bar chart**, one bar will be equal to half the *size* of the other.

Graphs are commonly presented as a line. Any point on that line is fixed by two co-ordinates, often referred to as x and y. In a graph related to rainfall over a period of one year, the x co-ordinate might be the month when the rain fell, and the y co-ordinate the quantity of rain that fell in the month (Fig G.7).

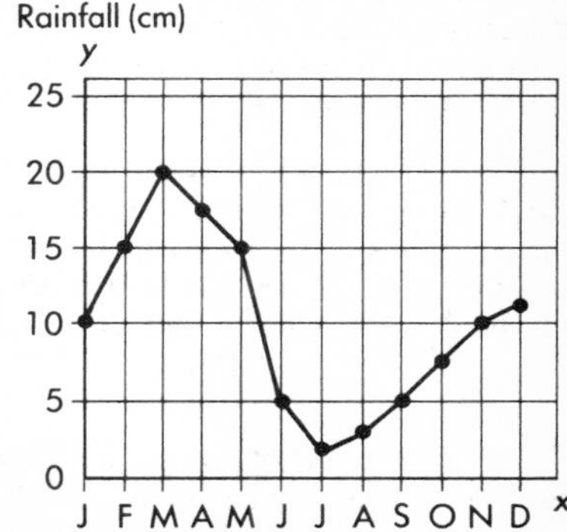

Fig G.7 Graphs

Graphs have the advantage of making it easy to *see* information at a glance. The information can then be understood more easily than if just figures and words were used.

GREENPEACE

This is an organisation concerned with environmental issues. Its main objective is to protect the natural environment of the seas and the land. It strongly opposed the dumping of toxic and radioactive waste in the seas and the pollution of the air through the release of waste gases from various industries.

GREEN STAGE

When a synthetic resin is in the process of **curing**, the first stage of hardening occurs in a space of several minutes to an hour or so; but the resin may not become really hard for several months. During this time the resin, though firm, can be quite flexible; it is then said to be in the *green stage*, i.e. still curing.

GREEN TIMBER

After a tree has been felled, the timber is still full of sap. This means that a lot of moisture is still contained in the vessels, so that the tree is still quite wet. Timber in this state is referred to as being 'green'. The term green timber has nothing to do with colour.

GROOVE

This is a hollow channel cut into a material. A groove can form part of a joint, such as a tongue and groove joint, or be a key way in a shaft. It can also be used as a means by which a lubricant can reach the surfaces of mechanical parts.

GOUGE

A *gouge* is a type of chisel that has a curved blade. There are two main types. Those with the grinding angle on the outside edge are called *firmer gouges*; those with the grinding angle on the inside edge are called *scribing gouges*. Firmer gouges are used for hollowing and turning wood on a lathe; scribing gouges are used for cutting grooves (Fig G.8).
Remember: Only the long handled firmer gouge can be used on a lathe. The long handle provides the support that is needed.

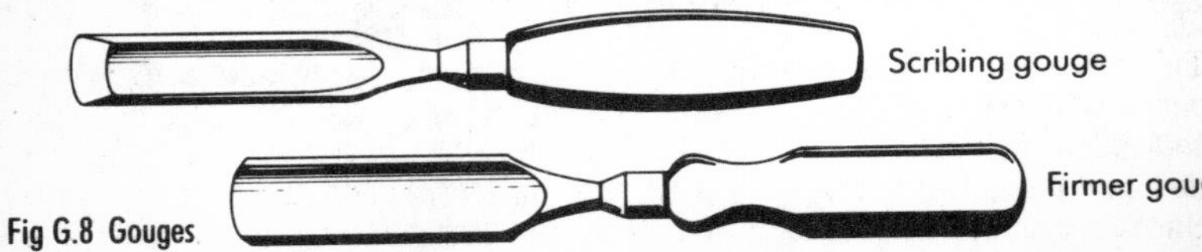

Fig G.8 Gouges

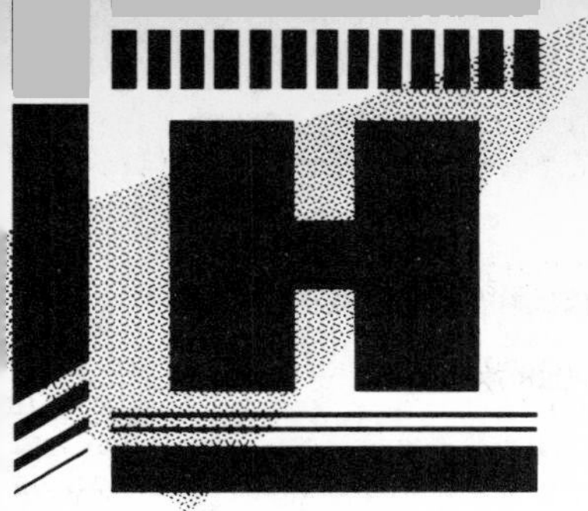

HALF SECTION

To show a half sectioned and a half not-sectioned in the single view is only acceptable when the object is symmetrical. The half showing the outside view does not need any hidden detail to be shown since the half that is sectioned should provide all the information (Fig H.1).

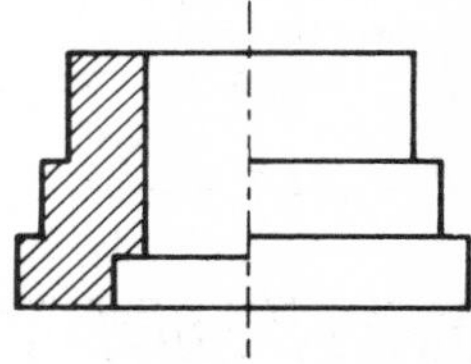

Fig H.1 Half section view

HALVING JOINTS

Here, two pieces of material are joined by a joint in which half the thickness of the material is removed from each piece; such a joint is called a *halving joint*. The most commonly used halving joints are a *cross halving* and a *tee halving* joint. When a pulling force may occur in a structure, a '*dovetail halving*' joint is used (Fig H.2). These types of joint are mainly used in solid wood constructions.

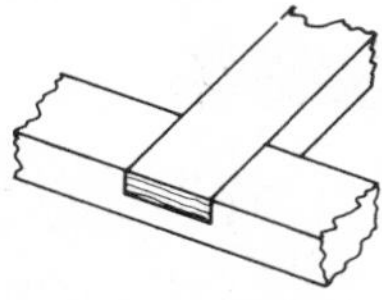

Tee halving joint

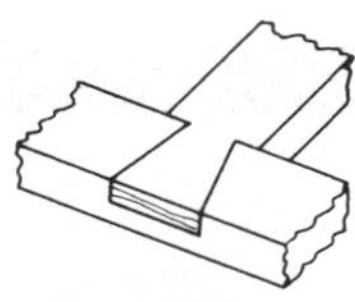

Dovetail halving joint

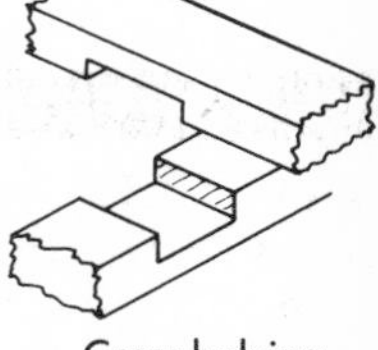

Cross halving

Fig H.2 Halving joints

HAND TOOLS

This is the name given to a tool that relies on the hand of the user to make it perform a function. The force and direction in which the tool moves is controlled by hand only. Tools that rely on electrical power do *not* come into this category. You would expect to find that tools such as hammers, saws, chisels, punches, snips, pliers, spanners, and screwdrivers fall into this group.

HARDBOARD

Hardboard is a man-made product. It is made into sheets 2440mm × 1220 mm and of 3 mm – 5 mm thickness. One side is smooth and the other side is textured with a pattern that is produced in the manufacturing.

Hardboard is made from the waste material of the sawmills, after wood has been subjected to the plywood peelers and the trimmers, the sanding and planing machines, etc. Even the bark that is stripped from the tree is a source for making hardboard. Current research is directed at using the whole tree, including the stems, branches, and roots, so that very soon manufactured boards will be made from almost every part of a tree.

HARDEN

Most materials can be hardened, though some will *harden* through age. Metals such as carbon steel can be made hard by heating to red heat and then quenching in water. Steels containing less carbon can be heated in a furnace containing a carbon compound, so that carbon is absorbed into the metal. This too can be quenched in water to make it hard. Aluminium, brass, copper and gilding metal become hardened when beaten with a hammer, which is why, when working with these metals, it is necessary to **anneal** (soften) them every so often.

Thermosetting plastics harden naturally by ageing, but the process is too slow for practical purposes, so an **activator** and **catalyst** is added to make the resin harden much more quickly.

HARDENER

This is either a liquid or a paste **catalyst** used to assist in the **curing** (hardening) of resins used in **Glass Reinforced Plastics** (GRP) work. It will only harden resins that have been pre-activated. A solution of cobalt octoate in styrene is usually added to the resin during its manufacture, so you should not need to add a pre-activator. If you are unsure, check the label of the resin container.

Manufacturers have produced pre-activated resins to avoid the danger of mixing a *hardener* with an **activator**, since such a mixture without a resin reacts very violently and could cause serious damage. The quantity of hardener needed, compared with the quantity of resin to be used, is very small and should not exceed 2%. In fact if too much hardener is used, the hardening process will be less effective and the resin will not harden.

Some two-part adhesives such as 'Araldite' have one tube containing resin and a second tube containing a hardener. To prepare the adhesive, two equal quantities of resin and hardener (paste) are thoroughly mixed to start the hardening process. If you are using the 'Rapid' variety, you only have a few minutes in which to work before the resin starts hardening, so make sure you have everything that is to be joined ready. This type of adhesive is only used in small quantities but has the ability of bonding most hard materials.

HARDENING AND TEMPERING

This is a process that can only be done with carbon steel, i.e. a steel containing between 0.75% and 1.5% carbon. The purpose is to make the steel suitable for producing tools to use on other metals and materials. Such tools as hammer heads, drill bits, centre punches, screwdrivers, etc., can be made from carbon steel. They then need to be hardened and tempered to perform the task that they are designed to do well.

The hardening process is achieved by heating the metal to red heat and quenching it in cold water. The metal should be either quenched under running cold water or stirred vigorously in a tank of cold water. The stirring action stops pockets of steam forming on the surface and allows the cold water to be directly in contact with the surface of the metal. The grain structure of the metal is frozen by the quenching at this stage, making it not only hard but extremely brittle. A second process is therefore necessary to keep the metal hard but to avoid it being brittle. This is called tempering.

Before the metal can be tempered, the oxide produced in the hardening stage has to be removed with an old file so that the silvery grey metal is showing. The metal will be reheated to a temperature between 200°C and 300°C. The colours formed by the oxides on the surface of the metal act as a guide to tell you the temperature of the metal. The colour that appears first, around 200°C, is a *pale yellow*. As the temperature rises, the yellow darkens, and as long as heat is applied to the metal so the oxide colours will progress to brown, dark brown, purple and finally blue. A metal that is quenched when a blue-colour oxide has formed is extremely tough and less hard than metals that are quenched when a yellow-colour oxide has formed. The metals quenched at this stage can still be slightly brittle. The different degrees of hardness and *toughness* that are created in the metal by this process make it possible to *select* the appropriate properties to suit a variety of needs. The list below will serve as an example:

Hammer face, scribers	230°C	Yellow
Drills, taps, dies	245°C	Dark Yellow
Punches	260°C	Brown
Letter punches	265°C	Dark Brown
Cold chisels, screwdrivers, hack-saw blades	270°C	Purple
Tape rules, springs, hand saws	295°C	Blue

HARDWARE

In computers, *hardware* is the actual equipment that is used, such as the Central Processing Unit (CPU), Visual Display Unit (VDU), etc. ◄ Software ►

HARDWOOD

This is a botanical classification to separate hardwoods from **softwoods**. The classification is based upon the type of tree from which the wood was prepared; whether from a broad-leaved tree that sheds its leaves in autumn (hardwood) or a tree with needle-shaped leaves that does not shed its leaves in autumn (softwood).

Though in general the type of woods that come from the broad-leaved trees are indeed hard, this is an unreliable yardstick. For example, Balsa wood is a hardwood, yet physically it is the softest and lightest wood in use. Beech, oak, ash, ramin, walnut, afrormosia, mahogany, teak and obeche are all examples of hardwoods that, in general, have the property of being hard.

HATCHING

These are diagonal lines that are used to show the part of a view that has been sectioned. They are normally drawn at an angle of 45°. They may be drawn at a different angle, but to avoid confusion only when the outline of the view is also at 45°. When the section goes through two or more items that are next to each other, the *hatching* lines are drawn at 45°, but at a right angle to each other. It is also helpful to make the spaces smaller in one set of hatching lines compared to the other set, so that the two neighbouring areas are clearly seen. The larger areas are usually selected for the larger spaces between the hatching lines. Remember that the spaces between the lines must be even, and drawn with a thinner line than that used for the outline. For more information read BS PP7308. ◀ Sectioning ▶

HEARTWOOD

The *heartwood* of a tree is the centre or the core of the tree where no more growth is taking place. The growing cells, which transport the sap, lie between the heartwood and the bark. As each new layer of growing cells is formed on top of the previous year's layer, so last year's cells become less active, until eventually they become completely inactive. The contents of the cells also undergo a chemical change. The new substances that are now produced result in a distinctive darker area, called the *heartwood,* while the lighter area is called the *sap wood.*

The heartwood is a much more durable wood than the sap wood, because the cell contents are of no real value as a food for wood beetles and fungi. So the best wood for furniture, building, etc., is the heartwood.
◀ Cellular structure ▶

HEATING SYMBOLS

These are the *symbols* that can be used when drawing the **plan view** and cross-sectional view of a building that is heated. For full details you are recommended to refer to British Standards 1553 part 1. Some examples of *symbols* are shown in Figure H.3.

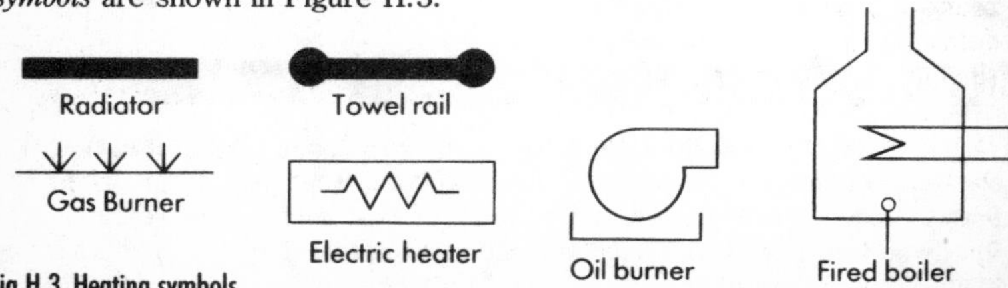

Fig H.3 Heating symbols

HEAT-SENSITIVE CIRCUIT

If two different metal wires, such as iron and copper, are joined at one end and the two free ends are attached to the terminals of a **multimeter** set to measure in the microampere range, a complete electrical circuit will have been formed. When the joined end is warmed by a small flame, an emf (electromotive force) develops in the wires. It is detected in the multimeter by the movement of the needle pointer and a reading in microamps can be taken. The scale could be re-calibrated to read in degrees Celsius, so that the multimeter could be used as a *thermometer*, i.e. an instrument for measuring temperature. Such a device would be called a *thermocouple*.

A silicon temperature sensor is a highly sensitive solid-state device. It consists of a single crystal of almost pure **silicon**. The sensors are available with an operating temperature range from −170°C to +300°C. A circuit containing a heat-sensitive device is often used in fire alarms.

HEAT SINK

This is a device used to get rid of unwanted heat in a circuit. It is particularly useful for protecting **transistors** in power applications. The heat sink is a metal structure which radiates heat out of the collector.

HEAT-TREATMENT

When a piece of high-carbon steel is gently heated to a temperature of about 700°C, an important change begins to take place. The carbon, in the form of cementite or pearlite, begins to dissolve into the iron to form a solution of carbon and iron called Austenite. The temperature at which the change takes place depends on the amount of carbon in the steel. With as little as 0.1% carbon, the temperature will have to reach as high as 900°C. It is only when the carbon content of the steel is at 0.9% that the change will take place at 700°C. The change is very rapid and the term *eutectic point* refers to the temperature at which an alloy changes from a solid into a liquid.

When steels have been kept at a high temperature, the grain size grows. If the steel is allowed to cool very slowly the grain size will get smaller. This process is called full annealing, and is also known as 'heat treatment'.

◄ **Harden, Tempering, Annealing** ►

HELIX

A helix is the path of a moving point round a cylinder. Another way of defining it is to say that a helix is a sloping plane wrapped round a cylinder. If you draw a straight line at an angle to the bottom edge of a piece of paper and then wrap the paper round a cylinder, the line will form a helix (Fig H.4). A practical application of the helix is a screw thread or a coil spring.

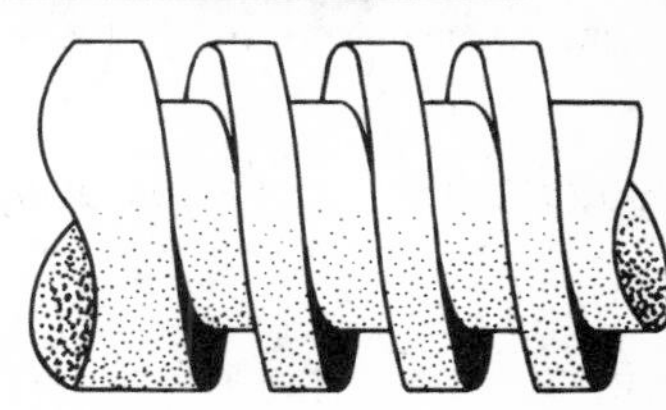

Fig H.4 Helix

HENRY (H)

The Henry is a unit of **inductance**. An American scientist, Joseph Henry, recognised that a changing current in a coil induces an emf in the *same* coil (self inductance). The property is known as inductance and the unit by which it can be measured is named after Henry. A coil has an inductance of one Henry if an electromagnetic force (emf) of one volt is induced when the current passing through it changes at the rate of one amp every second.

HEPTAGON

This is a seven-sided plane figure (Fig H.5).

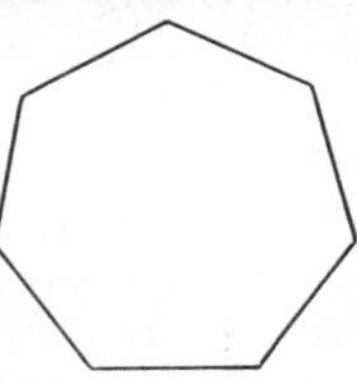

Fig H.5 Heptagon

HERTZ (Hz)

A unit of frequency. One *hertz* is equal to one complete cycle every second. The alternating voltage or current occurs 50 times a second and is measured as 50Hz. The unit is named after the 19th century German physicist, Heinrich Hertz.

HEXADECIMAL COUNTING SYSTEM

Decimal counting is done with a base 10, and the count runs from 0 to 9. The hexadecimal system uses a base 16. It has been used for many years and is still used today to count pounds and ounces; 16oz = 1lb.

The *hexidecimal* system counts from 0 to 9 and continues from A to F. This means that from 0 to 9 the decimal and hexadecimal are identical, but for the remainder 10 = A, 11 = B, 12 = C, 13 = D, 14 = E, and 15 = F. Hexadecimal values are used in microcomputers because they are much shorter than **binary** numbers, e.g. hexadecimal 9F is the equivalent to 1001 1111 binary.

HEXADECIMAL SEVEN SEGMENT DISPLAY

The seven segment display is a low voltage way of displaying numbers, and the letters A to F. The letters are displayed as upper and lower case letters and look like this: AbCdEF

The figures from 0 to 9 look like this: 0123456789

Care must be taken when reading the hexadecimal display not to confuse the letter b with the figure 6.

HEXAGON

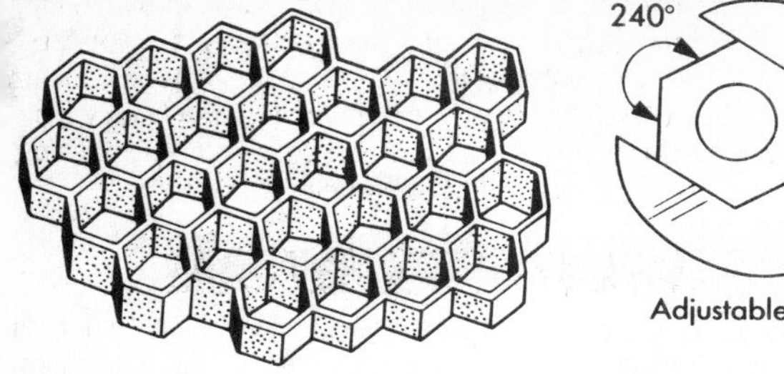

Fig H.6 Hexagon

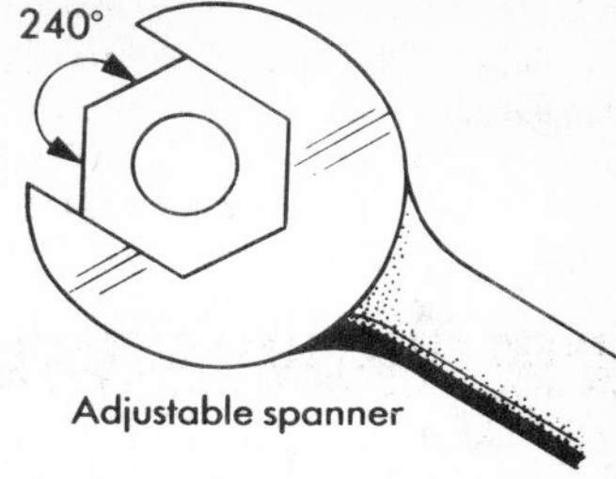

Fig H.7 Hexagonal prism

This is a six-sided figure. As a regular *hexagon* (all sides and angles equal), this figure can form **tessellations** (continuous patterns). In nature, the cross-section view of part of a bees honeycomb shows this pattern clearly (Fig H.6).

The hexagonal prism has a useful mechanical application in the form of nut and bolt heads. The opposite sides are parallel and are able to be gripped quite firmly by an instrument with parallel jaws, such as an open-ended spanner or an adjustable spanner (Fig H.7). The internal angle of 60° is also an asset in the design of a nut, in that the rotating movement of a nut can be made in small stages where movement is restricted. The external angle of 240° on the corners is able to resist damage more readily than, say, a square nut that has an external angle of 270°. Aluminium hexagonal honeycombing in-between two outer sheets of aluminium forms a light and very strong structure widely used in aircraft construction.

HEXAGONAL PYRAMID

This is a pointed figure that has a hexagonal base (Fig H.8).

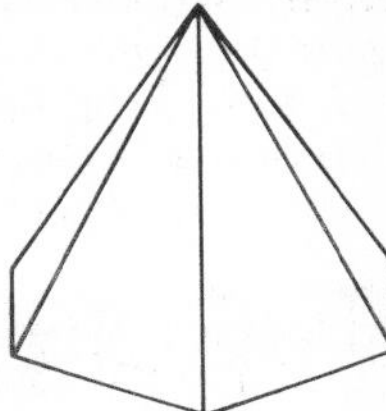

Fig H.8 Hexagonal pyramid

HIDDEN DETAIL

Objects made from opaque materials cannot show the detail of what lies below their surface. The draughtsman, however, can either do a section view to show the *hidden detail* or use a dotted line. When dotted lines are used they are referred to as hidden detail.

To comply with the standards set by the British Standards Institute, the line is not really dotted but is rather a series of short dashes.

These are drawn with a thinner line than that used for the outline, and the first and last dash always finishes on an outline (Fig H.9). For more information see B.S.I. PD7308.

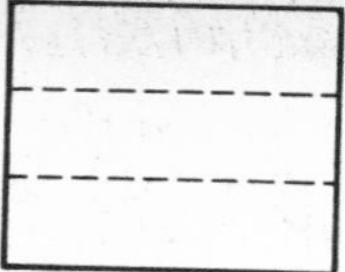

Fig H.9 Hidden detail

HIGHLIGHTING

Highlighting is a technique used in drawing to help surfaces to stand out from each other. Careful observation of how light falls on a surface will show you that the areas on a surface are not all of equal density. Some areas are darker or lighter than others. On a flat surface the highlights fall near the edges. On a curved, cylindrical surface the main highlight falls slightly to the left or right of the centre, but two other important highlights fall near the edges (Fig H.10). Adding the correct highlights to a drawing will considerably improve the effect and appearance of your work. It is well worthwhile studying where highlights fall on objects.

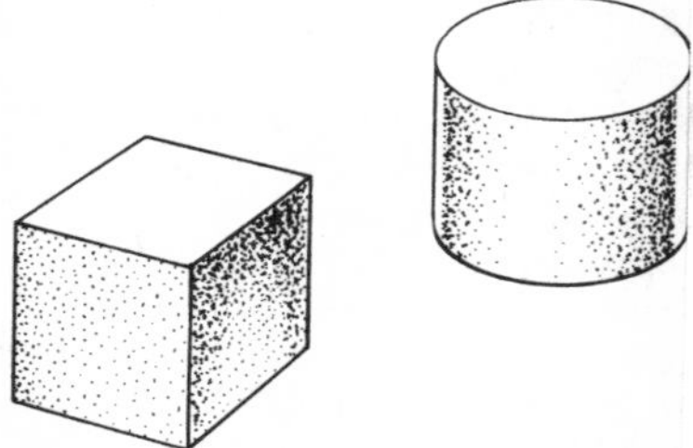

Fig H.10 Highlighting

HIGHLIGHTING PENS

These are used to help particular pieces of information stand out from other, less relevant, information. Titles are sometimes coloured with a highlighting pen. If you are using highlighting pens on design sheets, do be careful not to overdo it! The fluorescence or luminous quality of the colours can be overpowering.

HIGH-SPEED STEEL

Most drilling and cutting tools are made from High-Speed Steel. The initials HSS are often engraved on the tool. High-Speed Steel is an alloy of 4% chromium, 18% tungsten and 1.5% vanadium. It is a very hard steel and does not soften at high temperatures. It is possible for such a cutting tool to work at a higher speed than a carbon steel tool because it will keep its sharp edge much longer.

Drills and lathe cutting tools made from HSS cost approximately three times as much as the equivalent made from carbon steel. Their main advantage is that they can be used for cutting most metals, as well as for cutting other materials such as wood and plastics.

HINGE

The hinge is an important mechanism. To be able to move a component through an angle, while still remaining in firm contact with a supporting component, is tremendously important and has many practical applications.

A door hinge is perhaps the most well-known application of a hinge. Most lids of containers rely on a hinge for their controlled movement, the design of which is influenced by the material being hinged. For hinging wooden components, a butt hinge is well suited, but for hinging two metal components a much different design is needed. Some types of hinge are shown in Figure H.11.

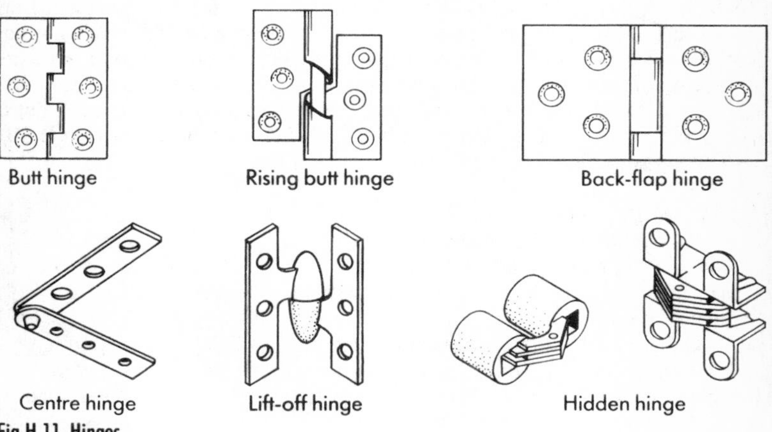

Fig H.11 Hinges

Sheet plastics present a different problem again. Trying to fix a conventional butt hinge would be extremely difficult and the end result would look ugly and probably be very impracticable. So when hinging is needed in plastics, the lid and box are made from a single sheet, to maintain rigidity, and the line between lid and the box is made flexible. Because plastics can be made to adopt particular properties, so a combination of properties can be produced in a single sheet. Have a look at an egg box.

HOLDING DEVICES

The three main families of *holding devices* are vices, clamps and chucks. Their main design function is to hold a piece of material while sawing, filing, planing, etc., or to hold components together while a process is taking place, e.g. glue setting.

Items like paper clips and drawing board clips are also holding devices and they all have one design feature in common. Namely that they are a temporary means of holding something, and when removed do not leave any marks on the material held.

Chucks are used mainly to hold round section material and is the main holding device for drills. The jaws are opened and closed with a key.

HOLLOWING

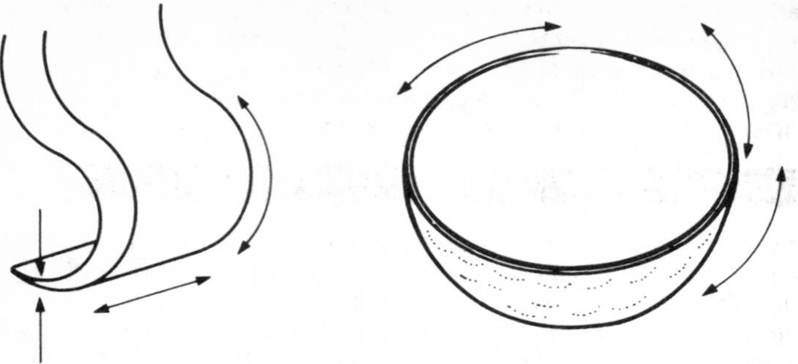

Fig H.12 Beaten metalwork

Fig H.13 Hollowing a piece of wood

This is a process of making a hollow shape. In beaten metalwork, the beating of a sheet of gilding metal with a mallet on a sand bag is an early stage in changing a flat material into a hollow form (Fig H.12). Hollowing a piece of wood has to be done by removing the unwanted material with a mallet and gouge (Fig H.13).

To make a hollow form in thermosetting plastics it is necessary to have a mould into which resin and glass mat can be worked and allowed to set. With thermoplastics, the plastic can be heated until softened and then vacuum formed. ◀ Vacuum forming ▶

HOOKE'S LAW

Hooke's Law says that the **stress** (the force acting on an object divided by its area) divided by the **strain** (change in size) is constant for any given material and is called the **modulus of elasticity**.
◀ Elasticity, Modulus of elasticity ▶

HORIZON LINE

The horizon line in **perspective** drawing is sometimes referrd to as the 'eye level'. It represents the height of the observer's eye in relation to the object (Fig H.14). The *vanishing point* or points are placed on this line. ◀ Perspective ▶

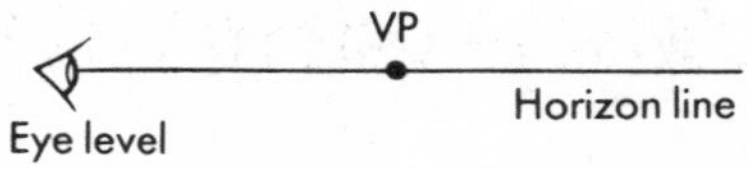

VP

Horizon line

Eye level

Fig H.14 Horizon line

HORIZONTAL PLANE

This is the flat surface of an object that is level and at right angles to the vertical surface. The lines indicating the area of the horizontal plane or surface on a **perspective** or **isometric** drawing need not be drawn at right angles to the vertical planes, and this may seem confusing when trying to draw objects in three dimensions. The horizontal plane in isometric drawing is drawn at an angle of 30° in **oblique projection**, and 45° in **planometric projection**.

HOUSING

In general terms this means a recess into which another component can fit. In woodworking techniques, a *housing* is used to fit shelves or divisions in a unit. The two common types of housing are *through housing* and *stopped housing*. Though there is no real difference in strength, there is a difference in appearance. The stopped housing is preferred in cabinet work, while through housing is acceptable in general fitting and where the appearance is not so important (Fig H.15).

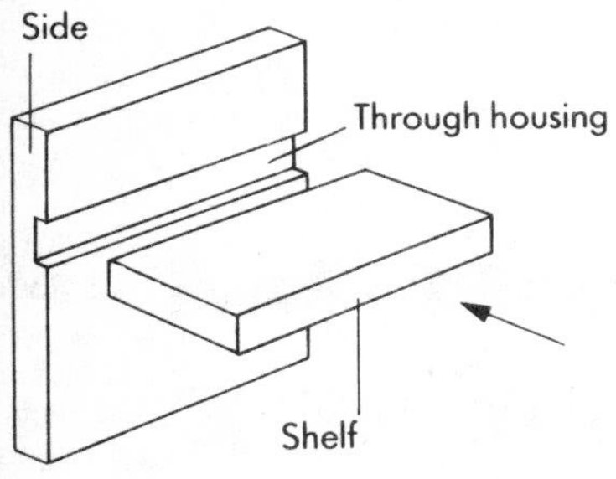

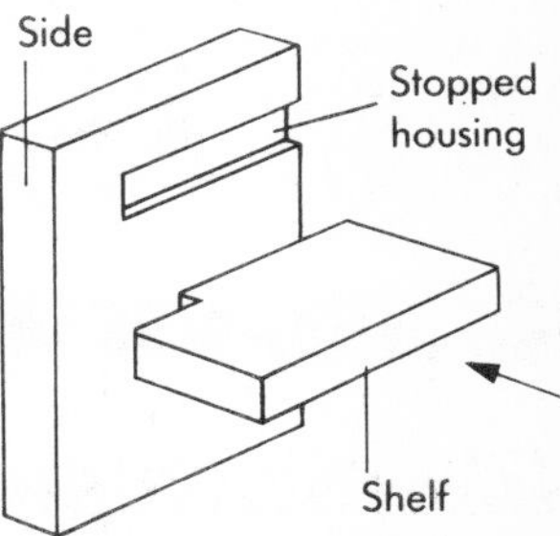

Fig H.15 Housing

HYDRAULICS

The knowledge that water or other liquids could resist considerable pressure, i.e. *compressive forces*, was put to limited use in the last century. Joseph Bramah, in 1795, used the power exerted by water under compression to drive a press. *Hydraulic* power was also used in the mining industry to support the roof. Today, hydraulic power is still used in mining but is also used in fork-lift trucks and jacks.

HYPERBOLA

When a cone is sliced through its side and base, the curve produced is called a hyperbola. It is one of the conic sections, the others being a **circle**, **ellipse**, and **parabola**.

In nature, or more precisely in *astronomy*, heavenly bodies such as planets or comets follow one of the conic sections. In geometric terms the hyperbola is the locus of a point which moves so that its distance from a focal point (focus) and a straight line (directrix) is constant, with a ratio greater than one. The ratio is 3:2 and the two halves are completely symmetrical (Fig H.16). ◄ Cone ►

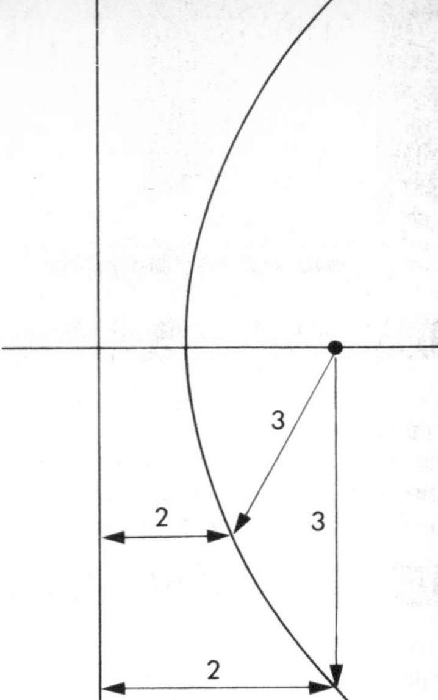

Fig H.16 Hyperbola

HYSTERESIS

Sometimes known as the 'deadband', the *hysteresis* is the band between the rising input voltage and the changeover from logic 0 to logic 1 in a TTL device.

The **Schmitt trigger** sign is based on the graphs formed by these two input and output voltage levels. The gap in the graph represents the hysteresis band. This gap, where nothing happens, prevents the logic from wondering which level to accept. If there was no difference in the rising and falling input threshold, the voltages would be the same and the logic level would oscillate. Such oscillation would be useless in any counting circuit.

Hz

The abbreviation for **Hertz**. Waves have two basic properties; one is **amplitude** and the other is **frequency**. Frequency is the number of complete vibrations made in a given time. Since waves move very quickly, the time is measured in a part of a second. A wave of 50 hertz contains 50 vibrations a second.

IDENTIFICATION

To identify something is to recognise it or to realise that it exists. The term *identification* is most commonly used with the word 'need'. To identify a need is to recognise that a need exists. Conservationalists recognise the need to protect much of our wild life. You may recognise needs, such as avoiding polluting the air, or providing a container for rubbish, etc.

IDEOGRAMS

An ideogram is a sign or symbol that is used to convey an idea easily and quickly. They are in common use in display instruments in cars, etc. These symbols are easily understood internationally, so there is no need for words (Fig I.1). Ideograms should not be confused with **pictograms** that are used to illustrate statistical information.

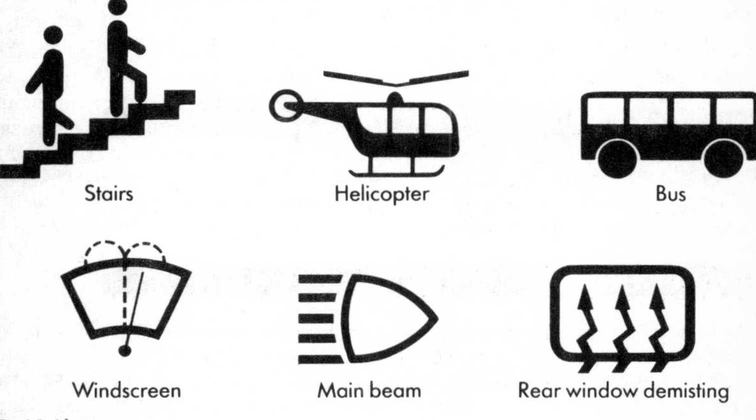

Fig I.1 Ideograms

IDLER GEAR

This is an intermediate gear that does not affect speed of rotation or direction of rotation. ◀ Gears ▶

IMPACT

A striking force. When a hammer strikes a piece of metal, the metal is receiving a blow or force from the hammer. It is a *compression force* that lasts for a short time.

IMPACT ADHESIVES

This is an adhesive which is applied to the two surfaces to be bonded, and allowed to go tacky. When the two surfaces are brought together under slight pressure the surfaces, on contact, become immediately joined together. Another name for this type of adhesive is 'Contact adhesive'.

IMPEDANCE

◀ Electrical resistance ▶

IMPLEMENTATION

To complete a process or activity. The *implementation* of an idea is to put that idea into practice and to see if it fulfils the particular requirements of the **Design Brief**. Whenever you are *testing* an idea, you are implementing it to see if it will work.

INCANDESCENT DISPLAY

This is a display that uses a filament for each segment of a seven segment display. It is an alternative display system to the seven segment LED display. Another name for this display is 'Minitron'. It is commonly used on petrol pump displays.

INCISE CARVING

Incise carving is the cutting into a surface to produce a shape, pattern, lettering, etc. It is the opposite to relief carving, where the shape, pattern, letter, etc., is raised and the background is removed.

INCLINED PLANE

Planes can be horizontal, vertical or at an angle to the horizontal. An inclined plane can be at *any* angle to the horizontal. The effort to move a load along an *inclined plane* is less than the effort required to lift a load vertically. The Egyptians raised the heavy stones to build the pyramids by sliding them along an inclined plane. Since the effort required to move the stone along the plane was less than the effort required to raise it vertically, a **'mechanical advantage'** had been achieved (Fig I.2).

The wedge is another example where a mechanical advantage is gained. The wedge can take the form of a *chisel blade* or, when wrapped round a cylindrical bar, a *screw thread.* A screw thread is an inclined plane around a

:ylinder and can be used to convert ·otary motion into linear motion, as vhen you move the cross slide on a athe or tighten a screw in a piece of naterial or a nut.

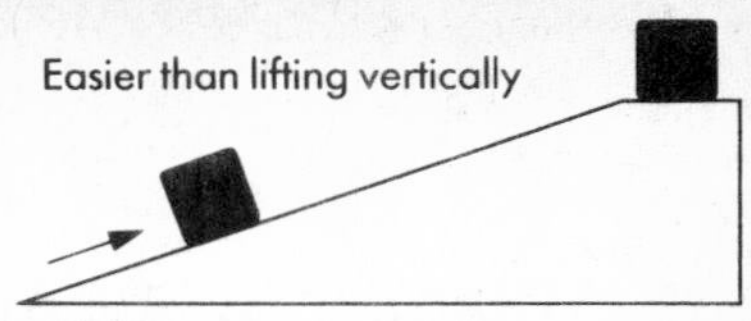

Fig I.2 Inclined plane

NDUCTANCE

◄ Electrical resistance ►

NDUSTRIAL DESIGN

ıny product designed by industry, e.g. cars, televisions, clocks, etc., must ıot only fulfil a need, but must above all be highly functional and economic to nake. Appearance is also important of course, but if the product is not unctional and economic to make in the first place then appearance is of little :onsequence. Industrial design is concerned with making a product which neets the various requirements deemed necessary for 'success' in the market ›lace.

NDUSTRIAL WASTE

Vhenever a process uses energy and modifies the structure and appearance ›f a material, there are some by-products which, because they are classified ıs having no use, are called waste materials. Though more effort is now being nade to create as little waste as possible, unwanted materials still result. Some are burnt in large incinerators to reduce their bulk and to burn off ınwanted gases. Ships have been designed as floating incinerators to burn ndustrial waste and to dump remaining materials in the sea. Conservationists ıave long been concerned about the effects of such actions.

Some by-products such as wood chippings and shavings, were once ·egarded as waste materials but have now been put to good use in the ›roduction of chipboard and fibre board.

NDUSTRY: PRIMARY, SECONDARY AND TERTIARY

?rimary industry is concerned with the production of *raw materials* such as :oal, oil, timber etc. It is sometimes extended to man-made raw materials such as plastics, glass, etc.

Secondary industry is concerned with the manufacturing of *goods*, i.e. urning the raw materials into a product.

Tertiary industry is concerned with *services*, such as publicity, distribution, selling, etc. Indeed another name for tertiary industry is service industry, vhich also includes education, banking, insurance, law, medicine, etc.

INERT SUBSTANCES

These are substances that have no action, force, or resistance. For instance substances such as pigments or fillers used to give colour to resins do not add any structural strength. In fact, if they are used in excess they will cause a structural weakness.

INHIBITOR

This is a substance that will prevent polymerisation taking place in a resin that has been activated and mixed with a catalyst. Colouring pigments are made from **inert** materials and, if used excessively, they will inhibit, or slow down, the polymerisation process. However, if they are used in the correct quantities recommended by the manufacturer, they should not seriously retard the **curing** process.

INJECTION MOULDING

Injecting a molten material under pressure into a mould is known as *injection moulding*. It is a process that is commonly used in industry but, since thermoplastics became commonly used materials in schools, it is now also used on a smaller scale there (Fig I.3).

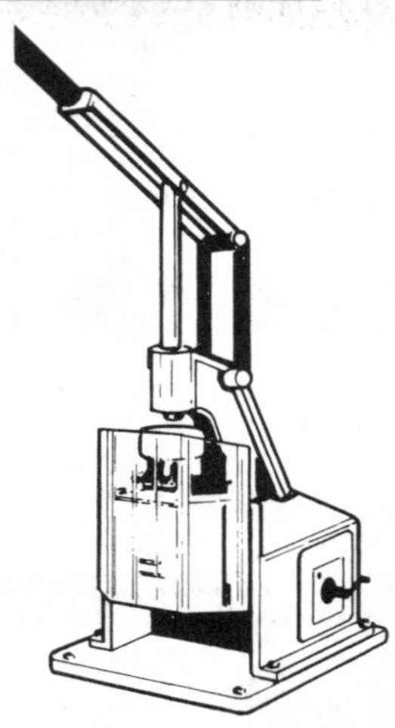

Fig I.3 Injection moulding machine

INKS

There are two main types: *waterproof* inks and *non-waterproof* inks. The waterproof ink is more commonly used in drawing because of its colour density and because it reproduces well when photocopied.

The quality of drawing inks became very important with the development of the new steel pen (it replaced the old quills). In 1834 Henry Stephens produced an ink that was highly suited to the steel pen. This set the standard on which further refinements were built, leading to the high quality and wide range of colours with which we are familiar today.

Other types of ink are used in the ball point pen and the felt tip pen. *Ballpoint* inks have a glycol base, similar to inks used for printing. *Felt-tipped*

inks have a spirit base that quickly evaporates, and so such pens have a short life. Because of the wide variety of inks that are used today there is always a chance of spoiling work by using the wrong type, so do check the label first.

NPUT CONTROL SYSTEMS

An input is a driving force or signal that is applied to a **circuit**, **device**, **machine**, **computer**, etc. When that signal is received, it can be controlled and an output generated.

The most common **control system** is an electric switch. It is either on or off, with nothing in-between, i.e. it cannot be half-on, or half-off. However, do not confuse this with a dimmer switch which is an **analogue** system.

In electronics and pneumatics, logic circuits are used. The **Integrated Circuits** are used as decision-making devices. They contain a number of switches and only when the switches are in the *correct position* will an output signal be generated. ◀ **Logic gates** ▶

NSCRIBED CIRCLES

A circle that is drawn inside another figure, with the sides of both figures touching, is called an *inscribed cirle*. The circle in a square, triangle, and hexagon are all examples of inscribed circles (Fig I.4). The *centre* of the circle is obtained by bisecting the angles. Where the bisectors meet or cross is the centre for the circle. The *radius* is perpendicular to the sides of the figure, and the *sides* are tangents to the circle.

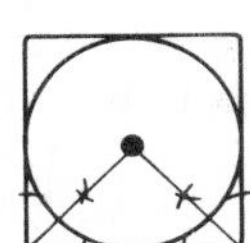
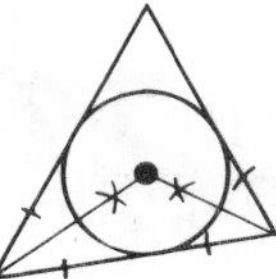
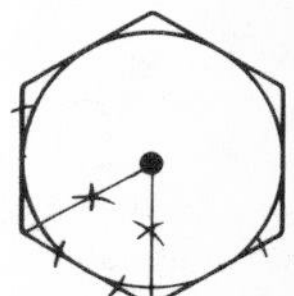

Fig I.4 Inscribed circles

NSTRUMENTATION

In general terms an instrument has a measuring function which can be displayed on a dial or screen, and read or understood by a use. An **oscilloscope** is perhaps the most commonly used instrument. It belongs to the same group as the television and is referred to as a Visual Display Unit or VDU. The *dial* family include such instruments as the **ammeter**, **voltmeter** or **multimeter**. Pressure gauges also come into this family, but are used to measure air pressure in pneumatic circuits.

NSULATION/INSULATOR

To insulate something is to stop the flow of an electric current, heat or sound. To insulate something is to 'isolate' or 'prevent'. The PVC of a cable isolates the wire carrying the electric current; expanded polystyrene prevents warm things getting cold or cold things getting warm; a cavity containing sound absorbing material prevents sound travelling. Materials such as porcelain, glass, air or a vacuum, mica, synthetic resins, paper, etc., are all insulators. Even water is an insulator, but only when pure.

An insulator cannot conduct a current when a voltage is applied. It does one of two things. It can isolate **conductors** to prevent them conducting a current, or it can store an electrical charge when a voltage is applied. In this second case an insulator keeps its charge because electrons cannot flow to neutralize the charge. These insulators are called *dielectric* materials.

INTEGRATED CIRCUITS

Microelectronic technology has progressed considerably, so that, **transistors, diodes, capacitors** and **resistors** can now be contained on a single piece of silicon. They are sometimes referred to as 'monolithic integrated circuits'. Bipolar and metal oxide semiconductors (MOS) can be used to form transistors in *integrated circuits* (ICs).

The complexity of ICs varies and can be coded in the following way:

SSI	Small Scale Integration	Fairly simple circuits
MSI	Medium Scale Integration	Medium complexity
LSI	Large Scale Integration	Quite complex and can be described as having a complexity of 16 Kilobits
VLSI	Very Large Scale Integration	Describes a circuit with a capability of between 16K and one megabit.

There are many types of integrated circuit. They are used in all new electronic equipment, such as clocks, watches, microcomputers, calculators, games, etc. They are also used in modern **analogue** devices such as audio amplifiers and television receivers. ◀ **Chips, Linear IC, Monolithic IC** ▶

INTERPENETRATIONS

This is another word for **intersection**. It is the point where one solid penetrates another. Though the term 'solid' is often used, the shapes can in fact be hollow.

INTERSECTION

The point where two or more *lines* meet or cross. The meeting point of *solids*, such as two cylinders of equal diameter, or of different diameter (Fig I.5). There are many situations where shapes are formed by combining one with another, e.g. a cone sitting on the end of a cylinder. For the shape to be made from a *single* sheet of material, a knowledge of intersection is necessary.

A practical application involves sheet metal workers e.g. the meeting point of the wings of an aeroplane with the fuselage. As far as GCSE is concerned you may be required to make models from sheet material, or from differently shaped containers that could be used in packaging design.
◀ **Developments** ▶

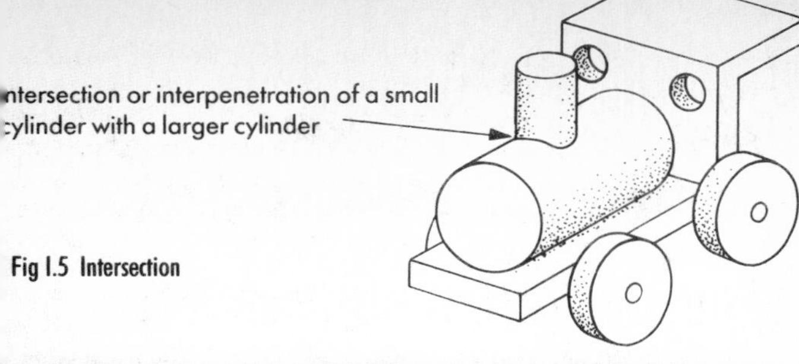

Fig I.5 Intersection

NVESTIGATION

ooking for information in books, magazines, data files, discs, etc., is one way f finding information to help you with a project. Another way is to get hold of ome material or device and try to see if it will *perform* the task in which you re interested. Will the material bend, twist, withstand the load, etc? Will the evice produce sufficient power to drive the buggy, etc? Information obtained rom your *own observation and testing* is called 'Primary Investigation'. Where ou use other people's observations, such as those you read in books, it is alled 'Secondary Investigation'. **Research** is another word commonly used in his connection.

NVESTMENT CASTING

his is a method of **casting** used mainly for producing small and complicated hapes. It is a process used in industry, dentistry and in making jewellery. You re most likely to meet the process in the context of casting in silver.

A wax pattern is made by careful carving, bending and melting to the shape ou require. This is then coated with an *investment* liquid plaster which sets uickly and is contained in a small flask. The moisture is then removed by eating gently, and the wax is then melted away by sustained heating. The nvestment is now dry, and a cavity is left in the mould. The molten silver is oured onto the top surface and allowed to run into the cavity of the mould. he final stage is completed by forcing the molten silver into the cavity entrifugally, or by steam pressure (Fig I.6).

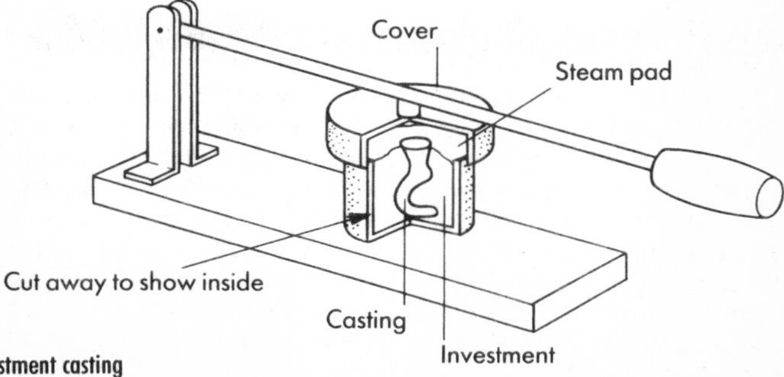

ig I.6 Investment casting

The plaster has to be broken away once it has had time to cool. Hence the mould and pattern are *not* available for a repeat process. The only way in which this process could be used for *batch production* is by having a mould for casting the wax that would allow for a number of wax patterns to be made.

INVOLUTE

An involute is the path of a moving point (locus). If you hold the end of a piece of string that is wound round a cylinder and then unwind the string, keeping it tightly pulled for one complete revolution, your hand will have moved in an 'involute'. If you had made a *loop* in the string and put a pencil in the loop and unwound the string, you would be able to draw an *involute curve*. If the cylinder was replaced with a square prism, or any number sided prism, and you performed the same exercise, an involute could be drawn to these prisms.

For accurate drawings of involutes you are advised to learn the precise methods of construction (Fig I.7). The involute curve is very important in mechanical engineering. It is the curve used in the profile of *gear teeth* and permits the gear teeth of one gear wheel to trasmit rotary motion to another by making good surface contact during rotation. This is sometimes referred to as 'meshing'.

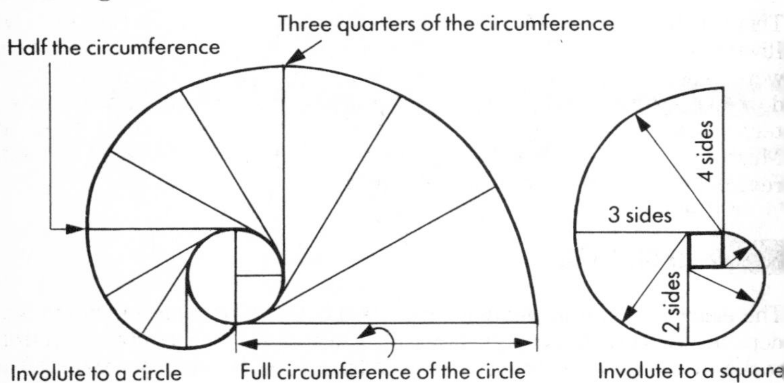

Fig I.7 Involute

IRON

This is one of the most common metallic elements. It is easy to extract from its ores and can be readily made into steel. It is the metal most widely used by man. It is a greyish-white metal that is highly **ductile** and **malleable** and therefore easy to shape. It is also magnetic and plays an important role in the production of magnetic fields and electricity.

Iron has been used by man for over 3000 years. It was the metal that replaced bronze in the production of weapons, and in 1200 BC the 'Iron Age' is officially regarded as having begun. It was not however until 1856, when Henry Bessemer developed the steel making process, that iron was used in large quantities.

IRON BRIDGE

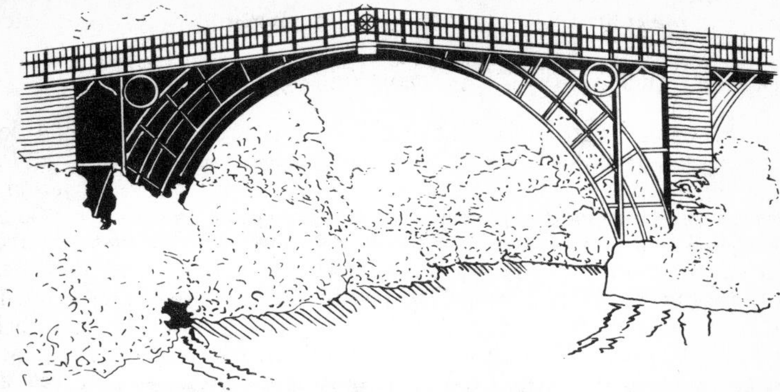

Fig I.8 Iron bridge

This was the first bridge to be built using iron. It was built in 1779 over the River Severn, near Coalbrookdale (Fig I.8). The construction techniques were those used to join wood together, e.g. mortice and tenon, lapped dovetail, wedged tenon (Fig J.1), because this was the extent of the technology of the time. The Iron Bridge is now part of the Iron Gorge Museum. It is just one exhibit of many related to this period of industrial revolution, and the museum is well worth a visit.

IRON ORE

The element iron is in plentiful supply, but it is available mixed with mineral deposits (rock) that have been given the name 'ore'. The mixture of metal and rock is not in a usable form and the iron has to be extracted (separated) from the minerals. This is done by heating the ore to a high temperature, 1500°C, so that the iron melts. This is done in a *blast furnace* which is designed so that the molten metal can be released from the furnace and into moulds called *pigs*. Hence the name 'pig iron'. ◀ Cast iron ▶

RREGULAR FORM

Any object or outline that has sides of varying length and an asymmetrical shape may be described as being an *irregular form*. It is the opposite to a regular form.

IRREGULAR POLYGONS

A polygon that has sides and angles *unequal* (Fig I.9). ◀ Polygons ▶

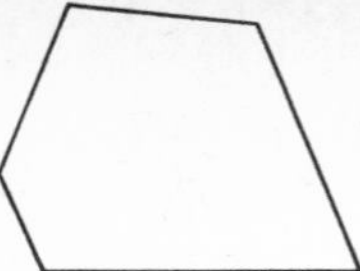

Fig I.9 Irregular polygon

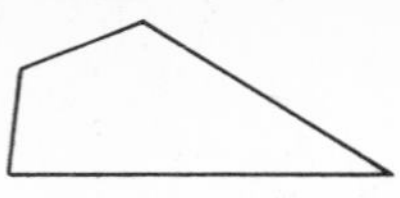

Fig I.10 Irregular quadrilateral

IRREGULAR QUADRILATERAL

A quadrilateral that has sides and angles *unequal* (Fig I.10).
◀ Quadrilaterals ▶

ISOLATING

Disconnecting a device or circuit from an electrical supply.

ISOLATOR

A device that allows microwave energy to *pass* in one direction with little loss, and *absorbs* power in the reverse direction.

ISOMETRIC DRAWING

This is a method of drawing that is commonly used to produce three-dimensional views of an object. *Horizontal lines* are drawn at 30° to the horizontal plane, and *vertical lines* are drawn parallel to the vertical plane (Fig I.11).

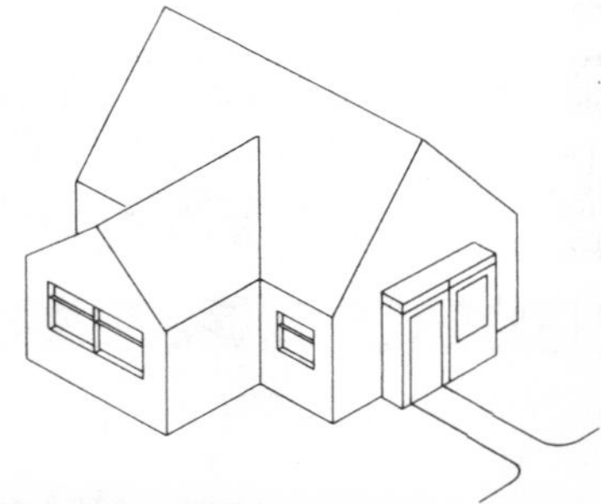

Fig I.11 Isometric drawing

ISOMETRIC GRID

These are the thin lines that are printed to represent the horizontal and vertical planes (Fig I.12). If you have difficulty drawing in three dimensions, you will find using a grid most helpful.

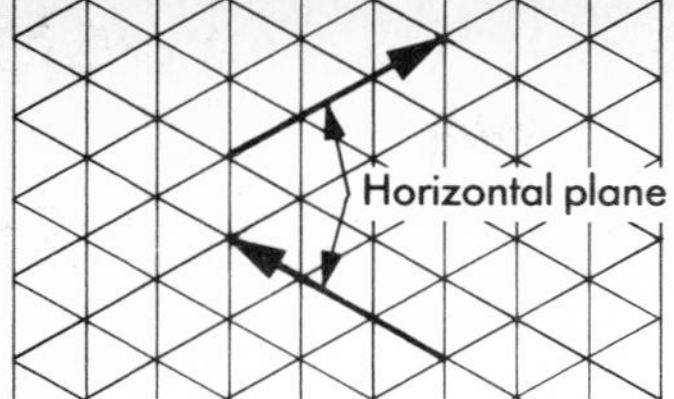

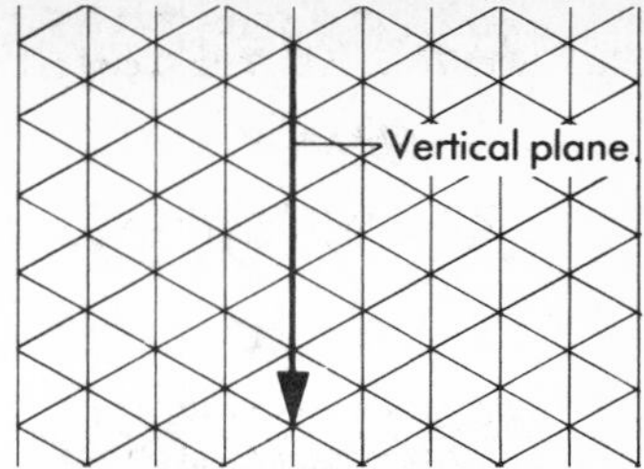

Fig I.12 Isometric grid

ISOMETRIC PROJECTION

◀ Isometric drawing ▶

ISOMETRIC TEMPLATE

This is a protractor that is designed to help the user draw ellipses in isometric projection (Fig I. 13).

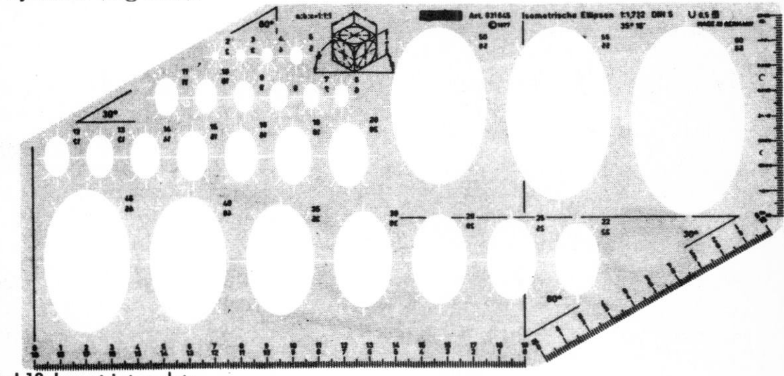

Fig I.13 Isometric template

ISOSCELES TRIANGLE

This is a triangle that has two sides and two angles equal. All angles are less than 90° (Fig I. 14).

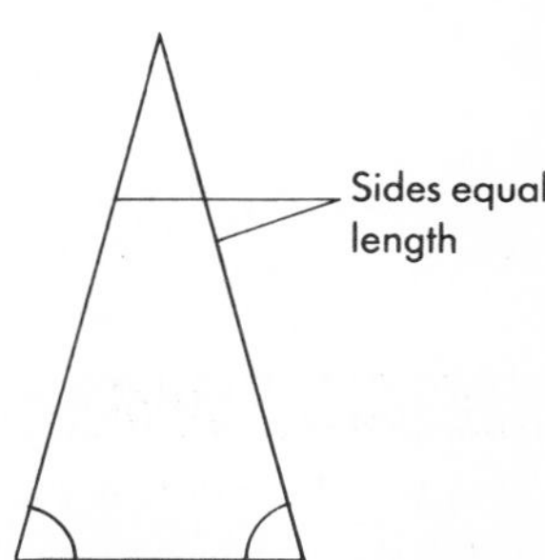

Fig I.14 Isosceles triangle

JIG

This is a device that will assist in the production of a particular component. Jigs are only worthwhile making if a *number* of identical components are to be made. To judge whether or not a jig would be helpful, consider how long it would take to produce the jig and then the number of components to be made; this should then be compared with how long it would take to make the components without the jig. If the time difference is *not* significant, then it is probably not worthwhile making the jig.

However another factor to be considered is *accuracy*. Using jigs is one way of ensuring a high degree of accuracy and similarity in the components produced. A *marking out template* for a number of holes will ensure that there is consistency in the marking out. A *profile* of a shape that has to be repeatedly cut in a suitable material, will ensure that the tracings are similar in size and shape.

Jigs can be used to assist in marking out, in cutting materials to particular lengths, in bending material to given angles, in masking areas to be sprayed, and so on. Whenever an object is designed for *batch production*, ways should be sought to achieve accuracy, uniformity, in the minimum time. A well designed jig will make a valuable contribution to these three aspects.

JOINTS

When two or more pieces of material are to be held together, they can be *joined* in a number of ways. A joint is created when the pieces are shaped by cutting and are held together. The joints can be permanent or temporary. A *permanent joint* is one that is not expected to be taken apart in the lifetime of the object, e.g. the welding together of the components of a bicycle frame. A *temporary joint* is one that can be taken apart many times in the lifetime of the object, e.g. an electric plug.

However, some components may need to be taken apart occasionally, yet causing as little damage to the parts as possible, e.g. a screwed cover of a wooden box. While the screws can be removed quite easily with a screwdriver, the wood tends to wear and even the screw can become damaged, so this means of joining will have a limited life.

PERMANENT JOINTS

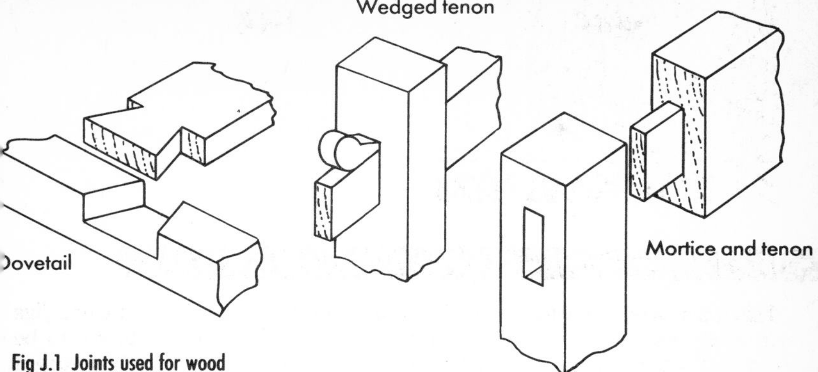

Fig J.1 Joints used for wood

For permanent methods of joining *wood* you should be familiar with the following families of construction: mortice and tenon, halving joints, dovetailing, housing, and dowelling. Most of these joinings should be finally held together with a strong adhesive (Fig J.1) For *metal* you should be familiar with riveting, brazing, welding, soldering.

For permanent methods of joining *plastics* you should be concerned with heatwelding and using adhesives. It is difficult to make joints in plastic, so other methods of forming are often preferred, e.g. vacuum forming, blow moulding, etc.

For joining *paper*, adhesives are mainly used, but stapling has become a common practice where speed is essential and appearance is not important. Double-sided tape is particularly useful for speed and neatness.

TEMPORARY JOINTS

For temporary methods of joining *wood* you should be familiar with: nailing, screwing, stapling, etc. For *metal* and *plastics* you should be familiar with nuts and bolts, pins, split pins, circlips, pegs, etc. For *paper* there are paper clips and masking tape, which has a light adhesive and can be readily removed without leaving a mark on the paper.

JOULES

A joule is a unit used for measuring the work done. When a force causes a movement, work is done. The amount of work done is equal to the force multiplied by the distance travelled. The SI unit is the joule and one joule is equal to the force that will move a load of one **newton** a distance of one metre.

The SI unit joule is named after James Prescot Joule (1818 – 89), a British physicist who showed how one form of energy could be converted into another without loss or gain of energy. You will need to use this unit of measurement in projects related to energy and movement.

JUNCTION DIODES

◄ Diodes ►

JUNCTION VOLTAGE

◄ Diodes ►

KERF

The name given to a cut made by a saw. This is a term commonly used by people who work with wood.

KEYBOARD

A kind of typewriting board which sends electrical signals. Information is tapped out on the individual keys and then converted into electrical signals. These are received by an electronic circuit and stored or used to perform functions. Computers are fed information via such a keyboard.

KEYS

In engineering terms a *key* is a device for stopping a wheel gear, pulley, etc, from slipping on a shaft during rotation. A *keyway* is slotted into the hub of the component to be fitted and into the shaft so that a key may be used to occupy the space. There are two types of key in common use, a *Gib Head Key* and a *Woodruff Key* (Fig K.1). You will find examples of these keys and keyways in use on lathes, drilling and milling machines.

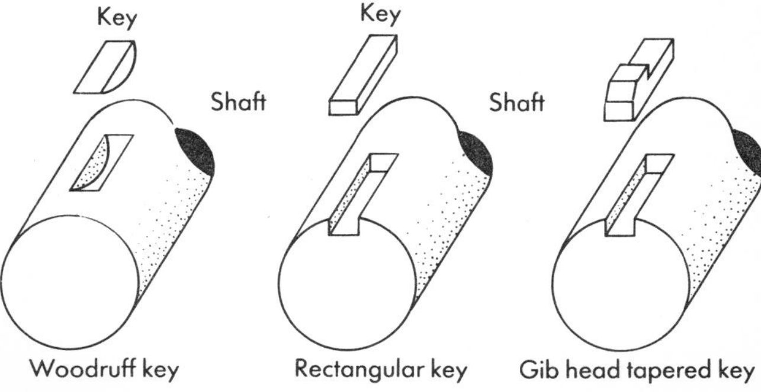

Fig K.1 Keys

KILOWATT

The watt is a unit of power and the prefix kilo means 1000 or 10^3, so a kilowatt is 1000 watts. However the term kilowatt is preferred, especially when referring to the rating of electrical items, e.g. an electric fire may be one or two kilowatt instead of 1000 or 2000 watts.

KILOWATT HOUR

This is the unit of energy that can be used in one hour. It helps consumers of electricity to know how much they have used and how much it will cost. One Kilowatt Hour is equal to 3.6 **joules.** ◀ **Watt** ▶

KINETIC ENERGY

Kinetic energy is 'moving' energy. Anything that is moving has energy, and the faster it moves the more kinetic enregy it has. Also the heavier an object is, the greater its kinetic energy when moving. Mechanical devices such as cars, lathes, power drills, etc., that use a motor or engine, also produce kinetic energy, though in these cases it is often termed *mechanical energy*. The blades of a windmill have kinetic energy when they are rotating, and this is referred to as *wind energy*. Vibrating objects possess kinetic energy. Sound waves, which are a form of vibration, are also a form of kinetic energy. Because atoms or molecules move in elements when heated, this too is a form of kinetic energy, though it is commonly referred to as *heat* or *thermal energy*.

KIRCHOFF'S FIRST LAW

The first law, of which there are two, relates to electric current. It states that the *sum of the currents meeting at any one point is zero.*

KITE

This is a type of **quadrilateral** (four-sided figure). It is also referred to as a *deltoid*. It has two pairs of adjacent sides equal in length, and diagonals which intersect at 90°. The smaller diagonal is bisected and it has one pair of opposite angles which are equal. (Fig K.2).

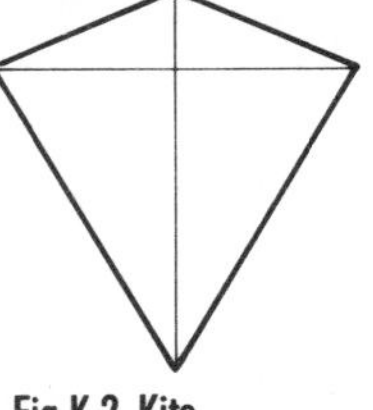

Fig K.2 Kite

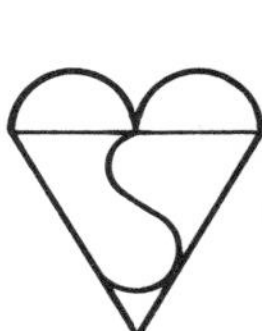

Fig K.3 Kitemark

KITEMARK

The Kitemark symbol on a product is an indication that it meets standards that have been accepted by the British Standards Institution(BSI). Purchasing any goods bearing this mark is an assurance of quality (Fig K.3). If you wish to draw the kitemark you will need to refer to BSI publication PP7307 for full details.

KNURLING

This is a type of finish or treatment of a surface, and is used mainly in engineering on cylindrical surfaces. There are a variety of knurling patterns that can be applied to a surface (Fig K.4). Knurling is done with a tool that has a wheel or wheels made from a hardened steel and which have their outer surfaces groved. The grooved surfaces are forced against the work while it is rotating slowly in a lathe. The pattern of the wheels leaves an impression on the work. This surface treatment has two functions. The first is to provide a surface that can be firmly gripped, especially on tools, wheels, handles etc., that are held in the hand. The second is to improve the appearance. So good knurling will improve both function and appearance.

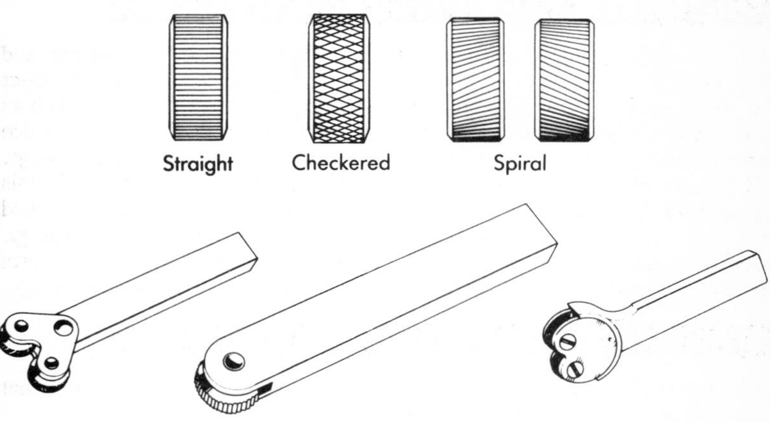

Fig K.4 Knurling

LABOUR-INTENSIVE PRODUCTION

This is a term used to identify industry according to the methods used in production. Where a large proportion of the cost of producing the item goes in the form of pay to the individual labourer, foreman, clerk, manager, etc. the industry is said to be labour-intensive. In *industrial countries* the labour-intensive industries are mainly the services (i.e. tertiary industries), such as teaching, administration, law, medical, retail services etc. In *developing countries*, where labour is plentiful, the labour-intensive industries tend to include manufacturing and farming. This is because machinery is expensive and needs to be operated by skilled labour or operatives, who are often scarce in such countries.

LAMINA

A lamina is a thin sheet, layer, flake, etc. When a number of lamina are put together to form a thicker sheet, the end product is called a **laminate.** Lamina or laminae (many lamina) are also terms used in drawing when concerned with drawing true shapes. A lamina is a *plane shape* that has no thickness.

◀ True length ▶

LAMINAR FLOW

When a fluid moves through a smooth pipe it flows in a stream of lines or layers and the particles between the layers do not move. this movement is called a *laminar flow* (Fig L.1).

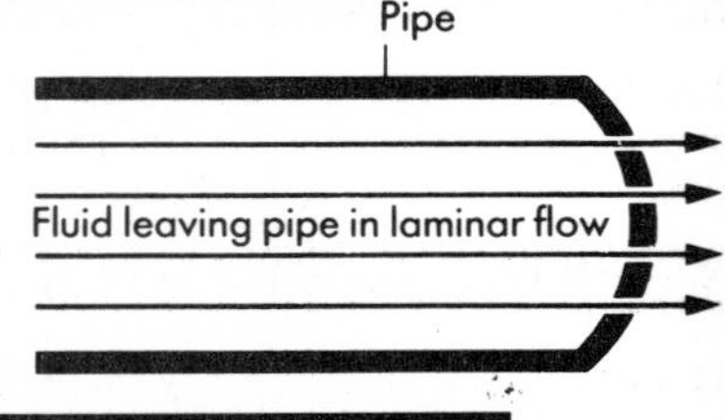

Fig L.1 Laminar flow

LAMINATE

A laminate is made up from a number of lamina, bonded together. *Plastic laminates* are made from a number of sheets of brown paper, with a top decorative paper, bonded together with a synthetic thermosetting resin. They are used as the decorative surface and working surface for kitchen furniture.

A *wood laminate* is made from a number of thin layers of wood bonded together. The grain of the wood is always in line and not at right angles to the next layer, as in plywood. Wood laminates are particularly strong because the adhesive also contributes to their strength. Because laminates can be *added* where they are needed, i.e. to the parts which are going to be subjected to a load, they can be made into large sections for use in building construction, in the same way as iron girders and supports are used to hold up the roof of large buildings. An added advantage of laminate structures is that they provide an aesthetic quality and form a visually interesting building.

On a smaller scale you can build up laminates to form thin, but strong, lightweight structures. Often the structures can take on a curved form, so you will need a **former** to hold the lamina in position while the adhesive is setting.

LAMINATED CORE

The iron *core* of a **transformer** is made up of a number of laminations. Each laminated section is insulated by a thin coating of iron oxide and varnish. The insulation increases the **resistance** in the cross-section of the core and reduces the eddy currents, but still allows a low **reluctance** path for high flux density around the core.

LAPPED JOINTS

This is where one piece of material overlaps another piece. A sheet of paper that is to be enlarged by adding another sheet of paper will have one surface overlapping another. This will help provide a reasonable area for bonding with an adhesive or a staple. Sheet metal is also overlapped to provide a suitable area for rivetting. Where an edge-to-edge join will not provide sufficient strength, then overlapping is one way of increasing strength in the bond.

LATHE TOOL

◀ Centre , Clearance angles ▶

LAYING UP

This term is commonly used in the process of building up layers of glass fibre mat in **glass reinforced plastic** (GRP). The mat is penetrated with a synthetic resin and allowed to cure before the next layer is applied.

LAYOUT

The way in which words and pictures are presented on page or sheet of paper is referred to as the **layout**. The arrangement of items on the pages of a newspaper, book, magazine, poster, design folio, etc. is covered by the term layout.

LENZ'S LAW

◀ Electrical resistance ▶

LEVER

A lever consists of a *beam* and a *pivot*. ◀ Fulcrum, Load, Mechanical efficiency, Pulley, Velocity ratio ▶

LIGHT DEPENDENT RESISTOR (LDR)

The LDR is highly sensitive to changes of light intensity. It can be used in circuits where outputs such as buzzers, counters, relays, motors, etc. can be made to function at particular levels of light intensity. As the light intensity *increases*, so the resistance in the LDR *decreases*.

The LDR commonly used is the ORP12 (Fig L.2). In the dark it has a resistance of 10MΩ, which in the light reduces to 130Ω. The change can take place in less than one second.

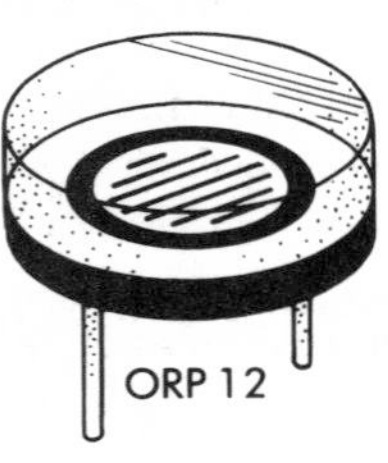

Fig L.2 Light dependent resistor

LIGHT EMITTING DIODES (LED)

LEDs are N (negative) P (positive) semiconductors. The junction is made from gallium phosphide and gallium arsenide phosphide. These diodes light up, very much like a small bulb, but unlike a bulb doe not have a filament, and use very much less current. The current through the LED must always be limited by a **resistor** that is in series with it. The value of the resistor (R) can be worked out using the following formula:

$$R = (V_s - V_f)/I_f$$

where V_s = voltage supply;
I_f = the LED's typical forward current;
V_f = the LED's forward voltage drop at I_f.

Remember: When including LEDs in a circuit, the cathode lead is next to the flat on its rim. To fit the connections the wrong way round will destroy the LED. Care should also be taken not to overheat the leads when soldering. LEDs are available in red, green, yellow and white (Fig L.3).

Fig L.3 Light emitting diode (LED)

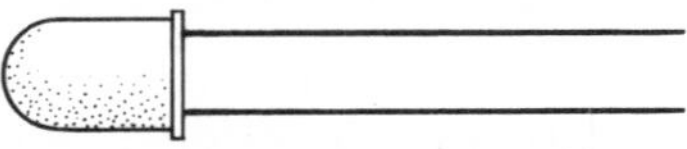

LIGHT-SENSITIVE CIRCUITS

These are circuits that contain *light-sensing devices*, such as Light Dependent Resistor, e.g. the ORP12. In a simple light-sensing circuit where the **LDR** receives a gradual change of light intensity, the resistance of the LDR will also change gradually. This will cause the voltage level, V_A, to rise gradually at the output (Fig L.4) The V_A moves from the correct voltage level for logic 0 to the correct voltage level for logic 1. Such a circuit can control a TTL (**Transistor-Transistor Logic**) logic gate with a **Schmitt trigger** input circuit.

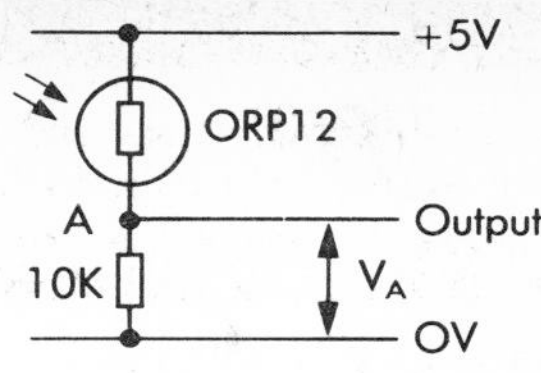

Fig L.4 Light-sensitive circuit

Remember: Although there are many types of sensors and sensing circuits, logic circuits must always be connected through a Schmitt trigger circuit.

LINE

A line has length, but no width or thickness. It can be straight, curved, or made up from a *combination* of straight and curved lines. A line is a method showing the outline of an object or the meeting point of two or more planes. Lines are used to indicate position on a graph in relation to vertical and horizontal axes.

In engineering drawing, lines are used in a number of different ways. Some examples are shown below:

Type	*Description*	*Use*
————————	Thick and continuous	Outlines
————————	Thin and continuous	Dimension, leader projection, hatching outline of revolved sections
～～～	Thin continuous and wavy	Boundaries of partial views or sections
- - - - - - - - - - -	Thin short dashes	Hidden detail of edges
—— – —— – —	Thin chain	Centre lines and the path of movable parts
—– – —— – —–	Thin chain with thick lines at the ends and where there is a change of direction	Cutting planes

Always remember that the *outline shape* of what is being drawn should stand out from all the other lines. For further details you should refer to BS PP7308.

LINEAR INTEGRATED CIRCUIT

Integrated Circuits (IC) are divided into two groups – **analogue** and **digital** circuits. The analogue circuits include linear amplifiers in which the output is a *linear function* of the input. Such circuits have a wide range of application and may be used in the following: voltage regulators, analogue switches, analogue-to-digital and digital-to-analogue converters, audio, radio and TV circuits.

LINEAR MEASUREMENT

Determining the size of an object by its length, width, thickness, etc.

LINEAR MOTION

Moving in a *straight* line. Many mechanical devices are required to move in a straight line, often vertically or horizontally. When the *linear motion* is backwards and forwards, it is said to be **reciprocating.** Such mechanisms as a **rack and pinion** or crank and slider change rotary motion into a linear motion. The compressed air in a cylinder moves the piston and piston rod in a linear motion.

LINK MECHANISMS

A device that joins one component with another component and transmits a motion or force through a link mechanism, is commonly referred to as a 'linkage'. Linkages can be used to change the direction of one motion through an angle of 90° or even to reverse the direction entirely (Fig L.5).

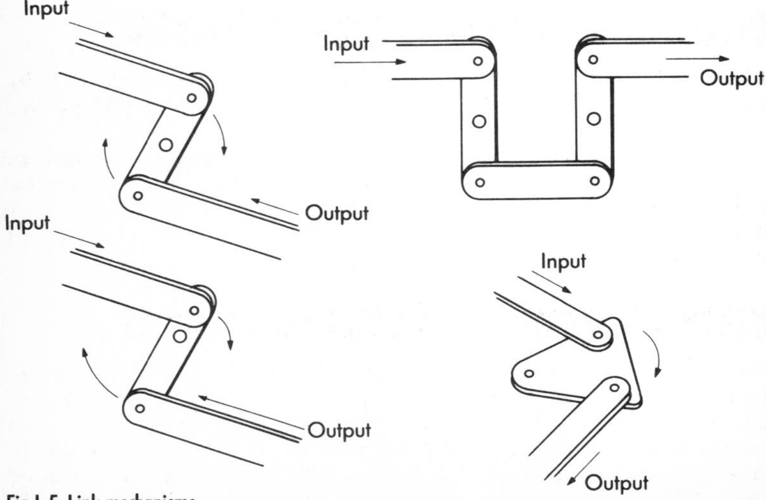

Fig L.5 Link mechanisms

LIPPED EDGE

A thin strip of wood that is attached to the edge of plywood so that the plies are not visible.

LIQUID CRYSTALS

These are substances that have their molecules arranged into set groups, like crystals, but which flow like liquids. Because the molecules are not fixed, as in solids, they can be easily changed, e.g. by passing an electric current through a transparent liquid crystal it will become opaque (cannot be seen through). Liquid crystals are used in seven segments displays in watches, calculators, etc.

Liquid crystals are also sensitive to temperature and respond by changing colour. For instance heat from a body will show up as a pattern of colours indicating the colder and warmer areas. Tumours are detected by looking at the colour patterns of a liquid crystal display.

LOAD

A load is an output force that often has to be moved or kept in balance by an input force known as *effort*. The *ratio* of effort to load is known as the **mechanical advantage**. When you lever you can lift a large load with very little effort, though the amount of effort is dependent upon the *length of the lever*. The longer the lever, the less the effort required to move the load. The ratio of the distance moved by the effort to the distance moved by the load, is called the **velocity ratio** (or **speed ratio**).

LOCUS/LOCI

A locus (singular of loci) is the path of a moving point. The orbits taken by planets round the earth and by electrons around a nucleus are examples of loci in nature.

You, however, will be expected to plot the path of loci in given situations as a means of constructing an ellipse, involute, cycloid, helix, hyperbola, Archimedian spiral, etc. In practical applications, determining the path of moving mechanisms is important, so that the path of one does not clash with another or with any stationary component.

LOGIC

The science of *logic* has been known for 2,000 years. It was first outlined by the Greek philosopher Aristotle in his treatise 'De Interpretatione'. It was not, however until 1854, when professor G.S. Boole published his own treatise called 'A Mathematical Analysis of Logic', that the science began to develop further. Even so, it took another 100 years before this reasoning could be applied to computers and pneumatics in a practical way. The debt owed to Professor Boole is indicated by the name Boolean algebra, given to mathematical reasoning of logic levels 0 and 1. These logic levels are a mathematical way of representing 'yes' and 'no', and in microcomputing they are another way of saying 'on' and 'off'.

Logic is also used by pneumatic engineers and is a very important means of control. ◄ **Logic gates** ►

LOGIC GATES

These are electronic circuits that act like switches. Though they have no moving parts they adopt either the 'on' position or the 'off' position. The 'on' position, which allows a current to flow, is represented by the digit 1; the 'off' position stops the current flowing and is represented by the digit 0. The circuit can be said to be 'open' or 'closed', just like a gate, hence the name *logic gate*.

In ***pneumatics***, the 'wall attachment device' for controlling an air supply in a pneumatic circuit has no moving parts. A fluid will not travel in a straight line between two diverging walls, (walls that are not parallel and which are opening out) but will bend towards one or the other (Fig L.6). Once the fluid has bent towards the wall, it attaches itself to that wall. Hence the name '*Wall attachment Device*'. The effect was first discovered by Henri Coanda in 1932 and is known as the *Coanda effect*.

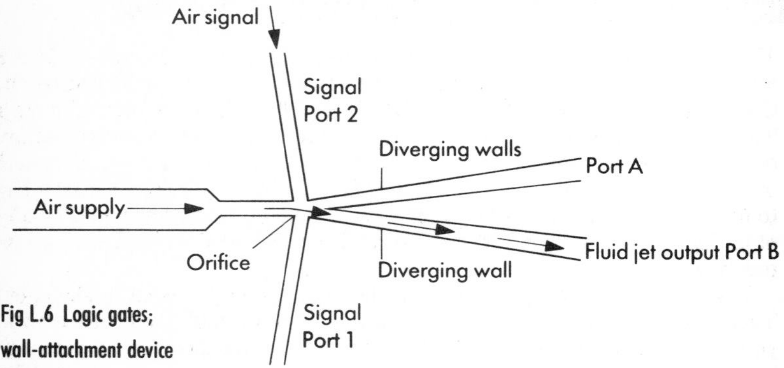

Fig L.6 Logic gates; wall-attachment device

Five logic gates are represented by the terms AND, OR, NOT, NAND and NOR. The AND gate has two or more inputs and one output. The output is at logic 1 when all the inputs are at logic 1 (Fig L.7a)).

The OR gate has two or more inputs and one output. The output is at logic 1 when one or more logic inputs are at logic 1 (Fig L.7b)).

Fig L.7 Logic gates

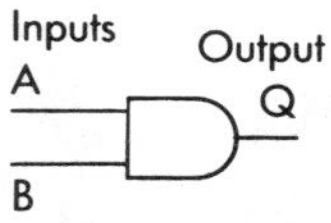

Inputs
A
B
Output
Q

a) AND gate

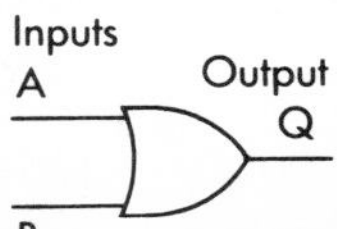

Inputs
A
B
Output
Q

b) OR gate

The NOT gate is like a beam on a pivot. When one end is up, the other is down. It is sometimes called an 'inverter' or an 'Inverting Buffer'. So whatever the input, the NOT gate gives the *opposite* in the ouput (Fig L.7c)).

c) NOT gate

The NAND gate has two or more inputs and one output. If all the inputs are at logic 1, the output is at logic 0. If one or more of the logic input is at 0, the output is at logic 1 (Fig L.7d)).

d) NAND gate

The NOR gate has two or more inputs and an output. If one or more of the inputs is at logic 1, the output is at logic 0. If all the inputs are at logic 0, the output is at logic 1 (Fig L.7e)).

e) NOR gate

LOGOGRAMS

The term 'logo' is more commonly used than the full name logogram. It is a form of symbolism that is used to identify a company and organisation. Companies such as W.H. Smith, British Rail, British Airways, etc. all have a 'logo' that is quickly and easily recognised. Images or words, or a combination of both, are used in the design of a logo. There are no rules as to what should or should not be in a logo, but the design brief for any logo would be that it has to be easily recognised and simple in outline. It must, of course, be unlike any other logo so that there is no confusion. Can you spot the Longman logo on this book?

When you design a logo, put down the information you want in sketches. Then rearrange the information in a variety of ways until you produce what you think is a possible solution. Now remove as much detail as you can, leaving just sufficient for you to still recognise what you have drawn. The example in Figure L.8 is a logo for a large superstore called 'Carefour', and the drawings are what possibly led to the final design.

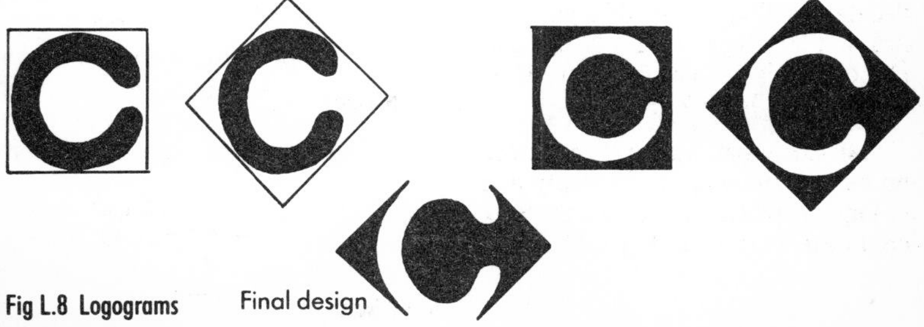

Fig L.8 Logograms

LOUDSPEAKER

An elecro-acoustic device that changes electrical energy into sound energy. It is the exact opposite of a **microphone,** which converts sound energy into electrical energy. It is designed to have sufficient power for weak sounds to still be heard and for moderate sounds to be heard more loudly.

Most loudspeakers use a coil, similar to that found in an electric motor, to convert electrical signals into sound waves. The signals are received by a coil which is placed between the poles of a circular permanent magnet. Variations in the signal strength cause the coil to move backwards and forwards (vibrate). These vibrations are conveyed to an attached cone, which emits the vibrations as sound waves, and they correspond to the variations in the electrical signal (Fig L.9).

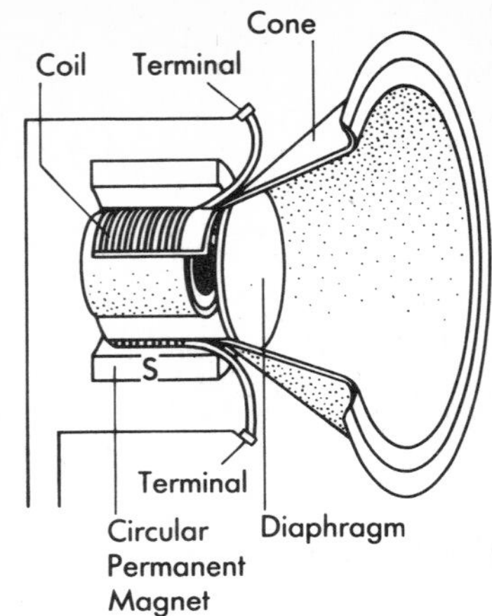

Moving coil loudspeaker (sectioned to show detail)

Fig L.9 Loudspeaker

LUBRICANTS/LUBRICATION

In order that moving mechanical parts which touch should move smoothly and with as little frictional resistance as possible, there is often a need for a substance to go between the touching surfaces. Most lubricants are mineral oils and greases that come from petroleum (crude oil). Some are soluble in water and, when mixed (often turning milky) are used to keep moving parts cool as well as running smoothly. Such oils are also used to keep cutting tools cool while cutting through metal; these are called *coolants.*

Lubricating greases are semi-solid and adhere to the surfaces they lubricate. They often have to be applied under pressure into casings through a *grease nipple* so that there is a constant supply of grease to the surface that needs lubricating. Many greases contain graphite, which is a flaky form of *carbon* that has excellent lubricating qualities. Some *waxes,* e.g. paraffin wax (mainly used to make candles), have a lubricating quality and can be used to rub on the sides of a handsaw blade to make the sawing action easier. *Cast iron* contains a high percentage of carbon. Parts that have machined surfaces made of cast iron, such as lathe beds, need very little lubrication because of their own natural lubricating supply.

Nylon has a waxy feel about its surface and can be used in light engineering without the need for a lubricating oil. Gears in domestic equipment, such as food mixers, are often made from nylon because there is no need for a lubricant.

LUG

A *lug* in engineering is a part that is sticking out from the rest of the component and is used for locating or fixing components together. *Bayonet fitting bulbs* are held in the bulb holder by two lugs. The *split die* for a wheel to be used in injection moulding has two locating lugs (Fig L. 10).

The cope of the *sand casting flask* has two small extensions so that it can locate with the drag (Fig L. 11).

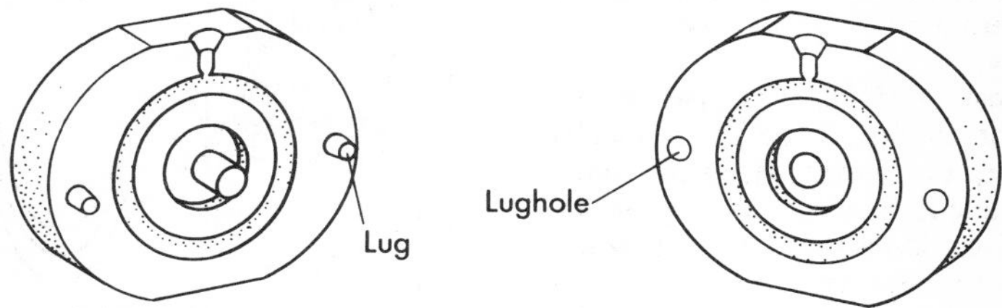

Fig L.10 Lug; split die

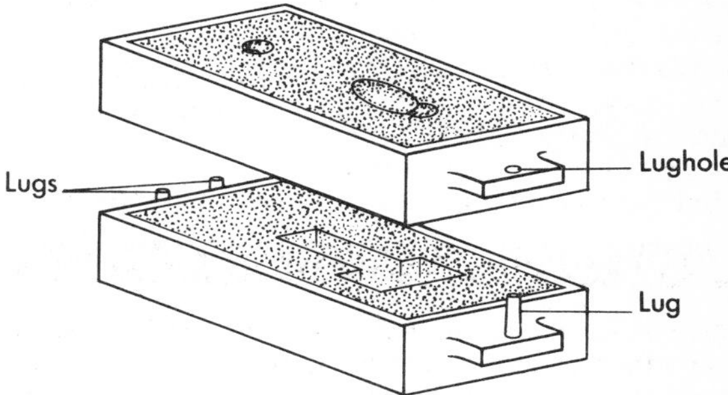

Fig L.11 Lug; sand casting flask

MACHINE

A machine is a mechanical device made up of mechanical elements such as gears, levers, cogs, wheels, pulleys, etc and can be driven by electrical, human or chemical energy. Machines are designed to do a variety of functions, such as sewing, printing, drilling, planing, sawing, transporting, flying, etc.

A machine should be capable of working to a higher degree of accuracy, and at a higher level of production, than in the case of a human being doing the equivalent work manually. Highly developed machines can also extend the capabilities of human activities, e.g. flying, travelling at speed, etc.

MACHINE TOOLS

These are tools designed to be used by machines to perform a specific function. Since they are designed to be held in a holding device, such as a *chuck* or tool holder, they are unsuitable for holding by hand. They should therefore not be confused with hand tools that are designed to be held in the hand. Examples of *machine tools* include lathe cutting tools, sewing machine needle; drill bits, etc.

MAGNITUDE OF LINEAR MOTION

When an object is to be moved, a **force** is required to move it. The *force needed* is proportional to the *area of contact* with the object and the *pressure required* to make it move. Hence the force is equal to the pressure × the area.

MAJOR AXIS

Where there is more than one axis, it is likely that one axis will be larger than the other. The larger axis is called the major axis. The most common and well-known example occurs in an **ellipse** (Fig M.1).

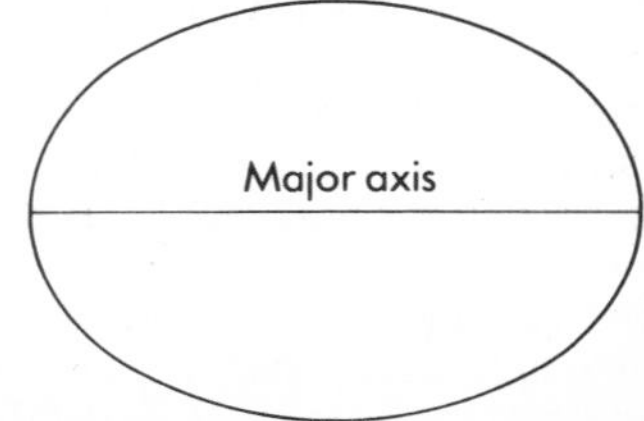

Fig M.1 Major axis

MAJOR PROJECT

This is a project that is allowed more time to complete than other projects in the syllabus. It can vary from one term, to three or four terms. The project or assignment will carry proportionately more marks and therefore may have a significant effect upon your final grade.

MAKE

In all courses that involve a practical element, there comes a time when the technology has to be put into some practical form. Putting that knowledge into practice is given the title *make* in CDT. This distinguishes it from the other activities such as research, design, analysis, etc.

Making something involves the use of materials and/or kits. Though the term 'make' mainly applies to the production of a solution using materials such as wood, metal and plastic, the act of making can still apply to products made from paper, card, fabric, etc.

MALE MOULD

Male moulds are distinct from **female moulds** in that they are raised and not hollow (Fig M.2). They are not commonly used, since the most important surface of a **casting** is generally the external surface. However male moulds are used in drape vacuum forming.

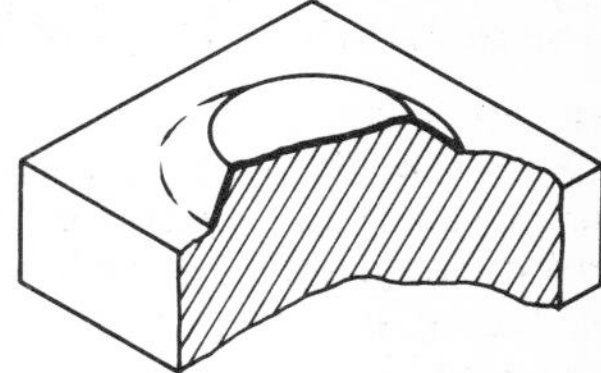

Fig M.2 Male mould

MALLEABLE

This is the ability of a material to change its shape under pressure without crumbling (breaking into small pieces) or cracking.

Plasticine that is used for modelling is an excellent example of a material that is malleable. Metals are also malleable. Some are malleable when they are cold, and can be beaten into various forms by hammering. Gold is the most malleable metal, closely followed by silver. This is one reason that these two metals can be used in jewellery. Other malleable metals include copper, aluminium, lead, zinc, and iron. The malleability of some metals is made more obvious when heated to red heat. Mild steel can be bent, drawn down (made longer and thinner) and upset (made shorter and fatter) by hammering when it is red hot.

The advantage of using materials that are malleable and forming them by hammering, rolling, etc., is that there is very little waste. Also, because the grain structure flows in the line of direction of the formed shape, it is stronger than the equivalent form achieved by machining (Fig M.3).

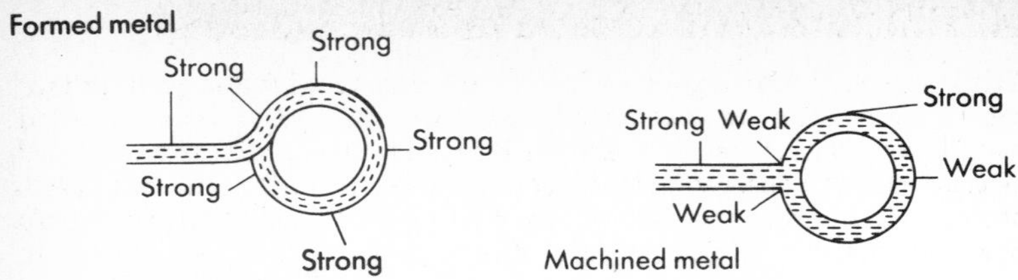

Fig M.3 Malleable

MANDREL

The shaft on which the main gears and pulleys are fitted in a lathe, drilling machine, etc.

MANIKIN

A manikin is a little man, a scale model of a human figure or a cut-out profile of a human figure with joints that enable the body, legs and arms to be put into a variety of positions.

Manikins are commonly made at 1/10th of the actual size of the human figure being represented. Therefore all sketches should be drawn to this scale. The suitability of, say, the design of a chair can then be evaluated by seeing how well the manikin sits in, or on, the chair.

Remember: A manikin is used to assess *measurement* only. You may have heard other names for this figure, such as 'Anthropod' or 'Ergonome'. The study of *anthropometrics* (man/measurement) is to do with sizes. A common mistake is to think that '*ergonomics*' is to do with measurement only.

MARKING OUT

This is the process of putting all the lines, centre punch marks, etc., on material to show *where* it has to be cut, drilled, sawn etc. On *wood*, the main *marking out* medium is *pencil*; on *metal* it is a *scriber*; and on *plastics* it is a *felt pen*. Marking gauges are used on wood to mark lines parallel to the face side and face edge. A surface plate and gauge is used to mark out parallel lines to a datum edge.

Remember: Use the correct marking out medium for the material being marked.

MASKING

This means placing a cover over an area to be protected from a paint, ink, etc. that is being applied to a neighbouring surface. *Masking* is more commonly used when work is being done using an air brush. A *masking tape* is specially designed to bond to paper and can be removed without leaving a mark or causing damage.

MATERIAL

This is a general term used to include anything from which an item or product can be made. The most commonly used materials for **making** are wood, metal, clay , plastics, paper and cloth. However 'expendable' materials, such as glass appear, adhesive, solders, etc. are also important during the making process. ◀ **Hardwoods, Softwoods, Ferrous metals, Non-ferrous metals, Synthetic materials, Thermoplastics, Thermosetting plastics** ▶

MATERIAL CHARACTERISTICS

These are the features by which a material can be recognised, e.g. colour, texture, feel, smell, weight, etc. The features of a well-known timber may be described as 'golden brown', but may in fact be medium to dark brown and have some black markings. Try to be *specific* in describing a material, e.g. it is a medium weight wood, heavier than mahogany and lighter than oak. It is, of course, *teak* that is being described.

Remember: material characteristics are descriptions of what the material looks like. Don't confuse the term with 'properties', which is convered with what the material can do, i.e. conduct electricity, bend, become soft when heated, etc.

MATERIAL HARDNESS

Hardness is a property of materials. Some materials are harder than others and they can be placed in order of hardness by a simple 'scratch test'. All this means is that if one material will leave a scratch on another, then that material is harder than the other. For instance, if you scratch a piece of glass with a diamond, the diamond is harder than the glass. Materials are given a *hardness number* 1 to 10, which is an indication of which material is harder than another, rather than a measurement of hardness.

Diamond, being the hardest material known, is given the number 10. *Quartz* is given a number 7 because it is softer than the diamond. The number indicates that there are two other materials that are harder than quartz but softer than diamond. The hardness scale number is also known as **Moh's Scale.**

The hardness of materials such as wood and plastics is not necessarily an important piece of information, but knowing the hardness of *metals* could be quite important, especially if you want to design a tool for cutting, say, aluminium or tin plate. It could also be important where two parts of a mechanism are rubbing on each other and you do not wish the one to wear away the other, e.g. the toothed gear wheels in a **gear train.**

MATERIAL HARDNESS TESTING

There are *hardness tests* carried out in industry that are precise and the results are the accepted scale of hardness. There are *five* tests that have been developed to test the hardness of metals that you should know.

Brinell hardness test

This is done by pressing a ball bearing into the surface of a piece of metal. The hardness is calculated by knowing the *load* on the ball bearing and the *diameter* of the impression made in the metal.

Vickers Pyramid hardness test

This is done by pressing a square-based, pyramid-shaped diamond into the surface of a piece of metal. The hardness is calculated by knowing the *load* used and the *length of the diagonal* of the impression.

Rockwell hardness test

This is done with a steel ball or a diamond cone and the *depth of the impression is used to calculate the hardness number.*

Izod hardness number

This is calculated by measuring the *angle* a pendulum hammer swings past the metal being tested. As the hammer hits the metal, which is firmly held in a vice, the swing of the pendulum is considerably slowed down by the impact. It only swings a small way past on hard metals, but further past on softer metals. The angle is measured by reading the position the marker comes to rest on the scale.

Shore Scleroscope

A diamond pointed tool is dropped down a glass tube and the hardness is calculated by knowing the *height of the first bounce.*

Here are some standard numbers that you should be aware of:

Metals
Aluminium 38; Brass 82; Bronze 70; Copper 45; Lead 6; Mild steel 188; Stainless steel 200.
Plastics
Acrylic M100; Cellulose acetate M90; Nylon R112; Polypropylene R90; Polystyrene (high density) R70; Polythene (High density) R50; (Low density) Shore D40; Polyvinyl chloride (PVC) rigid R60.

Wood is not tested for hardness since it is not regarded as a material used for making mechanical devices. Also there are considerable variations in the density and weight of a timber coming from a single family, therefore any calculations made would *not* provide a reliable set of figures.

MATERIAL PROPERTIES

When referring to the *properties of wood*, the following are considered – how easy or difficult it is to cut (working properties); whether or not it is stable i.e. will not warp, split, shrink, etc; its strength; how well it will finish (i.e. how easy it is to make smooth and polish etc); and its resistance to fungi or beetle attack (technical properties). For instance, the material properties of a piece of *walnut* are that it is easy to work; it is moderately stable; and it is noted for its excellent finish. It is also moderately resistant to fungi attack.

Properties of metals can also be described under different headings: e.g. malleability, ductility, electrical conductivity, thermal conductivity, magnetic qualities, rates of expansion, machinability, casting abilitity and mechanical properties (e.g. hardness, tensile strength, corrosion resistance, etc.) For instance the properties of an *aluminium alloy* could read; malleable and ductile when annealed; an excellent conductor of electricity; cannot be magnetised; has a hardness of 38; has a melting range of between 525°C and 625°C; has a coefficient of linear expansion at 20°C of 23.0; is fairly resistant to corrosion; and so on.

MATERIAL SOURCES

The three main sources of materials are mineral ores, oil, and trees. The *mineral ores* are compounds of chemical and metallic elements. An ore is a collection of minerals together with unwanted materials (technically called 'gangue'), and is to be found as part of the earth's crust. It is mainly quarried, but in some cases such as tin ore (Cassiterite, SnO), it is mined. The value of an ore is determined by the percentage of the wanted mineral and the gangue. The higher the quantity of the wanted mineral, the better the quality of the ore. But the value of the mineral to be extracted must also be considered. For instance, *Gold* is a highly valuable metal. Therefore to be able to extract 14 to 28 grams *per tonne of ore* is worth the high costs of extraction. However for *iron*, if *less than 250g per tonne* could be extracted, then the ore is not worthwhile extracting.

Here is a list of metals and the ores from which they are extracted: Aluminium – bauxite; Copper – chalcopyrite; Iron – haematite, magnetite, limonite and siderite; Lead – galena; Nickel – pentlandite; Tin – cassiterite; and Zinc – zincblende, calamine and hemimorphite.

Crude oil (petrolium) is the major source for *plastic* materials. Coal, wood and cotton waste, milk are also sources, but since the development of 'Oil cracking' processes, the major source is undoubtedly oil. Here is a list of some of the more commonly used plastics and their original source: Polystyrene – petroleum; Polyvinyl chloride – petroleum/coal; Nylon – coal; Cellulose – wood/cotton; Acrylic – petroleum, Urea and Melamine – coal; Polyester resin – coal/petroleum; Polyurethane – petroleum.

Wood is a natural product that comes from plants – the *Angiosperms* (broad leaf trees) and the *Gymnnosperms* (conifer trees). The conifer (cone-bearing) trees, e.g. Scots Pine, produce the 'softwoods' and the broad leaf trees, e.g. Oak, produce the hardwoods. This is a *botanical classification* and is not a reliable description of the hardness of wood. Before the timber from the trees can be used for manufacturing purposes, the timber has to be seasoned. In other words its moisture content has to be reduced to between 11% and 15% so that it will not warp, shrink, expand or split. Wood will either absorb moisture or release moisture to the air until it has the same moisture content as the air surrounding it. Paper is also a material that comes from wood that is made into a pulp.

MATERIAL STRAIN

These are the forces acting upon a material when it is changing size or shape, e.g. when it is being *stretched, compressed* or *twisted.* The strain can be calculated by dividing the eventual shape by the original size or by measuring the angle through which it is twisted. The strain on a material can also be measured using a **strain gauge.**

MATERIAL STRESS

There are three stress forces; compressive, tensile and shear. The *compressive force* tries to reduce the size of the material; rubber can be compressed into a smaller shape. The *tensile force* is a stretching force and is measured by *Young's* **modulus of elasticity**. The *shear force* is a sideways force that tries to separate the material into layers and can be measured by *shear modulus of elasticity*.

The three diagrams in Fig M.4 illustrate how the atoms in a lattice are pulled from their original position.

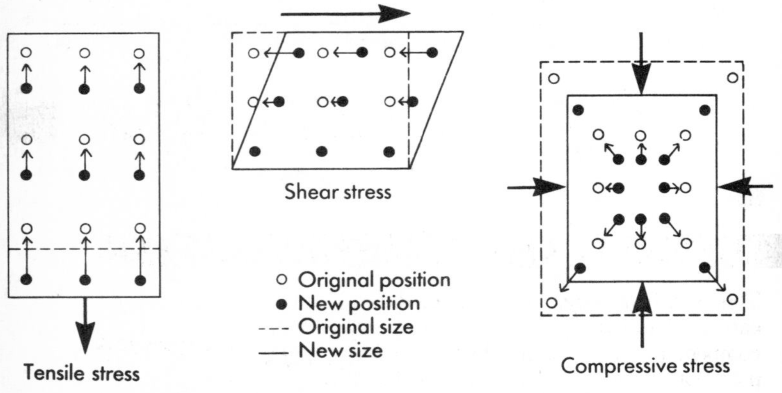

Fig M.4 Material stress

MATERIAL TESTING

Materials and structures must be thoroughly tested, particularly if they are to be used in buildings, bridges, cars, trains, aeroplanes, etc. A material will withstand a load or force up to its **'elastic limit'**. Beyond this point a material will begin to deform. First it stretches, twists, etc. slowly until it reaches its yield point; then it *deforms* rapidly until it finally *fractures* (Fig M.5).

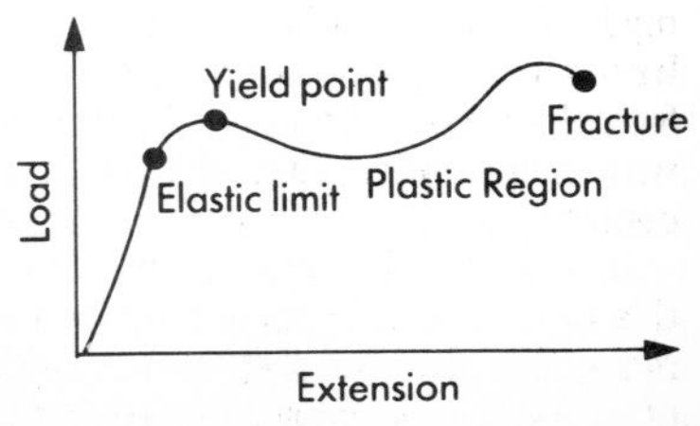

Fig M.5 Material testing

There are set procedures and standards for testing materials that are laid down by the British Standards Institute. The ones that may concern you are as follows: Metals BS 18; Wood BS 373 to determine strength and effect on strength of various treatments; BS 3962 and BS 5910 finishes; BS 5669 Chipboard specification and testing; Plastics BS 2782; Rubber BS 903; Textiles BS 1006; Adhesives BS 647; bone and fish glues BS 3544; polyvinyl acetate and BS 5350 for bond strength and longitudinal shear.

There are other standards, but you are only likely to refer to such information if you are doing a project that involves the testing of materials.

MATERIALS IN SECTION

When a section view is given, there are conventional symbols for showing the type of material that has been sectioned. Fig M.6 shows some examples that you are likely to need.

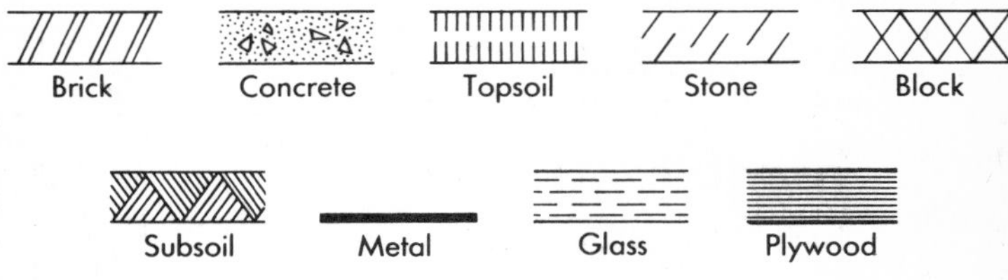

Fig M.6 Materials in section

MATRIX BOARD

This is a board upon which circuits can be temporarily arranged. The components can be attached with pins that fit tightly in small holes that are 1.3 mm in diameter. When the circuit is developed, the components may be soldered either to the pins or on the underside of the board (Fig M.7). The board is available as small panels 150 mm × 100 mm and is made from a synthetic laminate of brown paper and phenol-formaldehyde. The board is pierced with many holes that are 2.5 mm centres apart.

If you intend leaving a circuit on this type of board, you are advised to mount the board on some small strips of wood to prevent any soldering joints getting knocked and damaged.

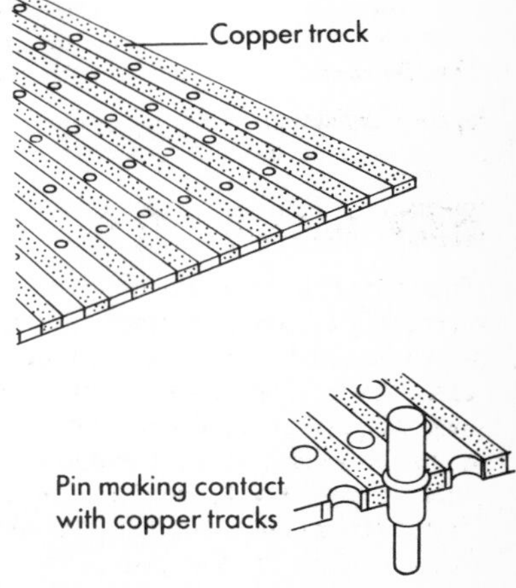

Fig M.7 Matrix board

MATT FINISH

This is a dull finish that does not reflect light. It is the opposite to a gloss finish that is shiny and reflects the light. *Matt finishes* are suitable for surfaces that are not perfectly smooth.

MECCANO

This is an early form of construction kit that required the use of nuts and small screws to keep the metal components together. Though it has been a commonly used kit, it is now less well-used and has been replaced with plastic kits that are quicker and easier to assemble and dismantle. These include **Fischertechnik**, Lego Technic and Hybridex.

MECHANICAL ADVANTAGE

When less human effort is required to move or lift a load because a mechanical device has been used, an *advantage* has been gained. This advantage is known as a *mechanical advantage*. The less effort that is required, the greater the mechanical advantage. Mechanical advantage can be calculated by the following formula:

$$\text{Mechanical advantage} = \frac{\text{Load}}{\text{Effort}}$$

The simplest mechanical device is the *lever*. To move a heavy stone, a metal bar can be supported on a smaller stone (fulcrum), and the heavy stone can then be levered to the position where it is required.

If the *effort* required was 200 newtons, to move a stone of *load* 600 newtons, then the *mechanical advantage* would be 3. Pulley systems are another mechanical device used to gain mechanical advantage. Car engines are often removed from the car with the aid of a block and tackle; a kind of pulley system, with only one person providing the effort. ◀ **Lever** ▶

MECHANICAL EFFICIENCY

If friction did not exist, the effort input would equal the effort output. But in any machine or mechanical device, friction does take some of the effort so that the output is always less than the input. This means that no machine can be 100% efficient. Efficiency can be calculated by the following formula:

$$\text{Efficiency} = \frac{\text{work done on the load}}{\text{work done by the effort}} \times 100\%$$

Work is measured in joules. ◀ **Joules, Newton's laws of motion** ▶

MECHANISMS

This is the overall term given to all mechanical devices, e.g. pulleys, linkages, levers, gear wheels, ratchets, pistons, etc.

MEDULLARY RAY

These are the cells in wood that radiate horizontally to the centre of the tree. This only occurs in hardwoods, and it produces distinctive silvery streaks in oak. Only planks that are cut radially show the best results of this attractive feature.

METALLURGY

Metallurgy is the scientific study of metal and metal extraction from ores. Exactly how man became aware of the presence of metal on the earth is uncertain. It is believed that the earliest recognised form of iron came from meteorites, but exactly how man discovered that iron could be produced from minerals is not at all clear. The minerals in the form of an oxide (haematite) or a sulphide (iron pyrites) do not in any way look like a metal. It is widely believed that the first production of iron many thousands of years ago was a lucky accident, rather than resulting from a basic idea of how to extract iron from an ore.

METALS

Metals are extracted from the ore as pure elements, e.g. iron, copper, gold, silver, aluminium lead, tin and zinc. If they are mixed with other metals, or other elements such as carbon, they are then called **alloys**. Iron plus carbon provides a variety of grades of steel, such as mild steel, tool steel, etc. If chromium, tungsten, and vanadium are added, **High-Speed Steel** is the result. Copper and tin combine to provide a metal alloy of bronze, while a combination of copper and zinc provide an alloy called brass.

Metals play such an important role in our lives that it is difficult to think what could be done if they did not exist. They have been known to man for over 6000 years, but more metal has been used in the last 60 years than in the whole of the previous period. This is a largely due to the rapid advances in technology. The extraction, refining and carefully controlled alloying of metals have made metal the most versatile material. Metals are hard, shiny, strong and not easily broken when pulled (high tensile strength). They can be beaten into shape by hammering (malleable), are heavy, can conduct heat and electricity, bend, melt, and can be stretched into wire when pulled (ductile). Metals expand when heated. Some can become magnetised and some can be hardened by heating or hammering.

Metals corrode at different rates. Iron, or alloys of iron, rust very steadily but, because of an improved understanding of alloying, metals such as steel can be made so that they do *not* rust, e.g. stainless steel.

Each metal has its own characteristics but, unlike naturally produced materials like timber, tends to be homogenous, i.e. the same all the way through. Therefore when working with metal, it is not necessary to be concerned with the direction of grain, as it is when working with wood.

METER

A meter is a device that measures quantities, whether it be of water, gas or electricity, that are used in a give space of time. Meters are also used to *record* the quantities that have been used in the past.

The moving coil meter is still the most commonly used type of meter, but digital meters are increasing in number. Meters not only measure, but also help to detect faults in circuits or in components in circuits. These are sometimes called 'multitesters'. ◀ **Ammeter, Voltmeter** ▶

METHOD

The *way* in which something is achieved. It is a sequence of events that enables an activity to be successfully completed. Often the better the *method*, the easier the activity will be accomplished and the less time will be taken to complete the activity. Method often includes order and logic.

You are often asked to show your method of construction in a drawing. This is so that an examiner can see if you chose the most appropriate method, say to construct a hexagon, ellipse, cycloid, etc. When planning the production of an artefact you are concerned with selecting a method that will enable you to produce the artefact successfully, in the most economic manner.

METHODOLOGY

This is the 'science' of method. You do not have to have a scientific understanding, rather a commonsense approach to finding a way in which things can be achieved. Putting one particular activity before another is very much down to common sense, i.e. you investigate what is *needed* before thinking of possible solutions or ideas. Sensible planning is all that is looked for at this level.

METRE

This is a metric unit of linear measurement. It is equivalent to approximately 33.37 inches in the imperial system. The metre is divided into 1000 equal parts, or *millimetres*. The *decimetre* is 10th of a metre, but should be avoided as a unit of measurement on drawings. It is far easier to write 132 mm than it is to write 1.32 dm. Also, if a decimal point is used it is very easy to put it in the wrong place. Always use the mm unit (millimetre is 1000th of metre) on drawings so that a decimal point is *not* needed, so reducing the chance of making an error.

METRIC

Of the metre or *metric* system. All units are based on the metre. The system was first devised by French scientists at the Academy of Sciences in 1791, with the *metre* being a unit of length, *litre* the unit of capacity, and *kilogramme* the unit of mass.

MICROCOMPUTER

Microcomputers are computers that have integrated circuits. The prefix *micro* means small. The development of the silicon chip has reduced the space required for many transistors and has made it possible to contain integrated circuits on a single chip, 0.5 mm square. The circuit can contain hundreds of thousands of microscopic components, hence the name microcomputers.

The developemnt in 1965 of the integrated circuit (IC) so revolutionised the size and power of computers that the personal, portable, computer became possible. Pocket calculators can store information and be programmed in various ways and are in fact examples of microcomputers.

MICROELECTRONICS

There are two branches of *microelectronics* – *digital* and *analogue*. **Digital circuits** work on a binary system of 1 or 0; on or off; high or low. Most electrical circuits are digital. The light is either on or off, according to whether the switch is in the on or off position. The input must be discrete (made up of distinct parts) rather than continuous. A digital signal is therefore a group of pulses that have the same level and are on or off, etc. In the **analogue circuit** the signal information is continuous, so if the light switch is replaced with a dimmer switch, the light can change gradually from no light to a dull glow, then to various levels of brightness until fully on.

◀ Logic circuits, Logic gates ▶

MICROMETER

This is a precision measuring device used in engineering to measure the diameter of round objects or the thickness of flat material. It consists of an accurately ground spindle (screw) which, when turned, moves the end of the spindle forwards or backwards so that it either moves towards the anvil or away from it. The object is measured by placing it in the gap between the anvil and spindle, and then moving the spindle forward until it touches the surface of the object (Fig M.8).

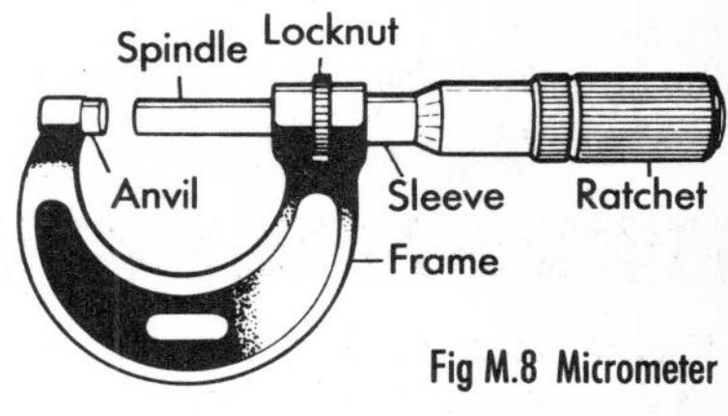

Fig M.8 Micrometer

A micrometer can be designed to measure in inches or in millimetres. The spindle of the micrometer designed to measure in inches has 40 threads to the inch; so with one complete turn the spindle moves 1/40th of an inch, i.e. 0.025 inch. Complete turns are marked by small cross lines on the sleeve. Each group of four is marked by a longer line. Four complete turns move the spindle 0.1 inch or 1/10th of an inch. For much smaller measurements, the partial turns can also be read from the divisions marked on the spindle. These are divided into 25 equal divisions; 1/25 of a turn moves the spindle 0.001 inch or 1000th of an inch. Hence the micrometer is capable of measuring to the nearest thousandth of an inch.

The *metric micrometer* works on the same principle. The thread pitch of the spindle is 0.5 mm therefore with one complete turn, the spindle moves half a millimetre, and with two complete turns it moves one millimetre. One complete turn is marked by short crosslines on the sleeve; two by a slightly longer line; and four by a longer line. The spindle is marked in 50 equal divisions so that each division equals 1/50 of half a millimeter or 0.01 mm. *Note:* Great care must be taken with such a precision instrument. It should never be banged, tapped, etc., and should always be returned to its protective case when not in use.

MICROPHONE

A microphone is an electro-mechanical device for converting sound energy into electrical energy. It has a flexible diaphragm which moves in response to the small changes in air pressure caused by the sound waves.

In the *carbon microphone,* the variation in the pressure from the sound waves causes the diaphragm to vibrate. The pressure on the carbon granules behind the diaphragm changes their electrical resistance. This imposes an alternating current on the direct current supply. The AC can be 'tapped off' as an output by means of a **transformer**. Such microphones do not provide high fidelity but they are cheap and are commonly used in telephones.

The *moving coil microphone* works on the electromagnet principle.

MICROPROCESSOR

A microprocessor is a very complex unit and is at the centre of computing activity. It basically receives, stores and obeys instructions. But it can only work when linked to other integrated circuits. It is sometimes referred to as a *Central Processing Unit* or CPU. A CPU on one or two chips, contained within a single package, is called a microprocessor.

There are many different microprocessors and they can be identified by their number. The 6502 is used in the BBC microcomputer. The Z80 is much more commonly used and can be found in the Amstrad and Spectrum computer systems.

The microprocessor in simple terms is the brain of the computer and controls the functions of all the other parts of the system.

MICRO SWITCH

◄ Switches ►

MID-ORDINATES

A mid-ordinate is a straight line representing an axis between two ordinates. Mid-ordinates are used to calculate the area of an irregularly shaped figure. The figure is divided up into approximate *trapezia.* The area of a trapezium is calculated by multiplying the average height by its width. The mid-ordinates can be used to find the average height of each trapezium constructed *within* the irregular figure. The average height is then multiplied by the width of the mid-ordinate to give the area of the trapezium. These are then added together for *all* the trapezia to give the area of the irregular shape ◀ **Area** ▶

MILD STEEL

This is a **ferrous metal** that is an **alloy** of 0.1–0.3% carbon and 99.9–99.7% iron. It is a general purpose steel and is avaliable in sheet, rod and tubular section. It is easy to work cold and to shape when red hot. It rusts very easily and needs a protective finish.

MINI-ENTERPRISE

These are essentially small group projects that are intended to be of help to the community. Projects are based around helping the elderly, the handicapped or the under-privleged. A team of five to ten pupils work together to research the problem and to follow a design procedure that will result in an idea to be **realised** as a product.

MINI-PROJECTS

These are projects that are usually completed in the space of several weeks and form the early part of the course. Sometimes the **realisation** element is developed to a stage where the idea can be demonstrated by using 'Off cut' materials, construction kits, etc. So the main emphasis in a mini-project is the *solving of a problem* rather than the production of an artefact.

MINOR AXIS

When a geometric figure has more than one axis, they are not usually the same size. The smaller one is called the minor axis, and the larger one the major axis. ◀ **Ellipse** ▶

MITRE

A mitre is an angle of 45°. A right angle that is bisected will form a mitre. Many right angle joints are mitred on the edge that is seen because the appearance is then pleasing. Picture frames are joined at the corners with a mitred joint. Many mouldings, covings, etc. that meet at right angles on internal and external corners are mitred. There are marking out tools such as a mitre square, an engineer's combination set; and a 45° set square. Jigs such as mitre blocks are used in cutting mitres.

MOCK-UP

This is a term used to describe something that has to made in three dimensions, fairly quickly and without too much attention being paid to precise measurements and to the quality of finish. In other words just sufficient for a function or appearance to be demonstrated.

MODEL

There are two types of model. One is a *small version* of something that is large and is accurately detailed. The other is a **'mock-up'** of an idea. You must be certain which of the two terms applies to what you have to do in a project. Sometimes you are asked specifically to produce a 'mock-up' of your ideas. If, however, you are involved with an idea for a new leisure centre or for the development of a city transport scheme, you will be expected to present some of your ideas in three dimensions, and a small version (scale) model is expected. In this case the accuracy and quality of finish are important, and materials might be used of the same quality as that expected in the finished product.

MODERATE/MODERATION

Because so much of the assessing and marking of coursework and examination papers is carried out by many different people, it is necessary for the results to be checked. By checking the marks awarded for each part of the examination, it is possible to see whether all the candidates from all the centres have been marked at the same standard. Some teachers and examiners mark 'harder' than others, i.e. some award fewer marks than others for the same piece of work. The opposite can obviously happen with an 'easy' examiner or assessor. So in order to be fair, some marks need to be raised and some lowered. There are of course many teachers and examiners who give marks that agree with the national standard and do not need to be moved up or down. The process of adjusting and confirming marks is called *moderation*.

MODIFICATION

During a designing activity, ideas do not usually come as a complete package, providing a perfect solution. Some adjustment or modification is necessary to improve upon the initial ideas. In fact the need to make adjustments occurs almost continuously, even after the product or solution has been realised. At that stage you can still say how you would change things in the future.

MODULUS OF ELASTICITY

Most materials are *elastic*, i.e. they will return to their original size if stretched or bent, when the force used to do the stretching or bending no longer exists. Some materials are less elastic than others. The 'stress' on a material divided by the 'strain' is constant for any material, and is called the modulus of elasticity. The size of the modulus gives a measure of how elastic that material is. ◀ Hooke's law ▶

MOHS' SCALE

Materials are known to have varying degrees of *hardness*, and a German minerologist, Friedrich Mohs, arranged 10 common minerals in order of increasing hardness. He started with *talc* as his softest material, number 1, and *diamond* as the hardest mineral, number 10. The complete scale is as follows:

No	*Mineral*	*Comments*
1	Talc	Crushed by finger nail
2	Gypsum	Scratched by finger nail
3	Calcite	Scratched by bronze coin
4	Flourite	Scratched by glass
5	Apatite	Scratched by penknife
6	Feldspar	Scratched by quartz
7	Quartz	Scratched by steel file
8	Topaz	Scratched by corundum
9	Corundum	Scratched by diamond
10	Diamond	Scratched only by itself

This scale has become accepted as a standard by which other *minerals* could be compared. Here is a list showing how some of the *materials* you are likely to meet on your course have been compared with Mohs' scale:

1	Paper, wood.
2	Plastics
3	Annealed aluminium, annealed brass.
4	Low carbon steels
5	Machining steels
6	Tool steel
7	High Speed Steel
8	
9	Tungsten carbide, silicon carbide, corundum (Emery cloth).
10	Diamond cutting tool (glass cutter)

Remember that the list is *comparative* only.

MOISTURE CONTENT

Most natural materials such as wood contain a percentage of moisture. Even wood that has been seasoned contains moisture, and it is important that the amount of moisture be the *same* as the normal amount in the air. In a centrally-heated building, the moisture content of the air is approximately 11%. If the timber has the same moisture content as the air, it is unlikely to warp.

If timber has *not* got the same moisture content as the air surrounding it, then it will either release some of its own moisture, or absorb moisture until the moisture content of the air and the timber are the same. If the adjusting period requires considerable changes in the levels of moisture, then this is the time when timber will warp and split.

MOLECULAR STRUCTURE

Materials are made up of tiny particles, called molecules. Molecules are made up of even tinier particles called **atoms**, but if we went on dividing we would lose the identity of the material. All the molecules of a substance are identical. But the molecules of one substance are different from the molecules of another substance. Every molecule of a given substance has the same number of atoms linked together in the same pattern. Another substance could have molecules with the identical number of atoms, but linked together in a *different pattern* so that it constitutes a different substance.

Any substance which is made up of molecules containing the identical *pattern* of atoms is called an **element.** ◀ **Crystals** ▶

MOMENTS

These are forces acting upon a lever to cause it to rotate about an axis. The effect of the force is dependent upon the distance the force is away from the *point of rotation*, i.e. the pivot or fulcrum. If you think of a see-saw, with the children on the see-saw being of equal weight and equal distance from the central pivoting point, then the children and the see-saw will remain balanced. This is said to be in a state of **equilibrium**. If one child moves nearer the centre, the see-saw will begin to rotate about the pivoting point. This turning force is known as a moment.

Moments can be used to work out the effort required to move a load. The ratio between the load to be moved and the effort required is known as the mechanical advantage. Moments can also be used to work out the load or distance required to keep a beam in equilibrium. Can you work out the answer for the unknown load in Figure M.9? It is 200N.
◀ **Mechanical advantage** ▶

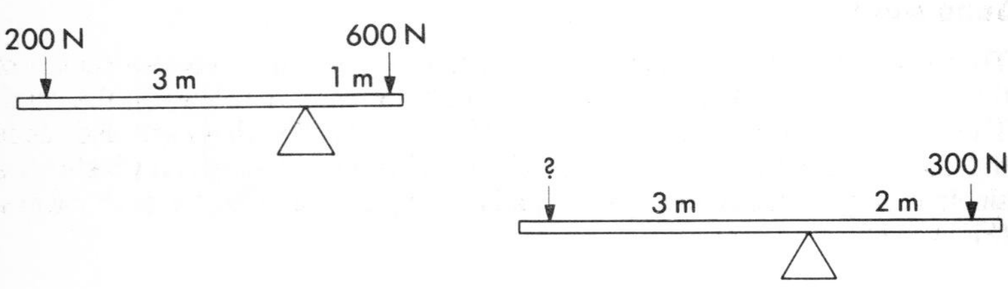

Fig M.9 Moments

MONO

Mono is often used as a prefix, i.e. in front of another word. On its own it means 'single' or 'one of'. Therefore *monochromatic radiation* means electromagnetic radiation of a single frequency. *Monostable* means a type of circuit that has only one stable mate. A *monolithic integrated circuit* has all its components on one side of a single chip of silicon, and so on.

MONOGRAM

A combination of two or more letters woven into a single form (Fig M.10). Monograms are often used on jewellery and personal property. Though monograms are a means of identity, they are more of a decorative feature. If you use one on your work, do make sure that your full name is also available since it is not always easy to identify a person by a monogram alone.

Fig M.10 Monograms

MONOLITHIC INTEGRATED CIRCUIT

These are circuits that have all their components on one side of a silicon chip.

MORTICE

A mortice is a hole. It is the part of a joint commonly used when working in wood, e.g. *mortice and tenon*. A *mortice lock* is one that is contained in a hole.

MOULDS

A mould is a device which has a cavity into which a material that is in a 'liquid' state can flow, taking upon itself the shape of the cavity. It is a device or means for producing many identical items. Sometimes the material can be used cold, e.g. epoxy resin, and sometimes hot, e.g. aluminium, gold, silver, etc.

MOULD TYPES

Sand moulds

These are used when casting molten metals. A pattern (a wooden replica of the shape to be cast) of the casting is used to provide the cavity in the sand. The sand is held together by a mixture of water and clay; there are also sands that have special additives, e.g. Petrabond. This type of mould only lasts for a single casting process and a new mould has to be prepared for each casting (Fig M.11).

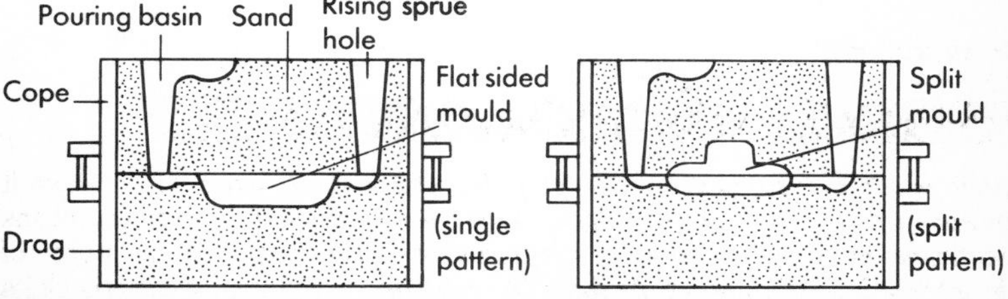

Fig M.11 Sand moulds

Cuttle fish moulds

These are suitable for small work such as jewellery. The bone of the cuttle fish is found on many sea shores and is available in pet shops where it is sold for birds such as canaries and budgerigars. The cavity is made by cutting the shape with a sharp knife or by pressing a metal form into the surface. Two pieces of cuttle fish bone are required to make the mould, or one piece and a charcoal block (Fig M.12).

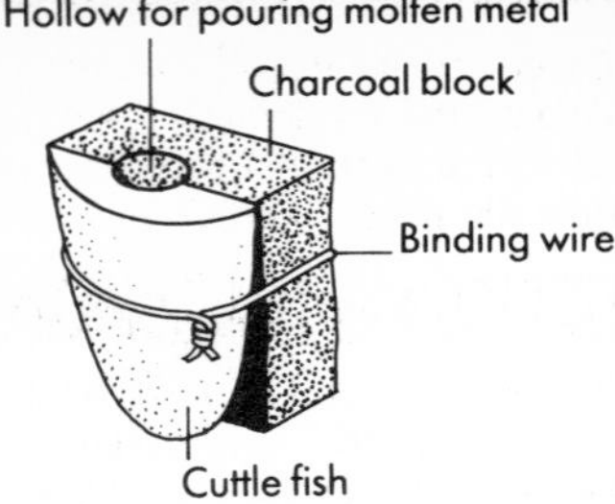

Fig M.12 Cuttle fish mould

Metal moulds

These are often called *dies*. They are suitable for producing a large number of castings. They are expensive to make, but, with correct use, they can be used many thousand times. Most thermoplastic castings are done in metal dies. When the material is forced into the cavity, the process is known as 'pressure die casting'.

Plaster moulds

These are made from a fine plaster called an 'investment'. They are used in casting fine pieces of jewellery.

Flexible moulds

These are rubbery and made from a plastic material. They are often called 'vinomoulds'. They are used to produce intricate shapes. Because the mould is pliable there is no need to worry about 'under cuts'. Wax is often used as the casting material and is poured into the mould when hot. Other materials such as plaster or cement can be used with these moulds. For support reading see Design and Technology Metal, by Hicks, Heddle and Bridge.

MOULD RELEASE AGENT

In some casting processes, the casting bonds to the surface of the mould. It is then necessary to apply a release agent to the surfaces of the cavity before casting begins. This is particularly the case with **glass reinforced plastics** where the resin has a natural tendency to bond to the surface of the mould cavity. A silicone wax or honey wax are excellent release agents. Polyvinyl alcohol is a liquid which is an alternative release agent.

Hot plastics have slight tendency to 'stick' in the metal moulds. A very light smear of oil will help make it easier to remove the casting from the mould. It is important that only a thin film of oil is used in the *injection moulding process* where pressure casting is done. Excess oil could cause 'spitting'.

◀ Casting, Flasks, Investment casting, Patterns ▶

MOUNTING

Most pictures are placed on a thick coloured card. This provides support for the picture and a coloured border. The mounting card can be expensive but especially for work that is to be exhibited, it is often worth the extra cost to improve the presentation.

MULTIMETERS

Multimeters are used to test circuits. They are available as analogue or digital meter (Fig M.13). Read pages 180–82 of Patient's *Digital Micro-Electronics*.

Fig M.13 Multimeters

MULTIVIBRATOR (MV)

This is a device for producing a pulse, such as a clock generator for timing digital circuits. It generates a pulse that produces a square wave output. Multivibrators are often classified by their stability. A stable stage remains in the OFF condition until it is triggered into operation by an external pulse. The three classes are:

- *Astable*, which is a free running multivibrator. It is an oscillating circuit that produces a continuous flow of digital pulses. It does not have a stable state (Fig M.14a)).
- *Bistable* or 'flip flop', where the input pulse reverses the state of the output. Figure M.14b) shows how the input pulse causes the output state to drop from High to Low and remain in this state. The Bistable MV is always in one or the other stable state.

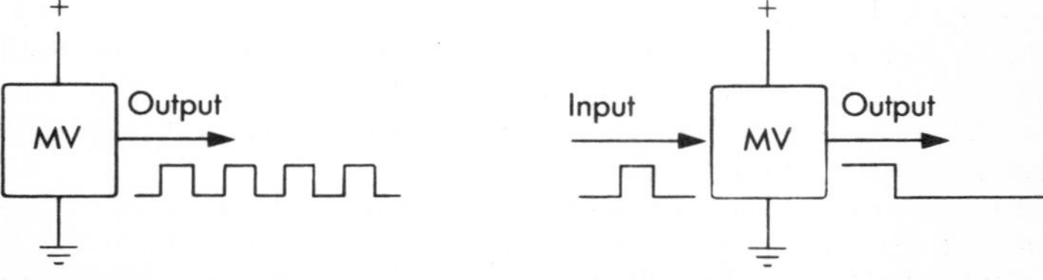

a) Astable multivibrator

b) Bistable multivibrator or flip flop

Fig M.14 Multivibrator

- *Monostable*, which is sometimes called a 'one shot multivibrator'. It has an unfixed input pulse that produces a single output pulse of a fixed duration (Fig M.14c))

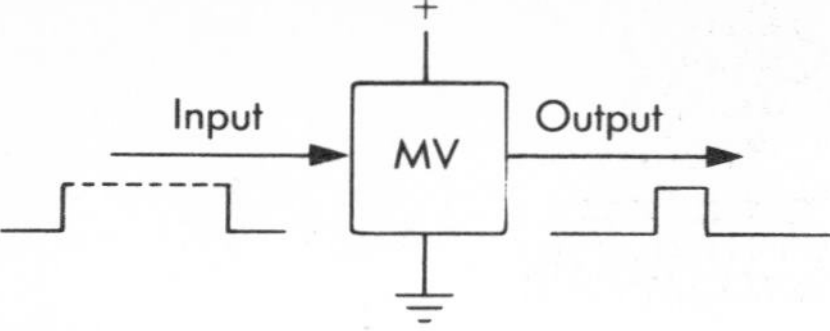

c) Monostable multivibrator

MUTUAL INDUCTANCE (M)

The ability of one coil to induce a voltage in another coil is called mutual inductance. This occurs in such electrical devices as a **transformer**. The current in one coil winding transfers the electrical energy to the other coil. Some of the energy is lost in the form of heat.

The unit of mutual inductance is the **henry** and the symbol is M. The two coils have M of one henry when a current of one ampere per second in the one coil induces one volt in the other. The schematic symbol for mutual inductance is shown below in Figure M.15 when a) there is just space between the coils and b) when an iron core is between the coils.
◀ Transformer ▶

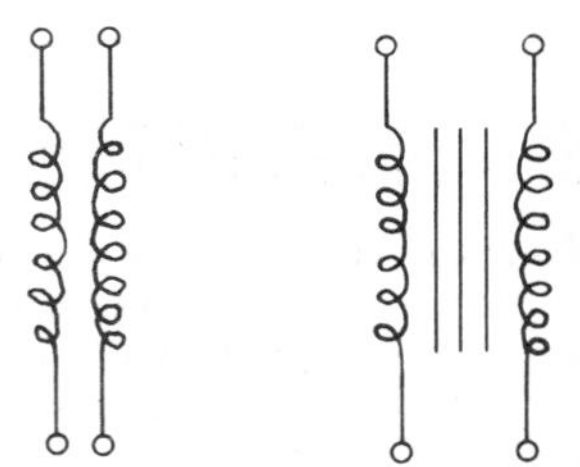

a) Space between coils b) Iron Core between coils

Fig M.15 Mutual inductance

NAND GATE

This is a logic gate that produces a low output 0 when the input is high at 1.
◀ Logic gates ▶

NANO (n)

This is a prefix to a unit of measurement that gives the submultiple of 10^9 of that unit; e.g. 5nA = 5 nanoamps = 5×10^{-9} amps.

NATIONAL CRITERIA

The National Criteria are a set of rules that have been laid down for *every* GCSE *subject. Still more precise criteria have been laid down for each subject. These are known as Subject Specific Criteria.* Under the heading of Craft Design and Technology, there are three subjects, namely CDT Design and Realisation, CDT Technology and CDT Design and Communication.

There is just one set of 8 'Aims'. These outline what it is hoped will be achieved by each pupil who follows the course. For instance, to encourage pupils to be creative, developing ideas while working with materials through investigation, planning, designing, making and evaluating. Also, to encourage and develop communication skills, technological awareness, etc.

Next comes a set of 17 *Assessment Objectives*. These say what a pupil should be able to do by the end of the course; e.g. be able to identify problems which can be solved through designing and making, to plan how to make a solution to a problem, and so on.

Then comes the *content* or *syllabus* indicating *what* you should know. Your teacher should have a syllabus if you do not have a copy of your own. The content of the syllabus has then to be related to the assessment objectives. To help make this easy to follow, the activities you will have to be doing on a CDT course have been put into three groups:

1 *Designing* This includes the identification of a need, the development of a solution and the evaluation of that solution.
2 *Skills* This includes communicating, planning, making, etc.
3 *Knowledge* This includes *what* you should know.

Your teacher should be able to give you the full details for the course you are following.

NATURAL SEASONING

This is the process of allowing timber to reduce its moisture content by being exposed to the air, but sheltered from the rain and snow. A 50 mm thick piece of wood would take approximately two years to season.
All timber was at one time naturally seasoned, but now most timber is kiln- or artificially-seasoned. *Kiln seasoning* is more expensive but is also approximately four times quicker.

NATURE

Nature refers to all living things, i.e. plants, animals and human beings. Natural forms are those that have been created by the growth of living things and the action of natural forces on materials, i.e. wind, rain, ice and snow when acting on stone, metal, wood, etc.

NEEDS

A need is a requirement, a necessity, something important. You are asked to identify a need when considering a project. If you do identify a need before starting to solve a problem it will help with your **evaluation**.

The needs to *eat* and to *keep warm* are two basic, but important, requirements. The need to *belong to a group* is also important and affects the way we behave. The need *to know* is crucial for understanding, and so on.

NEGATIVE

The opposite of positive, e.g. a negative mould is a hollow or female mould.

NEGATIVE POLARITIES

All materials, including solids, liquids, and gases, contain two basic particles of electric charge. These are known as the **electron** and the **proton**. The electron has a negative charge and the proton has a positive charge. The negative symbol is −; the positive symbol is +.

The negative and positive polarities are identified as opposites. On a battery, the negative terminal is the opposite of the positive terminal.

NETS

Nets are two-dimensional forms of something that is to be made into a three-dimensional form. Another name for this is *development.* Nets are often used to produce geometrical solid shapes, such as cones, cylinders, pyramids, etc. But this knowledge can be extended into the production packages that start from sheet material. ◀ **Developments** ▶

NEUTRAL AXIS

When a beam is under a load the top surface is in **compression** and the under surface is in **tension** (see Fig N.1). However in the middle, parallel to these surfaces, very little force is taking place. Engineers have for years designed beams so as to reduce material from the area carrying little force and add material where the forces are greatest. This provides a lighter, but still strong, beam. The most well known example is the I girder.

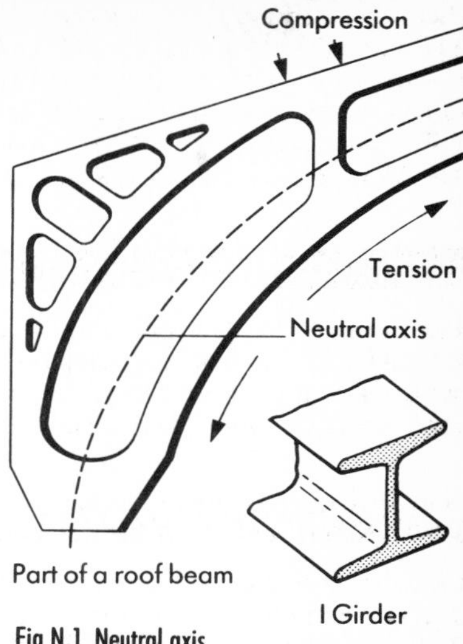

Fig N.1 Neutral axis

NEUTRON

This is a particle that has no electrical charge in the nucleus of an atom.

NEWTON

A newton is a unit of force. One Kilogram force (Kgf) equals approximately 10 newtons. If a mass of weight 1 kilogram is supported on a beam vertically downwards, the beam has to exert an equal and opposite force for the mass to remain supported. ◀ Newton's laws of motion ▶

NEWTON'S LAWS OF MOTION

In 1687 Sir Isaac Newton wrote a book called *Principia* which put forward some of the rules influencing mechanical forces. He found three laws of motion at work.

NEWTON'S FIRST LAW

'A body continues in a state of rest, or of motion at constant speed in a straight line, *except* when this state is changed by forces acting upon it.'

If you think of an arrow that has been fired from a bow, it will continue to move through the air until something either stops it or changes its motion. If there is nothing to stop or change its movement, then it will continue for ever. This is why planets are always moving in space. A *force* is therefore a push that *starts* a movement or one that *changes* a movement. *Gravity* is a kind of force and Newton discovered this when an apple fell from a tree. Such a downward force changes the movement of the arrow and eventually makes it land on the ground.

NEWTON'S SECOND LAW

'A body's rate of change of momentum is proportional to the force causing it.'

Another kind of force also acts on the arrow, affecting its momentum (the speed at which it was travelling forward). The arrow came to rest. It had stopped moving forward. This other kind of force is '*friction*'. Friction is produced by one medium coming into contact with the surface of another medium. The degree of friction is dependent upon the pressure. Try moving your finger along the surface of a table top, gradually pressing harder downwards. Eventually you will reach a stage when you can no longer push your finger forwards. With the *increase of pressure* so the friction between your finger and the table top *increases*. The surface of the arrow was in contact with the air, and this has had the effect of slowing down the arrow. The *combined* forces of gravity and friction were responsible for the arrow moving in a curved path and returning to earth.

NEWTON'S THIRD LAW

'To every action there is an equal and opposite reaction'.

This means that if a bullet is fired into a piece of wood it will exert a force on the wood which makes it go forward. But if the piece of wood is thick enough, it will apply an equal and opposite force and eventually stop the bullet going forward. The bullet will then be lodged in the wood.

◀ Mechanical efficiency ▶

NIBBLE

A binary word with four 'bits' which is equal to half a 'byte'. A 'bit' is a single unit of information, either 0 or 1 in the binary number system. Therefore a 'nibble' is four units of information.

NODE

This is a common connection for two or more branch currents. It is simply a connection for two or more components.

NOISE

These are unwanted electrical signals that occur in an electronic device or circuit and have undesirable results on the output. In television systems noise can result in unwanted lines appearing on the screen and spoil the quality of the picture.

NOISE INTENSITY

The amount of noise that occurs in a receiver is given by the noise factor F, Where $F = P_O/N_O$ and P_O is the power of the wave carrier and N_O is the noise output, measured in a given resistance. The noise factor F is expressed in decibels.

NOMINAL SIZE

The nominal size of a piece of planed wood is always the size it actually was before it was sawn. A piece of wood that started out as 25 mm thick by 75 mm wide will be *less* in actual size when planed, yet it will still be referred to as a piece of size 25 mm x 75 mm. So when buying wood it is always wise to measure the planed timber so that you know what you are buying.

NON-FERROUS METALS

There are two main groups of metals and they are classified by their content of iron, or lack of it. Since *ferro* is the prefix meaing iron, and *non-* means no, then a non-ferrous metal is one that does not contain iron. Metals such as aluminium, copper, gold, lead, tin and zinc, and alloys of these metals, are all non-ferrous.

A simple test is to see if they will respond to a magnet. If they are not attracted to the magnet, then they are non-ferrous. Also, non-ferrous metals do not rust.

NORMAL

A normal is a line at right angles to a tangent at the point of tangency. In the case of a circle, the radius is also a normal. Normals can also be constructed to other geometric frigures, such as an Involute, ellipse, cycloid etc; the normal is still at right angles to a tangent.

NOT VALVE

A NOT valve is a decision-making device. It is sometimes known as an *inverter* because if the input is ‘on’ the output will be ‘off’. The reverse happens when the input is ‘off’. A NOT valve has a single input and a single output. Think of the action of a see-saw, when one end is up, the other end is down.

The symbols used apply to all logic circuits, whether electronic or pneumatic. ◄ Logic gates ►

NPN TRANSISTOR

An NPN transistor has two opposite polarities of doped semiconductors. ◄ Transistors ►

N TYPE SEMICONDUCTORS

This is a semiconductor with excess electrons. The excess electrons in the pure semiconductor material is achieved by 'doping', i.e. adding negatively-charged impurities, such as the elements antimony, arsenic and phosphorus that have a **valence** of 5.

NUCLEUS

This is the central mass of an atom. It carries a positive charge, i.e. it is a **proton**. The number of protons in a nucleus is equal to the number of orbital **electrons**, and gives the atomic number of the atom.

In the atomic structure of a carbon atom, note that the number of protons shown with a + sign is equal to the number of the orbiting electrons shown with a – sign. ◀ **Atom** ▶

OBJECTIVE JUDGEMENTS/STATEMENTS

These are judgements based upon *facts* and not opinions. When you **evaluate** a product the most reliable judgements will be based upon facts. Does the device do what it is designed to do? Yes or no. For instance, if it is a warning device you should be able to *test* it. The test may show that it worked sometimes and not others, so the answer could be yes and no. A better and more specific answer would state the number of times it worked and the number of times it did not. This would be a factual answer which would indicated the reliability of the device.

When it comes to making objective judgements about *appearance*, this is a little more difficult. A single opinion is bound to be subjective (based upon what you like or dislike); but if a number of different people were able to make a judgement, at least you could report that, say, 8 out of 10 people liked the appearance and 2 did not. So you have now turned a subjective response into a factual one, i.e. into a more *objective statement.*

Remember: Subjective judgement are not helpful unless qualified by some factual evidence.

OBLIQUE

This simply means at an angle. Planes or surfaces that are at an angle are said to be oblique. They can be at an angle to either a vertical plane or a horizontal plane.

In **orthographic projection**, oblique auxiliary planes are used to show what an object looks like from a position that is not directly in front, to the side or above. The value of looking at an object from an angle is usually to establish the true shape; therefore the view would be parallel to the surface being drawn.

OBLIQUE PROJECTION

This is a form of three-dimensional drawing where the front view is drawn parallel to the vertical plane, and the top and side are drawn with lines that are at 45° to the horizontal plane (Fig O.1). This type of drawing

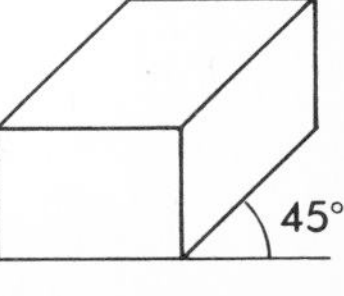

Fig O.1
Oblique projection

gives a rather distorted impression of the object. However, reducing the lines that go into the distance by half will help to give the impression of foreshortening. Though an acceptable method of drawing in three dimensions, it is not the preferred method. **Perspective drawing** comes first and **isometric drawing** second. But if you cannot use the other two methods, then you should at least attempt oblique projection.

OBTUSE ANGLES

These are angles that are more than 90° but less than 180° (Fig O.2).

Fig O.2 Obtuse angle

OCTAGON

An eight-sided figure (Fig O.3).

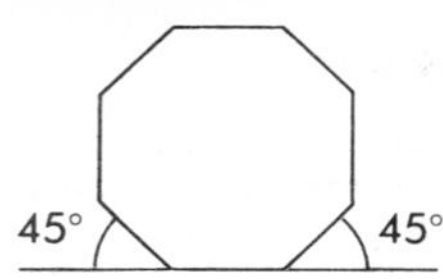

Fig O.3 Octagon

OCTAL BUFFER

◀ **Eight bit buffer** ▶

OCTAVE

A frequency ratio of 2 : 1.

OHM (Ω)

This is a unit of **resistance** (R). It is the unit by which resistors are valued, e.g. a common value is R = 100Ω. A resistance that develops 1.0 **joule** of heat when one **ampere** of current flows through it in one second, has a resistance of one *ohm*. A material that is a good conductor, like copper, can have a resistance of 0.032Ω for one metre length. The resistance of a wire heating element in a 600-watt toaster is 24Ω, while a tungsten filament in a 100-watt light bulb has a resistance of 144Ω from a 120 voltage supply.

OHMMETERS

An ohmmeter is a device for measuring the resistance in a circuit. It is also used for checking electronic components such as, capacitors, diodes and resistors.

The resistance is measured with the power *off* in the circuit. The only current used is that from the battery in the ohmmeter. For measuring resistance, the leads of the ohmmeter are connected across an external resistance to be measured. The resistance is measured by the amount of deflection in the meter movement.

Checking resistors

When checking **resistors** with an ohmmeter, it is important that the appropriate *scale* is selected (Fig O.4). To check resistors of less than 10Ω, an ohms scale of 100Ω or less is necessary; but to check a resistor of 10 MΩ, a scale of 100 MΩ or more should be used.

Remember: Do not touch the ohmmeter leads when checking, because this may affect the reading.

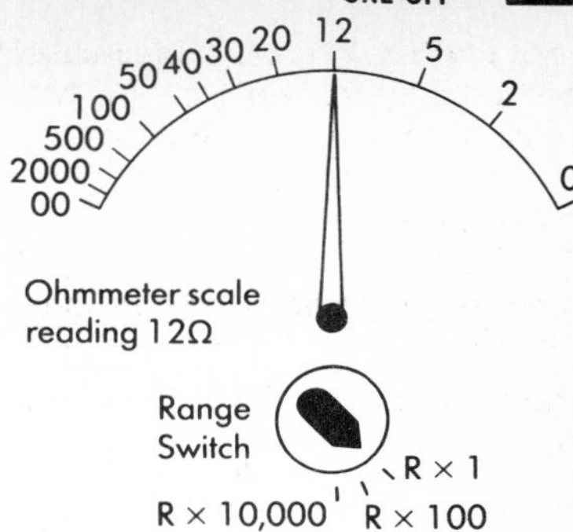

Fig O.4 Ohmmeter

Checking diodes

When checking a **diode**, the forward and reverse resistance can be checked by changing the connection of leads on the diode. The *forward resistance* should be low, i.e. 200Ω to 1 KΩ, and the reverse resistance should be high on all silicone diodes. When the resistance is high in both directions, the diode is open (there is a break in the circuit). When the resistance is low in both directions, the diode is shorted, (current is flowing).

When testing a **capacitor** it is appropriate to use the highest range, such as R = 1 MΩ. Disconnect one side of the capacitor to avoid any parallel resistance if already part of a circuit and then connect the leads across the capacitor. The meter pointer should move quickly towards the low resistance end of the scale, and then slowly towards infinity. When the pointer stops moving, *this* is the resistance of the capacitor. This reading should be high, between 500 to 1000 MΩ.

OHM'S LAW

The electric current I flowing in a conductor or resistor R is proportional to the applied voltage V. This means that if two values are known, the third can be calculated.

$$\text{Voltage} = \text{Current} \times \text{Resistance} \quad V = I \times R$$

$$\text{Current} = \frac{\text{Voltage}}{\text{Resistance}} \quad I = \frac{V}{R}$$

Remember: Voltage is in *volts*, current is in *amps* and the resistance is in *ohms*.

ONE-OFF

Only one to be made. This may refer to a component or an assembled product.

OPEN CIRCUIT

One that has a high resistance, resulting in zero current.

OPERATE

To function; to make an item work under control.

OPERATIONAL AMPLIFIER (OP AMP)

An operational amplifier is a high gain direct coupled amplifier. It relies on an external feedback from an output to an input to determine the operating characteristics. Operational amplifiers were used at one time in analogue computers to perform mathematical operations, and the term *operational* has been kept.

ORDINATES

An ordinate is a straight line that is parallel to one axis and at right angles to another. The ordinates finish either on a straight line or a curve. Ordinates are used to plot curved lines, as in Fig O.5. This is a very good method of plotting curved forms in Isometric Projection.

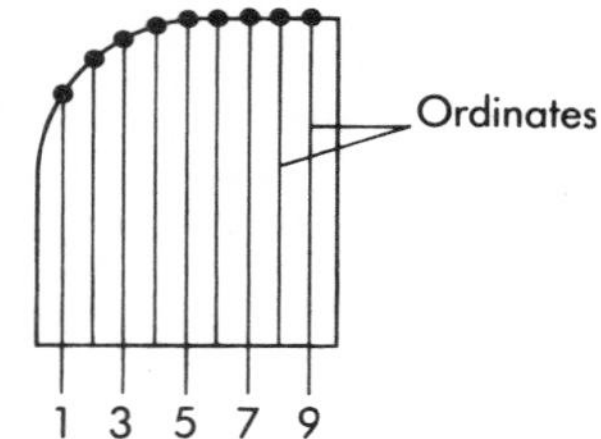

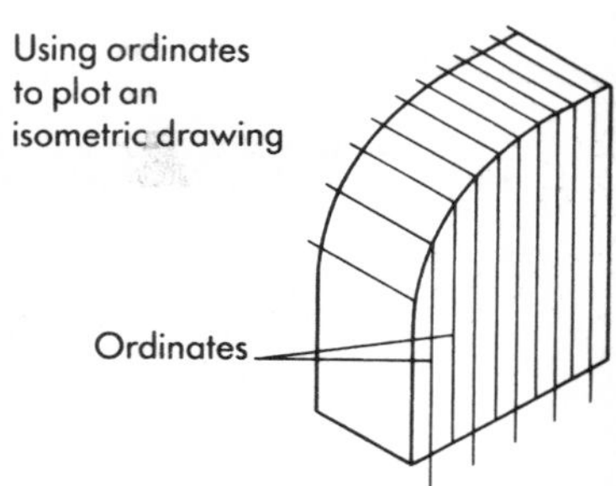

Fig O.5 Ordinates

ORGANISATION

There are two main types of organisation. One is concerned with the *order of events* in the production of a product, and the other is concerned with the *organisation of people*, say in a school, hospital, or office.

ORGANISATION CHART

The most commonly used chart for the *production of a product is the* **Bar chart** or Gantt chart (Gantt is the name of the person who developed this type of chart). To show the organisation of a firm or other institution the organisation chart is used.

Here we illustrate with a typical school:

Governing Body
Head Teacher
Assistant Head No 1 | Assistant Head No 2
Head of Department | Head of Department | Head of Department | Head of Department
Staff | Staff | Staff | Staff

This is a very simplified chart, and you should be able to apply such a chart to your own school.

The **bar chart** is also very useful for 'organisation', such as showing the work to be done set against the time in which it has to be completed:

Work to be done	*Week 1*	*Week 2*	*Week 3*	*Week 4*	*Week 5*	*Week 6*	*Week 7*	*Week 8*	*Week 9*	*Week 10*
Design Brief	■									
Analysis	■	■								
Investigation		■	■							
Ideas			■							
Development of chosen idea				■						
Make solution					■	■	■	■	■	
Evaluate										■

◀ **Flow charts** ▶

OR GATE

A digital logic circuit that produces a High Output of 1 when any of the inputs is High at 1. ◀ **Logic gates** ▶

ORTHOGRAPHIC PROJECTION

This is a type of drawing in which most of the views will produce a *true* shape or outline of the object being drawn. It will also be either the same size as the object, or drawn to *scale*, i.e. all the lines will be drawn proportionally larger or smaller. The views are drawn in two dimensions and they are the views that would be seen from directly in front, from the sides and a view as seen from directly above. This last view is known as the *plan view*. The arrangement of the views depends on the projection used. There are two commonly used types of projection: *First Angle* and *Third Angle*. The names First Angle and Third Angle are derived from the quadrant chosen for the intersecting vertical and horizontal planes (Fig O.6).

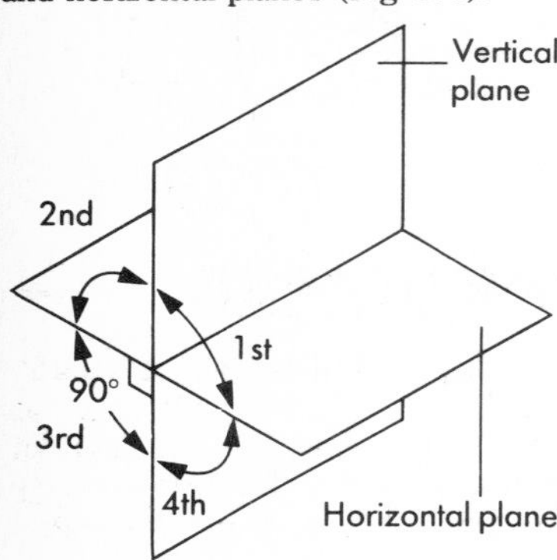

Fig O.6 Orthographic projection

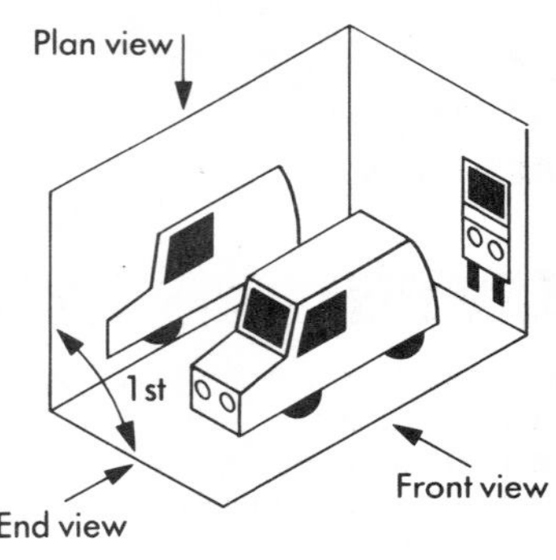

Fig O.7 First angle projection: how the views are obtained

 FIRST ANGLE PROJECTION

First Angle Projection has the following ruling for the position of the views: 'What you see from the right, you draw on the left of the front view; and what you see from above, you draw below the front view.' The *front view* and the *plan view* are the two most commonly used views. The *side views* are added if not all the information can be given in just the two views (Fig O.7). The views must all be in such a position that lines can be projected from one view to another, hence the name projection.

THIRD ANGLE PROJECTION

Third Angle Projection has a similar ruling for the position of the views: 'What you see from the left, you draw on the left of the front view; what you see from the right, you draw on the right of the front view; what you see from above you draw above the front view' (Fig O.8). A simple way of remembering which way the views are arranged, is to think First, *opposite sides*, and Third, *same side*.

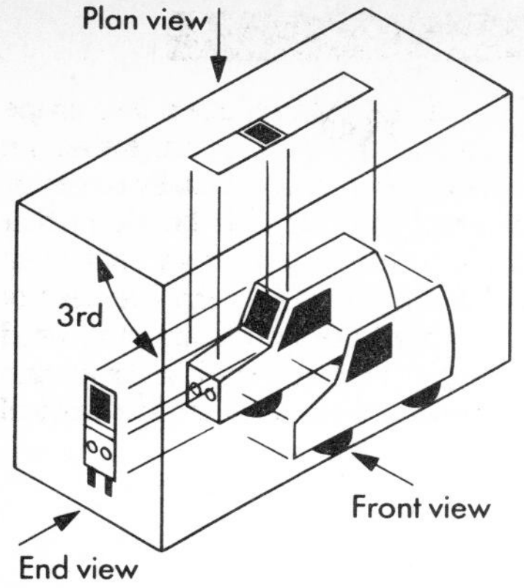

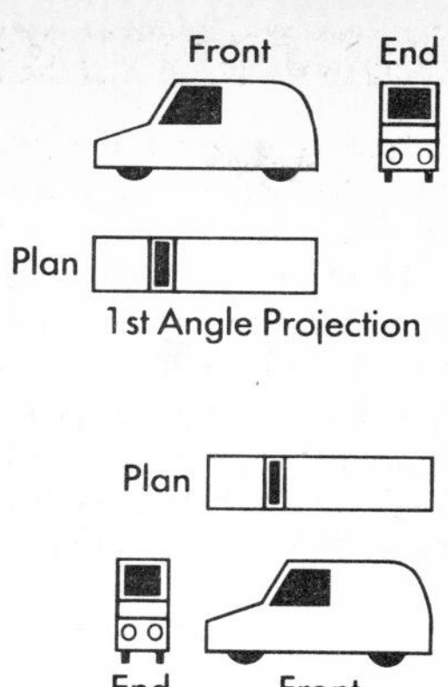

Fig 0.8 Third Angle Projection

OSCILLATION

The simplest form of oscillations is a weight swinging backwards and forwards on a piece of string. A pendulum is an oscillating mechanism. At rest the pendulum hangs vertically, but as it vibrates, it swings. The *potential energy* of the weight is at its maximum at the end of each swing. Its *kinetic energy* (moving energy) increases from zero to a maximum on the *downward* swing, and decreases on the *upward* swing back to zero.

The pendulum can continue as long as there is a restoring force, i.e. the *weight* in a grandfather clock, or the *pulse* in an electronic clock. Without the restoring force, the pendulum oscillations will get smaller and smaller (because of friction) until the pendulum eventually stops.

OSCILLATOR

An oscillator circuit is a circuit that generates an alternating current (AC) from a direct current (DC) supply without the input of an (AC) signal.

OSCILLOSCOPE

An oscilloscope is a versatile testing instrument and belongs to the television or VDU (Visual Display Unit) family. An electric signal can be displayed on the fluorescent screen and moved about by deflector plates, in this way making a trace on the screen.

To operate an oscilloscope, it has to have a mains power supply, just the same as a television. When the instrument is switched on, a bright spot appears in the centre of the screen. A vertical control knob will make the spot go either upwards or downwards. If the time-base control is switched off, and the horizontal control knob is operated, the spot will move left to right across the screen. If the time-base control is switched on, the spot will move automatically from left to right. By adjusting the time-base control, the spot can be made to move at varying rates. If a clock signal input is connected to the signal input of the oscilloscope, the spot will move slowly up and down at low frequency, and quickly up and down at a high frequency. A clock time/logic graph is traced out on the screen and will look similar to that shown in Fig O.9. Double-beam tubes are available to enable two signals to be displayed at the same time. This can be helpful when you need to compare waveforms in sequential logic, where the timing is important.

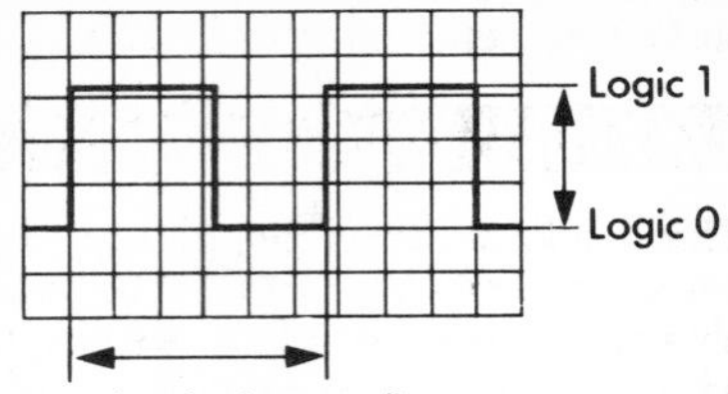

Fig O.9 Oscilloscope

OUTLINE

This is the outer line of a shape. In orthographic projection it is the darkest line so that it is distinguished from other continuous lines such as *construction lines* and *dimension lines*.

OVERLAP

This is where an allowance is made in sheet material so that two or more surfaces can be joined together by gluing, soldering, riveting, stapling, etc.

OVERLAY

These are illustrations that may be made up of a number of separate sheets. Each sheet has additional information and can be laid over the first sheet without stopping the previous information from being seen. Opaque pieces can be used, similar to some of the techniques used by the weather forecasters when they put the symbols of rain clouds or sunshine on the map.

You may find this technique helpful in projects that show a build up of information, such as the arrangement of furnishings in a room, the development of waste land for leisure pursuits, and so on.

OXIDISATION

Most metals try to combine with the oxygen in the air. Iron forms iron oxide (Fe_2O_3), aluminium forms aluminium oxide (Al_2O_3), and so on. When metals are heated, the process of oxidisation is quickened and can be seen taking place. The colours that form on the surface of bright steel, starting with a light straw-colour, then brown, purple and finally blue, are indications of the oxide layer getting thicker as the temperature rises. These colours can be frozen by dipping the metal in water. The practical application of this knowledge is used in tempering tool steel. It is also used for aesthetic reasons on mild steel. Rust is another example of oxidisation.

Some metals, such as gold and silver, do not oxidise so easily and this is the reason why they remain so shiny. Tarnish is a thin oxide that forms on the surface of metals such as brass and gilding metal.

OXYACETYLENE WELDING

This is a form of high temperature welding that melts the edge of the metal being joined and a filler rod of the same type of metal. The high temperature is obtained by using a special welding torch that combines a supply of oxygen with a supply of acetylene. This process is dangerous and the correct safety procedures must be followed. The gasses are normally stored in metal cylinders and are fed to the torch via a needle valve, a regulating valve, and a high pressure hose pipe (Fig O.10).

Remember: Before starting to weld, specially darkened glasses must be worn.

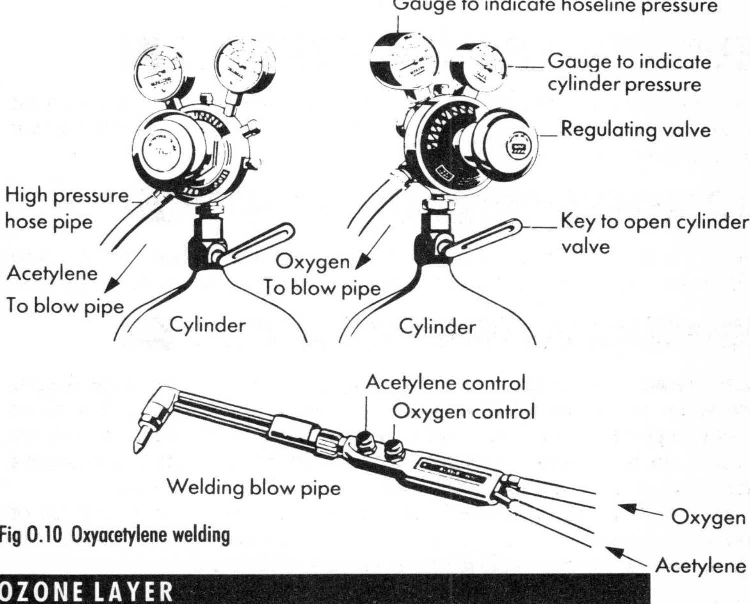

Fig O.10 Oxyacetylene welding

OZONE LAYER

This is a condensed form of oxygen which forms a layer above the earth, protecting it from the sun's rays. In particular it helps to filter out the harmful ultra-violet rays. Concern has been growing recently over the thinning of the ozone layer, particularly over the arctic and antarctic regions. Indeed 'holes' have been detected in the ozone layer. This has led to restrictions on the use of chemicals called CFCs (chlorofluorocarbons), that are used in aerosol sprays and refrigerators, and which have been blamed for much of the damage to the ozone layer.

PANTOGRAPH

This is a drawing device that is helpful in making a larger, or smaller, copy of an existing drawing. One end is fixed to the drawing board with a clamp, and the other end is where the tracing is done. The pencil or pen is held so that all the movements of the tracer produce an identical drawing, only one which is larger or smaller. The adjustment is made by moving the position of the two *cursors* (Fig P.1).

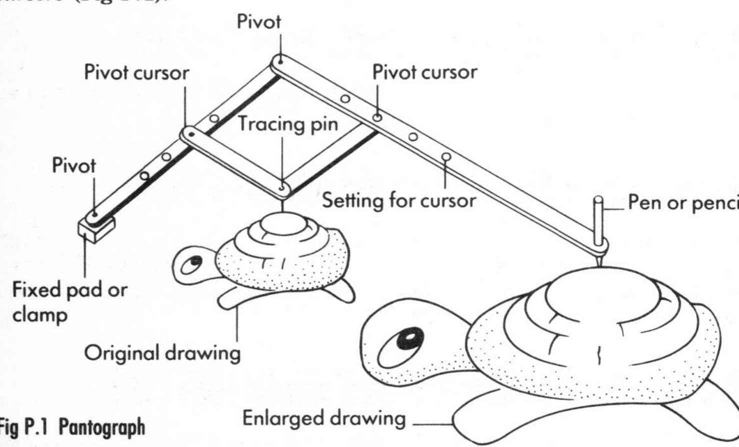

Fig P.1 Pantograph

PAPER SIZES

Paper sizes start with the letter A and are followed by a number. The higher the number, the smaller the size of paper:

A0	=	1189mm × 841mm
A1	=	841mm × 594mm
A2	=	594mm × 420mm
A3	=	420mm × 297mm
A4	=	297mm × 210mm

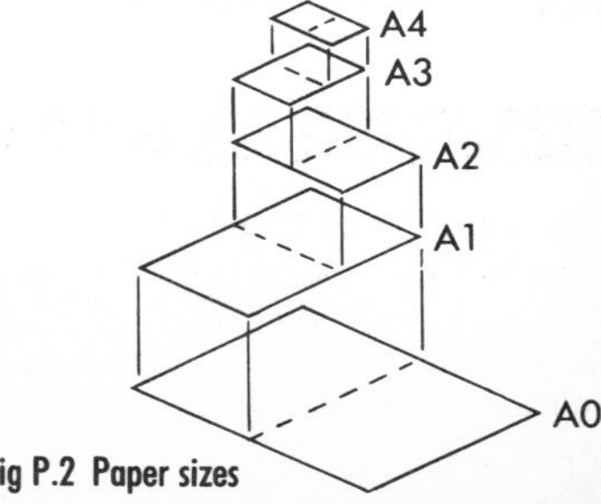

Fig P.2 Paper sizes

You will notice that each neighbouring sheet size from A0 is reduced by *halving* the long side (Fig P.2).

PARABOLA

The *parabola* is one of the four conic sections. It is a plane curve formed by the intersection of a cone with a plane parallel to its side. The parabola is also a natural curve. If you throw a ball into the air it will follow the path of a parabola.

The parabola can be used to generate a *paraboloid* (a hollow dish), and this curved dish has a practical application in light reflectors for torches, car lights, etc. If the filament of the bulb is placed at the focal point of the paraboloid, the rays of the light will bounce off the shiny surface parallel to the axis and form a beam of light. In car lights, the bulb has two filaments, so when the filament *not* at the focal point of the paraboloid is used, the light beam is in the dip position. Another application of the paraboloid is in focusing light or radio waves when acting as a receiver. The reflecting bowls of the many television receivers are paraboloid. ◀ Cone ▶

PARALLEL

These are two straight lines or flat surfaces that are the same distance apart at any point where the measurement is taken.

PARALLEL CIRCUITS

A parallel circuit is when two or more components share a common voltage supply. Therefore the components will receive the same **potential difference**. The parallel circuit is used where components require the same voltage. House wiring is a typical application.

PARALLEL MOTION

This is a device used on a drawing board to assist in drawing parallel lines. The parallel motion refers to the fact that the device can be moved up and down the board with its working edge parallel to the top and bottom edges of the board.

PARALLELOGRAM

This is a four-sided figure that has its *opposite sides* equal in length and parallel to each other. Also the *opposite angles* are equal and the diagonals bisect each other, i.e. they cut one another in half. Another name for this figure is a *rhomboid.* A rhombus is also a parallelogram, but with all its sides of equal length; its diagonals bisect each other at 90°.

PASSIVE TRANSDUCERS

A transducer is a sensing device that converts a non-electrical signal such as sound, pressure, light etc., into an electrical signal. A passive transducer is one in which there is 'no gain' i.e. it does not generate an electromagnetic force.

PATTERN

A repetitive design has continuity, balance and symmetry. *Pattern* often refers to the development of a three-dimensional shape to be made from a soft material, e.g. fabric, paper, etc. Sometimes pattern refers to the shape of a component to be cast in another material. Patterns for components that are to be cast in metal are often made from wood. The pattern is used to create the cavity into which the molten metal is to be poured. ◀ Casting ▶

PENTAGON

This is a five-sided figure. When all the sides are the same length and the angles are equal, it is called a *regular* pentagon (Fig P.3).

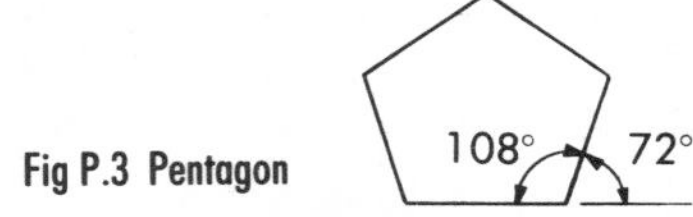

Fig P.3 Pentagon

PERMANENT JOINING

If components are joined in such a way that they cannot be taken apart without causing damage, then the method used must have been a permanent one. Such processes as welding, brazing, riveting, gluing, are examples of permanent joining.

PERPENDICULAR

Perpendicular means upright. A period in English architecture around the 15th century was called the *perpendicular period* because of the tall uprightness of the buildings, mainly churches and cathedrals. A *perpendicular line* is a line that is at right angles to another. When you bisect a line, the bisector is also a perpendicular line (Fig P.4).

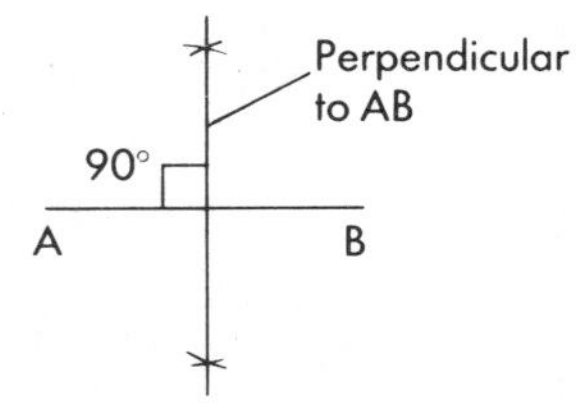

Fig P.4 Perpendicular

PERSPECTIVE

This is drawing things as they *appear*, i.e. the further items are away from you the smaller they appear. Most objects will be drawn in three dimensions and the nearest parts will appear larger than parts of the same size that are further away.

TYPES OF PERSPECTIVE

There are two commonly used forms of perspective that you are likely to meet and use. *One point* or *parallel* perspective and *two point* perspective.

One Point Perspective

This is quite often used to draw interior views of a room where all horizontal lines going into the picture meet at a single vanishing point (VP) on the eye level. All vertical and remaining horizontal lines are parallel with the edges of the paper (Fig P.5).

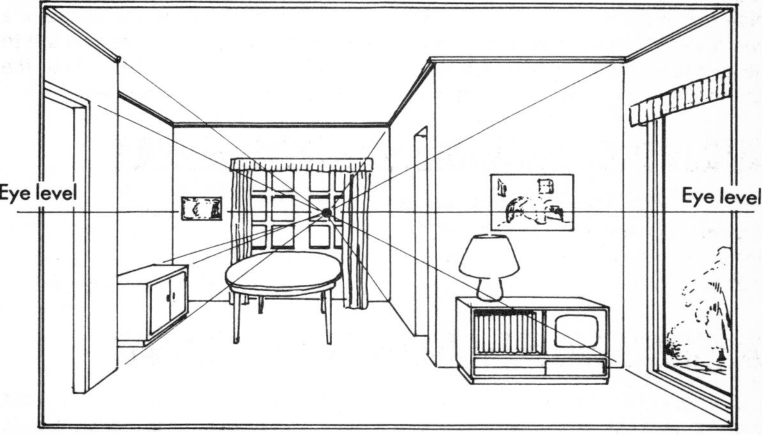

Fig P.5 One point perspective

Two Point Perspective

Fig P.6 Two point perspective

This has two vanishing points and all horizontal lines meet at either one or the other vanishing points. All vertical lines are parallel, and parallel with the edge of the paper, that is, at right angles to the eye level (Fig P.6).

Of the two types of perspective, the Two Point gives an image that is nearer to how we see things. Care, however, must be taken in deciding the *position of the vanishing points* on the eye level. The further they are apart, the truer the image that can be drawn. The closer they are, the more distorted the image will appear. It is quite common to have the vanishing points beyond the edge of the paper. This is not so difficult when using A4 *paper* on an A2 *drawing* board, but can present a problem when the paper and the drawing board are the same size.

For good composition, try to avoid placing a single perspective vanishing point in the centre of the paper, and in both types of perspective, avoid having the eye level on the halfway line. It tends to divide your picture. A ratio of 2:3 or 1:3 for the height of the eye level often produces reasonable results.

PHOTODIODE OR PHOTOTRANSISTOR

These are light-sensing devices that can respond quickly to a brief exposure to light. They can be used in devices where a clock pulse can be generated. For further details read *Digital Micro-Electronics* by Peter Patient, published by Olive Boyd, page 83.

PHOTOSYNTHESIS

This is the process by which the energy of sunlight is trapped by the chlorophyll of green plants and used to build up complex materials from carbon dioxide and water. Since plants and trees are a major source of material, man is very dependent upon this natural process taking place.

PICKLING

When a **non-ferrous** metal has been heated, an oxide forms on the surface. To remove this oxide without damaging the surface of the metal, it is put into a 'Pickling bath'. The pickle is diluted sulphuric and nitric acid. It is just sufficiently strong to remove an oxide in 3–5 minutes, so metal should not be left in the bath too long. Remember that even diluted acids are dangerous and care must be taken to ensure that the correct tongs are used and the appropriate protective clothing is worn. The work is always cleaned under running tap water in a porcelain sink. Copper, gilding metal and brass can be cleaned in this way.

PICO (p)

This is a prefix for 10^{-12}, e.g. one *picofarad* is 10^{-12} *farads*.

PICTOGRAMS

These are pictorial symbols that convey information quickly and are recognised internationally. They are often used to convey statistical information (Fig P.7).

Fig P.7 Pictograms

PICTORIAL DRAWING

This is the overall title for drawings in three dimensions, i.e. height, width and thickness. A pictorial view or representation is therefore a three-dimensional view or representation of an object.

During the *development of ideas* stage, it is possible that many of the solutions were drawn in two dimensions only. So a pictorial view, drawn when most of the problems have been resolved, helps to give an impression of the final solution. Most designers produce what is called an 'artist's impression' and this is exactly what you are asked to do when you draw a pictorial view of your chosen idea.

PIE CHARTS

As the name suggests, the charts takes the form of a *pie*. Then the divisions within the pie represent the sizes of the 'slices' of the pie. It is an easy way of showing the relative proportions going to each component, the sum of all proportions being 360°.

Pie charts can be drawn as a *flat circle* or in *three dimensions*, keeping the pie circular (Fig P.8). This is so that the proportions of the pie will not be foreshortened and pieces of identical size pie can be shown as identical on the chart. These charts are excellent for showing a comparison of quantities.

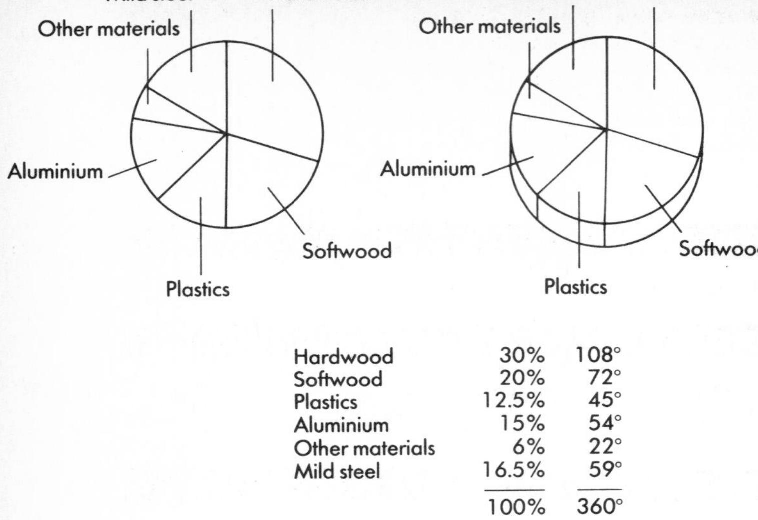

Hardwood	30%	108°
Softwood	20%	72°
Plastics	12.5%	45°
Aluminium	15%	54°
Other materials	6%	22°
Mild steel	16.5%	59°
	100%	360°

Fig P.8 Pie charts

PIEZO ELECTRIC EFFECT

When a voltage difference is applied across opposite faces of a crystal, the crystal becomes *strained* (squashed or stretched), and this is known as the piezo-electric effect. If a quartz crystal is used in an electronic circuit, an applied voltage difference and a generated voltage difference interact with each other, keeping the crystal moving from a 'strained' state to an 'unstrained' state. In other words, it is **oscillating**. The **frequency** at which it oscillates is dependent upon the size and shape of the crystal. Therefore with precision cutting and polishing, the frequency can be selected and the crystal used in an electronic clock system, strain gauge, etc.

PIGMENT

This is a colouring material added to resins to make them colourful. Some pigments are *opaque* (will not allow light through); others are *translucent* (will allow the light to pass through).

PILOT HOLE

When using screws to join two pieces of wood together, it is helpful if a hole is drilled into the piece that will be receiving the threaded part. This hole should be equal in diameter to the core diameter of the screw. This will make it easy for the screw to be turned and will not cause the wood to split (Fig P.9).

To select a drill for the pilot hole, the screw is held up to the light and a drill is placed in line with the screw threads to see if the silhouette of the drill is hidden. If the drill can still be seen, choose the next size down until you find the first drill that is hidden.

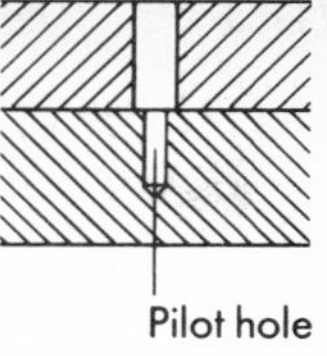

Fig P.9 Pilot hole

PILOT VALVE

◀ Valves ▶

PINCERS

These are a tool used for pulling out nails. They are often wrongly called 'pinchers'.

PINION

◀ Gears ▶

PIN OUT

Integrated circuits (ICs) are produced as packages. The IC is encapsulated in a plastic or ceramic material and the electronic circuits are connected to pins that come out at the side of the package. Some packages have as many as 40 pins and though not all the pins are connected to a circuit the user does need to know the function of the logic circuit. This can be shown on a pin-out diagram (Fig P.10).

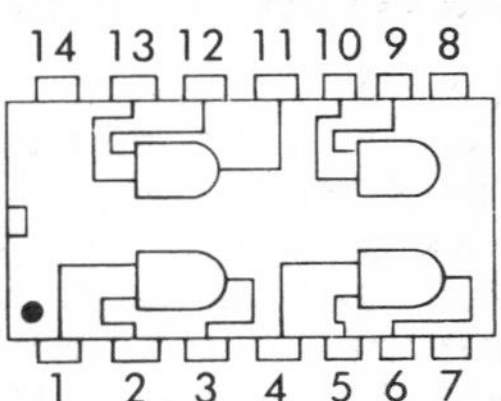

Pin out of 7408 quadruple 2-input AND gate

Fig P.10 Pin out

PIPED CIRCUITS

Pipes or tubes are required in a pneumatic circuit to convey air under pressure to components such as valves, cylinders, etc. A piped circuit is one in which pipes are used, e.g. an opening and closing door circuit.

PISTON

A component of a cylinder that is a specialised washer. It slides in a cylinder under pressure without letting air pass between it and the wall of the cylinder (Fig P.11).

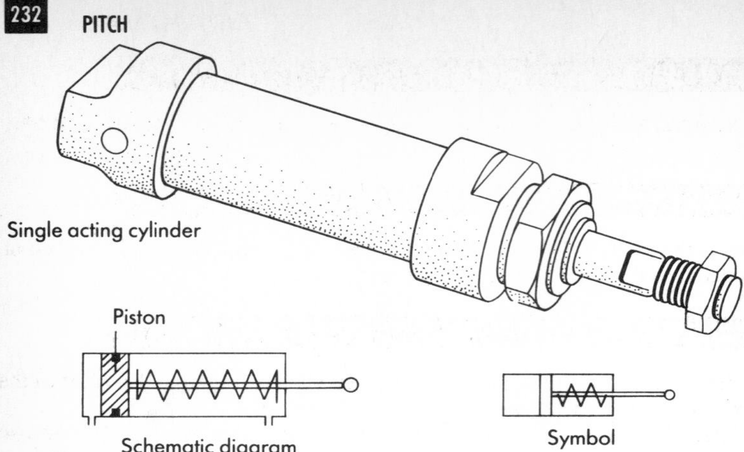

Fig P.11 Piston

PITCH

The pitch of a *saw* refers to the number of teeth per inch. The pitch of a *screw thread* is the number of threads per millimetre or per inch.

PIV (PEAK INPUT VOLTS)

This is the maximum alternating voltage that can be taken by a **diode**.

PLAN

This is the organisation or method by which something is going to be achieved. It is helpful to plan ahead so that each stage of a project follows smoothly and without delay. Putting down on paper a *list* of things to be done, and placing them in order, is all part of planning.
◀ **Method, Model, Organisation** ▶

PLANED SIZES

After wood has been sawn to size, the rough surface left from the saw blade is made smooth by a *planing machine*. The rotating blades of the planing machine just remove enough wood in the form of shavings to leave the surface smooth. The piece of wood has now been reduced in size, but quite often the wood is referred to by its *original size*, even though a piece of 50 mm × 25 mm will probably be only 46 mm × 21 mm after being planed. However, many timber merchants do sell timber planed and give the actual size of the timber for sale. There are standard planed sizes, e.g. 150 mm × 9 mm, 175 mm × 9 mm, 200 mm × 9 mm, 225 mm × 9 mm, 225 mm × 12 mm, 275 mm × 12 mm, 150 mm × 15 mm, 225 mm × 15 mm, etc. Such timber is sold by so much per linear metre. The prices vary according to the quality and the type of timber. Hardwoods are more expensive than softwoods.

PLANE FIGURES

Plane figures are *two dimensional* shapes, e.g. triangles, rectangles, circles, etc.

PLANE GEOMETRY

This is the method by which **plane figures** are constructed, lines bisected or divided into a given number of equal parts, etc.

PLANES

In drawing, this refers to the surfaces of an object. But it can also refer to the vertical or horizontal plane.

Planes are also *tools*. These are used to remove unwanted wood and to produce a smooth finish to natural wood. Planes should not be used on manufactured boards such as chipboard, plywood, etc. Not only will the board risk being damaged, but the plane will quickly lose its keen edge through trying to cut the resin adhesive that bonds the chips, veneers, etc. Planes are designed to perform specific functions and the appropriate plane should only be used for the purpose for which it was intended (Fig P.12).

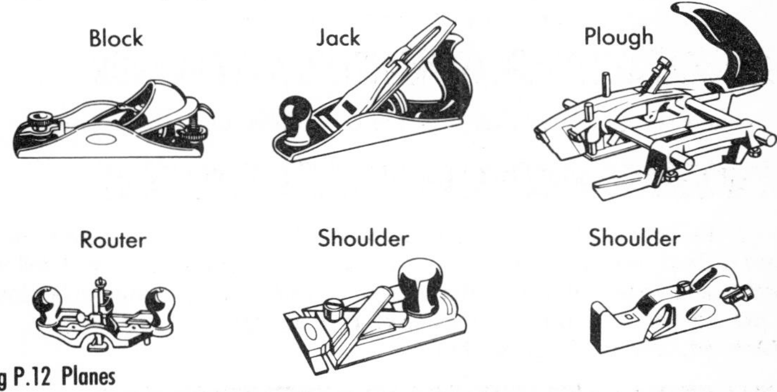

Fig P.12 Planes

PLAN VIEW

The view of an object when seen from above. The word 'view' is often left out and the word 'plan' is often used alone. ◀ **Orthographic projection** ▶

PLANISH/PLANISHING

Beaten metal such as gilding metal, copper and aluminium, is often finished by planishing. The surface is beaten with a planishing hammer that has a flat, very smooth and highly polished pein, while the metal is supported on a highly polished stake. By repeated hammering, the metal becomes smooth and highly polished. It also becomes hard. The overlapping blows of the hammer leave a pleasing appearance to the surface.

PLANK

The largest form of ready-to-use natural timber. It has a sawn finish and is more than 40 mm thick.

PLANOMETRIC PROJECTION

A planometric projection is created by revolving a plan view of an object through an angle of 30°, 45° or 60° and projecting the vertical sides either upwards or downwards to give a *three-dimensional drawing*. It will look a little distorted, but a reasonably good impression of what the object looks like is achieved (Fig P.13). This type of projection can be used to draw rooms straight from the plan, including furniture if required.

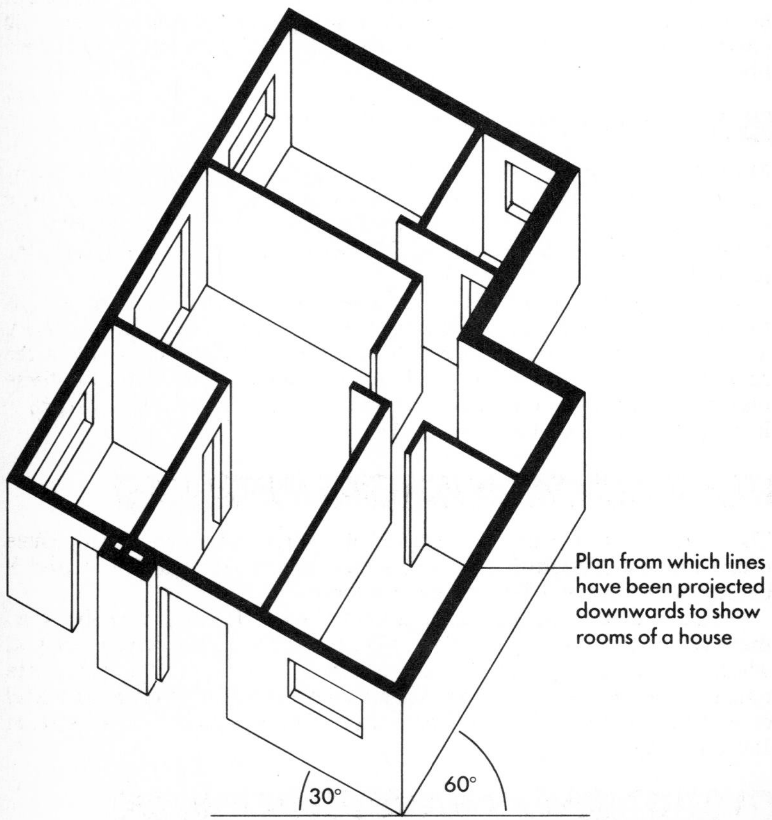

Fig P.13 Planometric projection

PLASTIC

This describes the *state of a material*. Metals, glass, clay, wax, etc., can all be moulded. These materials are either pliable when cold (e.g. clay and wax) or they are pliable when hot (e.g. glass and metal). The word plastic is often used incorrectly, to name a synthetic material.

PLASTIC MEMORY

The ability of some materials to return to their original moulded form when reheated. The most common example can be demonstrated by reheating a piece of acrylic that has been formed round a jig. The heating will soften the material and it will move on its own back to a flat shape. This ability is not confined to just some plastics materials used in some fire safety device, if heated, will return to their original form and trigger a mechanism that will operate a door. Such devices have been used in the newly rebuilt wing of York Minster.

PLASTIC PROPERTIES

Most metals are plastic when hot. They can be pressed, bent, drawn down, spread out, twisted, etc., by heating. Then by hammering or applying some mechanical force they can be changed in form. The blacksmith could not forge metal into so many different forms if it did not have the property of being plastic.

The advantage of a material being formed by squeezing, hammering, etc., is that the grain will flow and adopt the new form, as though it had been growing. This not only enables pleasing forms to be achieved, but it is *stronger* than the same form produced by cutting and removing waste material. So the three main advantages of having plastic properties are: a) aesthetic, b) strength, c) less wasteful. ◀ **Plasticity, Plastics** ▶

PLASTICITY

The ability to be moulded into shape. Often this state of being mouldable occurs when a material is hot, and as soon as the material has cooled it becomes fixed or set and keeps its new form.

A material in the state of plasticity is neither solid nor liquid, it is in-between these two states. It is important therefore to known the *temperature range* at which a material is plastic, so that it can be formed at the appropriate temperature. Most manufacturers of plastics materials indicate this on a label or in their literature. Nylon and polyethylene have a *plastic range* between 190°C and 220°C.

PLASTICIZER

A substance that is added to a plastics material to make it softer and more pliable.

PLASTICS

A group of synthetic resinous or other substances that can be moulded into any form.

PLIES

These are the thin slices of wood which, when bonded together with alternative slices, have their grain going at right angles to each other and from the manufactured board called *plywood*. ◀ Plywood ▶

PLUG

A plug is another name for a **pattern**. But the term is used in connection with GRP (**Glass Reinforced Plastics**). Plugs are made from wood and are used to make a mould in GRP. The mould is then used in the production of the product (Fig P.14). The plug is only useful for making new moulds when the original gets damaged or when more than one is required.

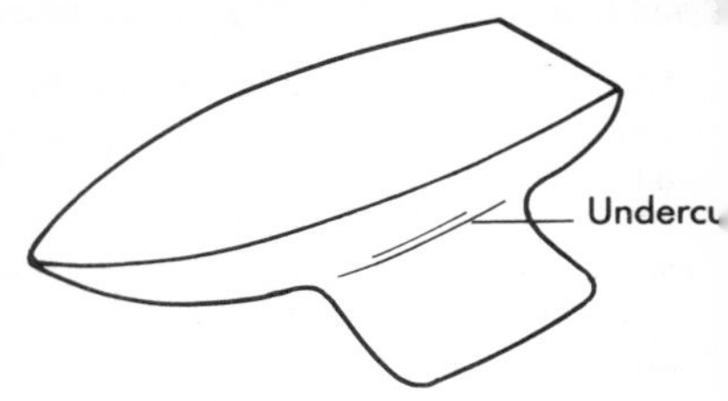

Fig P.14 Plug

PLYWOOD

A manufactured board that comes in sheet form. It is *stable*, i.e. it does not warp and is equally strong in both directions, unlike natural timber that is stronger *along* the grain than *across* the grain. There are always an uneven number of plies so that the outside veneers have their grain in the same direction.

If you require a piece of plywood cut to size, do check that you have the grain of the veneer going in the direction that you wish. Remember that the size is given by stating the length, width and thickness, in that order. This means that the direction of the grain will always be indicated by the first measurement, which may not be the longest length.

There are different grades of plywood. The factors that determine the grade of quality are a) the type of veneer used on the external surface, b) the number of plies in a given thickness, and c) the type of resin used to bond the plies and veneers. The high quality boards have carefully selected decorative hardwood veneers and many plies. The lower quality boards have unselected hardwood veneers and joins that can be seen and not many plies to a particular thickness. Special boards can be expensive because of the quality of the resin being used, i.e. waterproof or marine quality. Unless specified, plywood is produced for indoor use.

PNEUMATICS

Pneumatics is about controlling air under pressure and using it to operate mechanical devices. Compressed air is stored energy and can be used as and when it is needed. Any system that uses energy of this kind is a pneumatic system. Pneumatics are often combined with electronic control systems.

PNEUMATIC SYMBOLS

These are simplified diagrams that are used when designing a circuit. They are standardised and for more detail you are recommended to refer to British Standards Publication PP7307 Table 7. You will see that pneumatic and hydraulic symbols are the same.

PNEUMATIC TIME DELAY CIRCUITS

When machines are used to produce artefacts, there are often a number of repeated performances. Between each performance, there is often a need for no action, in other words there is a delay. The *delay time* has to be precise and consistent and this is achieved by using a *reservoir* (a cylinder that can withstand pressure) and a *flow regulator.*

Delay time is determined by the *volume of the reservoir* and the *rate at which the air pressure is increased.* The flow regulator controls the rate at which the air pressure increases in the reservoir; therefore adjustment to delay time is made by operating the flow regulator. Delays from 2 to 16 seconds can be achieved using a 130^3m capacity reservoir or from 4 to 32 seconds using a 250^3m capacity reservoir. Time delay circuits are used in clamping operations, car park barriers, etc. Read Pneumatics by Patient and Pickup; published by Oliver and Boyd; Chapter 6.

PN JUNCTION

When a piece of n-type silicon is joined to a p-type silicon, an electronic device is created. The join, however, is not made by using an adhesive. If this method were used, no electrons would be able to flow across the join. Instead the two semi-conductors are joined by solid state diffusion, i.e. they fuse together at a high temperature which is just below melting point. This means that the crystal structure is continuous between the two pieces, and an electron flow is possible. This is known as a pn junction.

POINT CONTACT DIODES

◀ Diodes ▶

POLARITY

The polarity of a Direct Current device will have its terminals marked red, or +, for positive, and black, or −, for negative. For the device to work its polarity must be connected so that the negative side of the source is connected to the negative side of the device, and the positive side of the source to the positive side of the device.

POLES

These are contacts or sets of contacts found in a switch or relay. A *single pole* switch controls a single circuit. A *double pole switch* controls two circuits that are independent of each other.

POLISH

This is a 'surface treatment' that is applied to most materials. It also comes under the heading of a **finish**. Woods, being porous (containing holes or cells), may require several coats of polish before the desired effect is achieved. A polished surface usually has a shine. The polish can be liquid or in the form of a wax.

LIQUID POLISHES

The liquid polishes can have an oil or spirit base. The oil based ones take far longer to dry than the spirit-based polishes and often have to be rubbed vigorously, whereas the spirit-based ones are normally left to dry on their own. Cellulose laquers can be sprayed on wood or metal surfaces. They dry quickly and provide a hard but easily scratched finish. Synthetic resins are known for their resistance to heat, moisture and chemicals. They are made from materials such as polyurethane, polyester, melamine, etc.

WAX POLISHES

Wax polishes provide a popular finish and are often used as a maintenance polish, i.e. used from time-to-time to keep a surface looking shiny. Beeswax and carnauba are two natural wax polishes used on wood. Honey wax and silicone waxes are used to polish the surfaces of GRP moulds so that the mouldings do not stick.

SPECIALISED POLISHES

There are also special polishes for *acrylic* (Perspex). Perspex No 1 which is used as an abrasive, 'cutting' polish, Perspex No 2, which is finer than number one, is used as a finishing polish. Note that the process of rubbing makes the acrylic charged with static electricity so that an anti-static cleaner may be necessary to give the acrylic a final finish. ◀ **Finish** ▶

POLYGON

These are figures that usually have more than four sides and internal angles. The prefix 'poly' means many.

If the length of the sides are equal it is known as a *regular polygon*; if the sides are of different lengths it is known as an *irregular polygon*. Polygons are identified by the number of sides they have, e.g. 5-sided, pentagon; 6-sided, hexagon; 7-sided, heptagon; 8-sided, octagon; 9-sided nonagon, etc.

Regular polygons can be constructed within a circle by dividing the diameter into the number of the sides of the polygon to be constructed. Then by drawing an arc equal to the diameter from either ends of the diameter of the circle. Where the two arcs cross, a straight line is drawn through the second division on the diameter until it crosses the circumference of the circle. The distance between this crossing and the diameter is equal to the *length of one side* of the polygon. The rest of the sides can then be marked off on the circumference by 'stepping them off' with a pair of dividers or by using a compass open to the length of the one side (Fig P.15a).

An octagon can be drawn using a 45° set square. When given a choice, this method is more suitable than the construction given above (Fig P.15b)).

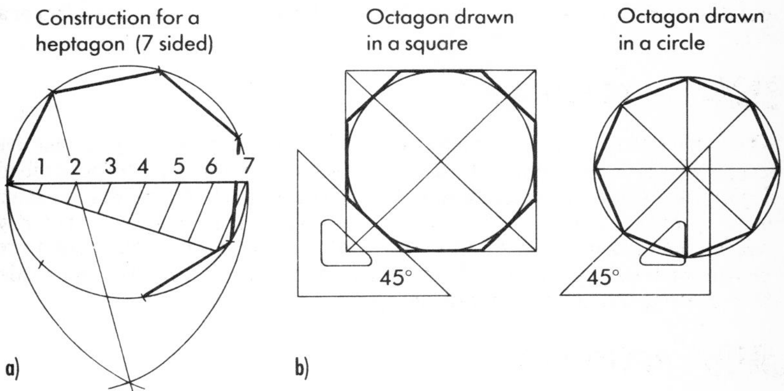

Fig P.15 Polygons

POLYGON OF FORCES

Poly means many and in this case means more than three, since there is a case for looking at triangular forces separately.

In most structures there are forces acting upon each member of the structure. One member assists another member by counteracting one force against another so that the structure is able to withstand all the forces it receives. When this is achieved, the structure is said to be in **equilibrium** (balance) or stability.

Forces can be calculated so that a structure is in equilibrium by drawing a polygon of forces diagram. If a member is to be held stationary by four forces, and the direction and magnitude (amount) of two of them are known, the other two can be calculated. Figure P.16 shows four forces acting upon a point P. The length of the lines are drawn to scale and are in proportion to load or force, i.e. 1 newton equals 10 millimetres. Therefore, a force of 4 newtons is represented by a line that is 40 millimetres in length.

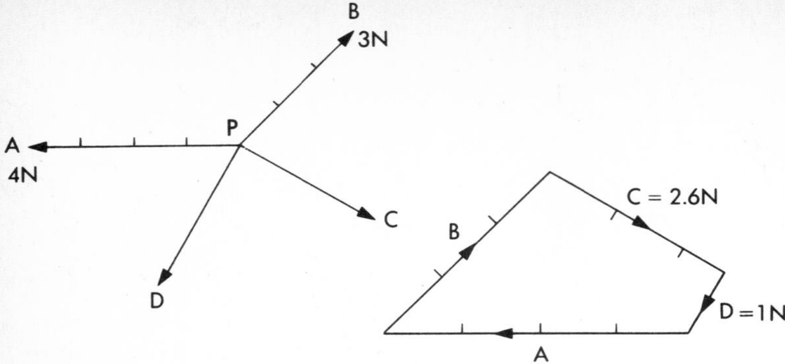

Fig P.16 Polygon of forces

To calculate the two unknown forces, the polygon is drawn to scale. First draw a line parallel to force A, 40 mm long. The, from the left hand end, draw a line parallel to force B, 30 mm long. Now draw a line parallel to force C, and another parallel to force D, to make a complete polygon. By measuring the length of each of these sides you can change the measurement into a force of so many newtons. In the example shown, C = 30 mm or 3N, and D = 10 mm or 1N.

You must remember that to use this method for calculating the forces that will ensure equilibrium, the polygon must be *complete*, the sides must be *parallel* to the direction of force, and must flow in one direction. See the arrows on the polygon.

POLYMERISATION

This is the process of making small molecules join together to form long-chain molecules. The long-chain molecules (polymers) are the main characteristic of plastic materials. The carbon atom has the ability to hold on to atoms of hydrogen and when the 'chain' has as many as 200 or more atoms, it is then regarded as a polymer (many small molecules) (Fig P.17).

The way the molecules are joined together affects the way the plastic material behaves, i.e. how rigid it is and whether or not it can be softened by heating. The long chain polymers are strongly bonded end-to-end, but one *chain* is held to another chain by a relatively weak bond known as a Van der Waals force. It is these forces that break down when heated and allow one chain to slide over another, and when cooled cause the chains to bond again in the new position. This is the characteristic of **thermoplastics** such as polythene, acrylic, polyvinyl chloride, etc. The long chain molecules that are *cross linked* bond strongly from end-to-end and from side-to-side and *cannot* slide over each other when heated. This is the characteristic of **thermosetting plastics** such as melamine formaldehyde, polyester resins, polyurethane, etc.

◀ Carbon, Curing ▶

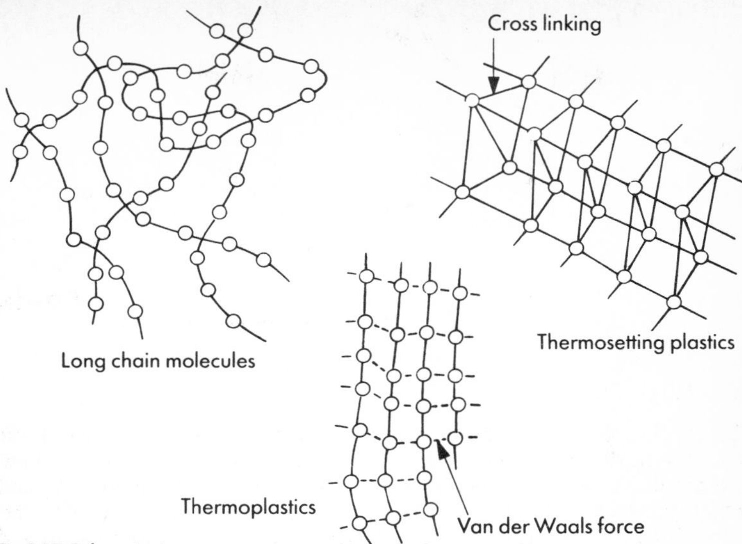

Fig P.17 Polymerisation

POP RIVET

This is a process of riveting sheet material, such as steel and aluminium, and some plastic materials, by using a special tool. It is quick and easy to use and is not likely to damage the material being joined (Fig P.18).

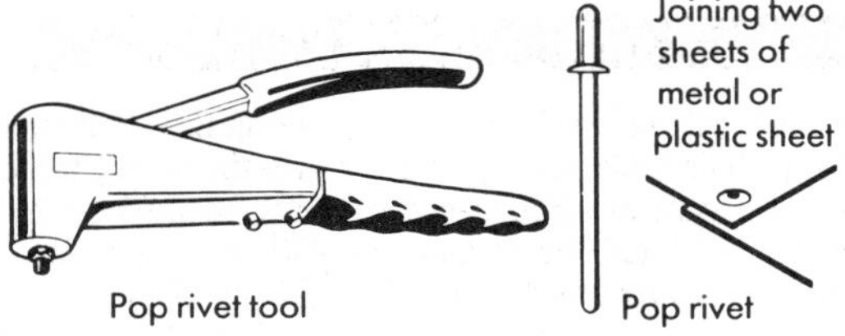

Fig P.18 Pop rivet

POTENTIAL DIFFERENCE

The word 'potential' refers to something that can happen in the future, e.g. work. Two unlike charges are the result of work done to separate electrons from protons. Since the electrons and protons have a natural desire to balance one another out, so reaching a neutral state, the difference in charge represents the *potential work* involved in getting together again. The greater the difference, the greater the work. The work is measured in volts, named after Alessandro Volta (1754–1827).

POTENTIAL DIVIDER

This device can give a continuous variation of current across the whole range from zero to the maximum current. It does this by controlling the voltage available across a component.

POTENTIAL ENERGY

Potential refers to the future and energy refers to the effort or work to be done. A stretched elastic band has potential energy. When one end is released, the elastic band uses energy to return to its original size. If you lift a brick in your hand, the brick has potential energy; it is now stationary, but when you let the brick go it falls to the ground.

POTTING

Another term for encapsulating objects, electrical devices such as integrated circuits, etc. in a resin. When the resin has cured, the objects become fixed in position and protected. Resin is a good insulator and so the silicon chip has to be connected by leads that are brought out to the sides of the package. ◀ **Encapsulation** ▶

PP NUMBER PUBLICATIONS

Namely PP7307, 7308, 7310, and 7320. These are all publications produced by the **British Standards Institution** that are available to help you present information correctly, clearly and simply.

■ **PP7307** is concerned with *graphic symbols*. It contains information of the following; Engineering diagrams; Electrical and electronic symbols; Welding symbols; Controls and indicators for road vehicles; Fluid power symbols; Public information symbols; Safety signs and colours; Piping and plant symbols; Symbols for data processing flow charts; Project network techniques; Therbligs; Pictorial marking of goods in transit; Symbols connected with British Standards Symbols for textile care labelling; Symbols for use on electrical equipment; Construction of the Kitemark; Standard colours and colour coding; and Resources.

■ **PP7308** is concerned with all that is needed to produce Engineering Drawings, e.g. layout, scale, lines, lettering, projection, dimensioning, etc.

■ **PP7310** is concerned with Anthropometrics and includes all the details you need to know related to the measurement of children and adults.

■ **PP7320** is concerned with Construction drawing practice. Construction here is related to buildings.

There are many other BSI publications, but if you have access to those mentioned above you will have ample resource material for presenting your drawings.

PREPARED TIMBER

Timber that has been planed to size. ◀ **Planed sizes** ▶

PRESENTATION

Presentation is about communicating information clearly and attractively. It is also concerned with the way in which items are displayed. In order to get someone interested in your work you need to take care and thought in presenting it. Think of presentation as 'selling' yourself, your ideas and your work. If your work is displayed carefully, you are much more likely to interest someone and, where you are being assessed, impress the assessor.

PRESERVATIVE

Most materials, especially timber, have a natural tendency to react with the air and life around them: wood will rot and decay if in a wet atmosphere, or be attacked by insects and fungi.

Timber can be treated with materials known as preservatives, with such trade names as 'Rentokil', 'Cuprinol', etc. They can be applied to the timber by brush or spray. However, some of them contain chemicals that are believed to be harmful to man if not used correctly. Care must therefore be taken to follow the manufacturer's instructions. Some timbers that are for outdoor use are already treated with a preservative. These have often been treated under pressure, so that the liquid preservative penetrates deeply into the wood. Wood treated this way has a chance of being preserved for many years.

PRIMARY COLOURS

Red, yellow and blue are the three primary colours. From these three colours *secondary colours* can be obtained.

Red and yellow gives *orange*; yellow and blue gives *green*; blue and red gives *violet.* By further mixing of the primary and secondary colours a third set of colours can be obtained, knows as *tertiary colours.* ◀ Colour ▶

PRIMARY INDUSTRY

This is the first stage of production of artefacts and products. The various raw materials are often included under this heading. ◀ Industry ▶

PRIMARY INVESTIGATION/RESEARCH

Information that is obtained by original research. This usually involves looking at materials and objects, and talking to people, as opposed to reading from books, magazines, etc.

In order to design an alarm system on a machine, you will need to find out what the alarm is exactly supposed to do. Is it to tell the person that a part of the machine is too hot or that the sliding mechanism needs lubricating? Or is it to indicate that a guard is not in position? You would have to find out this type of information yourself. This is called *primary investigation.*

PRINCIPAL PLANES

In **orthographic projection**, the vertical and the horizontal planes are the most used and are sometimes referred to as the principal planes.

PRISM

A prism is a solid that remains the same cross-sectional shape throughout its length or height. A solid with a circular cross - sectional shape is called a *cylindrical prism*. Other solid shapes include a triangle, rectangle, pentagon, hexagon, heptagon etc (Fig P.19).

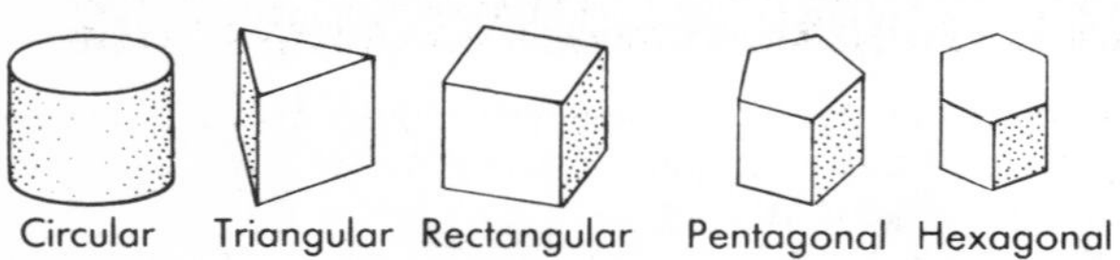

Fig P.19 Prisms

PROBLEM-SOLVING PROCESS

This is the process that will allow a problem to be resolved. There are a variety of ways of resolving a problem. Some ways rely on an inspired guess or personal intuition. Though these are not necessarily methodical approaches, they do produce results. The safest way of solving a problem is however by following a sequence of activities, commonly referred to as a 'design process'. ◀ **Design process** ▶

PROFILE

The outline or silhouette of a face or figure. The brief description of a person that is recorded in writing.

PROJECT

An assignment of work. Projects in CDT refer to the solving of a problem that requires research, analysis, testing, the development of ideas, etc.

To project, as in drawing, refers to lines that extend from one view to another view, especially in **orthographic projection**. The projection lines are thin so that they do not get confused with the outlines.
◀ **Orthographic projection** ▶

PROPORTION

The relationship of one part with another. Some sizes are said to be *in proportion* when they appeal to a sense of balance. The proportion of the sides of a rectangle are pleasing when they are in balance. ◀ **Golden Mean** ▶

PROTONS

These are elementary particles that have a positive charge equal to the electron negative charge. The number of protons in an atomic nucleus is the same as the number of orbital electrons. This number gives the atomic number of the atom.

PROTOTYPE

This is the first three-dimensional form of an object that will later be made with refinements. It is the first working model of an idea.

P TYPE SEMICONDUCTOR

This type of semiconductor is produced during the **'doping'** of a piece of pure silicon or pure germanium. Doping is the process of adding impurities to provide negative and positive charges.

Silicon and germanium are *tetravalent elements*, i.e. they have four electrons in their outer shell. Boron is an acceptor impurity because its atoms can accept an electon from other atoms nearby. When an atom of boron, that has three valence electrons (trivalent), is introduced normal covalent bonding occurs. But, in the area where the fourth bond ought to be, a 'hole' exists and attracts any moving electrons. The area is then said to be behaving *as though* it were positively charged.

Because the semiconductor behaves as though it was positive, it is called a P type semiconductor. ◀ **N type semiconductor** ▶

PULLEY

A pulley wheel is a wheel that has a groove in its rim. It is used in mechanical systems to lift loads. By having a combination of pulley wheels it is possible to gain considerable **mechanical advantage** (the effort is smaller than that actually required to lift the load *without* a mechanism). A pulley system is a 'First Class Lever' (Fig P.20).

Pulley systems are used mainly to lift loads vertically, e.g. lifts, block and tackle used to lift car engines in and out of car bodies, etc. They also transfer electrical energy into mechanical energy by linking the drive of an electric motor with the rotating part of a machine, e.g. electric drilling machine, lathe, circular saw, etc.

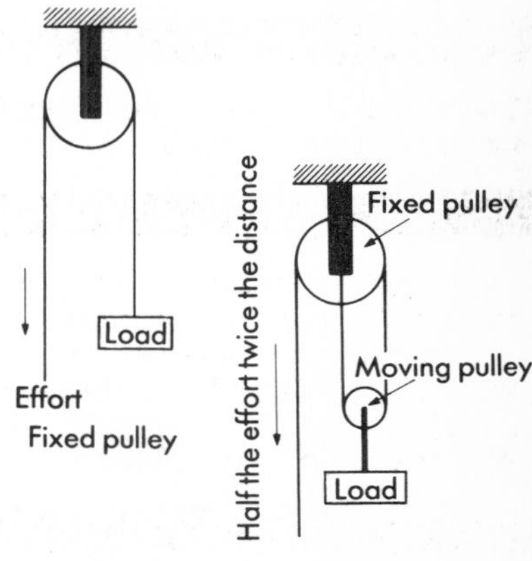

Fig P.20 Pulleys

PULSE DETECTOR

◀ Decoder ▶

PYRAMID

A pyramid has a regular shaped figure, with base and triangular sides meeting at the vertex (the vertical height above the centre of the base.) (Fig P.21).

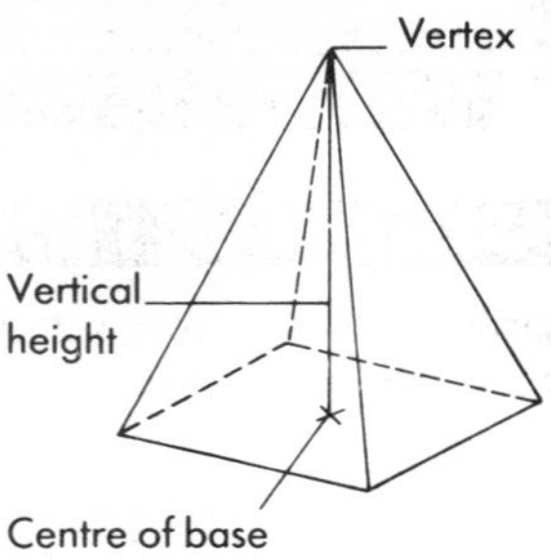

Fig P.21 Pyramid

PYTHAGORAS

The 'Pythagoras' theorem says that in a triangle with one right angle (i.e. 90°), the sum of the square on the longest side (hypotenuse) is equal to the sum of the squares on the other two sides. A right-angled triangle that has its sides in the ratio of 3:4:5 can be used as an example that shows clearly how the theorem works:

The longest side (hypotenuse)	= 5	the square	$= 5 \times 5$	= 25
shortest side	= 3	the square	$= 3 \times 3$	= 9
the remaining side	= 4	the square	$= 4 \times 4$	= 16

$$25 = 9 + 16.$$

If you know two sides of a right-angled triangle, the third one can be calculated using this theorem. For example, when the length of the longest side equals 13 units and another side = 5 units, let the third side = a

Then $a^2 + 5^2 = 13^2$

$$a^2 = 13^2 - 5^2$$
$$= 169 - 25 = 144$$
$$a^2 = 144$$
$$a = 12$$

By remembering these ratios 3:4:5 you can always construct a right angle without the need of a protractor.

QUADRILATERAL

A quadrilateral is a four-sided plane figure. Fig Q.1 shows examples of different quadrilaterals.

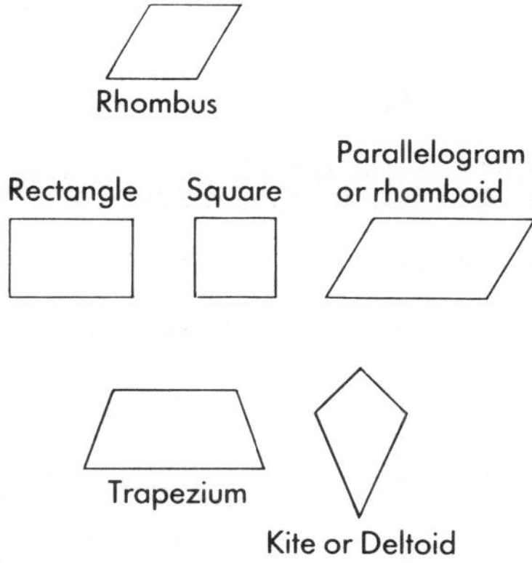

Fig Q.1 Quadrilaterals

QUENCH/QUENCHING

Cooling a piece of material in a liquid is called *quenching*. This process is important in the hardening process where carbon steel is first of all heated to about red heat (730°C – 910°C), the austenite range. This is the critical range where the structural changes take place: e.g. the ferrite and pearlite grains become pearlite and austenite in the low carbon steels, and the cementite and pearlite become the cementite and austenite in the carbon steels above 0.83%. Quenching the hot metal under running water at this stage produces a hardness in steel.

If the carbon steels are left in this condition, they will break very easily, i.e. they are brittle. To make them hard and tough, they need to be heated again and quenched at a particular stage. ◀ **Hardening and tempering** ▶

RACK AND PINION

This is a mechanism for converting linear motion to rotary motion, or vice versa (Fig R.1). You can find examples of this device on a lathe, e.g. for controlling the horizontal movement of the saddle on a metal-worker's lathe. You can also use this mechanism for controlling the rise and fall of the table on a drilling machine (Fig R.2).

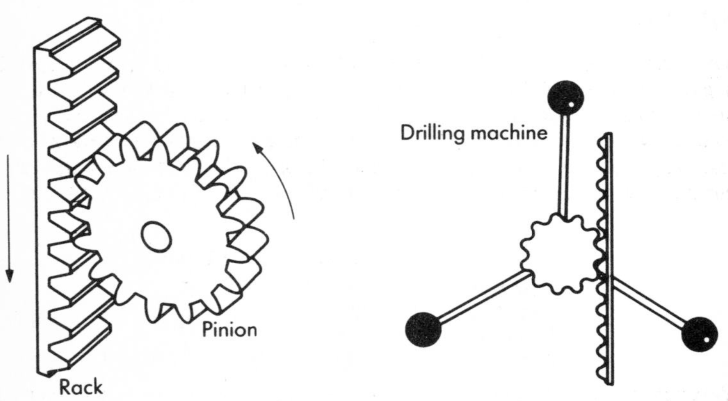

Fig R.1 Rack and pinion

Fig R.2 Drilling machine rack and pinion

RADIUS

Half the diameter of a circle. The distance from the centre of the circle to the circumference.

RADIUS CURVES

There is a drawing template that has a number of different size curves for drawing arcs of a circle. Though arcs can be drawn equally well with a compass, templates are useful for drawing small radiused arcs about 10 mm and less.

RADIUSED CORNERS

Rounded corners take away the sharp edge where two planes meet. This can be for practical reasons, as on a child's toy or on a pattern to be used to make a sand mould for casting hot molten metal. Plugs used in vacuum forming also have their corners rounded, helping the softened plastic sheet to follow the curve without it weakening.

RAKE ANGLE

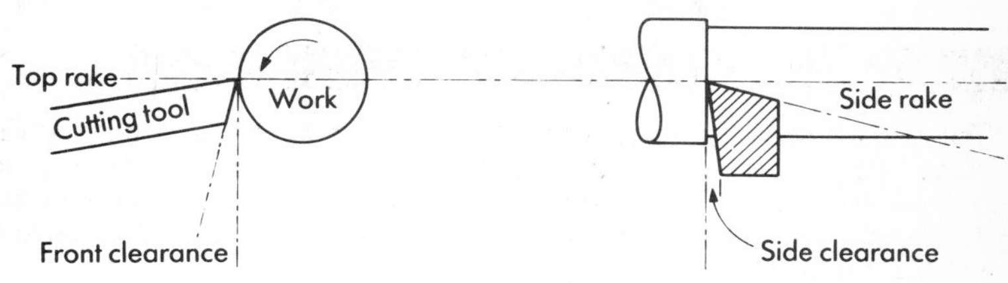

Fig R.3 Rake angle

The rake angles on a lathe cutting tool occur on the top surface. The first angle is concerned with the cutting angle and is called the *top rake*; the second angle is called the *side rake*, and allows the material that has been cut to clear the cutting tool (Fig R.3). Some tool holders hold the tool at the top rake angle so that there is only a need to grind the side rake angle of the cutting tool. Note that these angles are different for different materials:

Metal	*Top Rake*	*Side Rake*
Aluminium	30°	15°
Mild steel	20°	15°
Tool steel	10°	5°
Brass	0°	0°

Remember: the best results in *turning* are achieved when the tool is sharp and ground to the correct rake angles for a particular material.

RAM

RAM is an abbreviation for Random-Access Memory. Many digital devices contain a system of storing information, i.e. flip-flops, registers, etc. and when these are organised into large groups they are called RAMs and ROMs.

The RAM stores digital information quickly and the amount it can store is dependent upon its capacity. The RAM capacity of a computer/word processor could be 132K (132,000 bits). It can be read and written and is sometimes called the *read-write* memory. The disadvantage of the RAM memory is that it all disappears as soon as the power is switched off. This is why a *backing store* is needed for storing information that is to be kept, i.e. disks.

RATCHET AND PAWL

This is a mechanical device that has a wheel with teeth. The front edge of each tooth has a steel slope and the back edge has a gradual slope. The gradual slope allows the pawl to slide over the surface and the ratchet wheel to rotate; the steep slope stops it from rotating in the reverse direction (Fig R.4). Examples can be found in ratchet screwdriver, free-wheel in a bicycle and winding mechanisms. In the case of the screwdriver, the pawl can be moved to an adjacent wheel where the teeth are facing the opposite way round so that the screwing action works for both screwing and unscrewing.

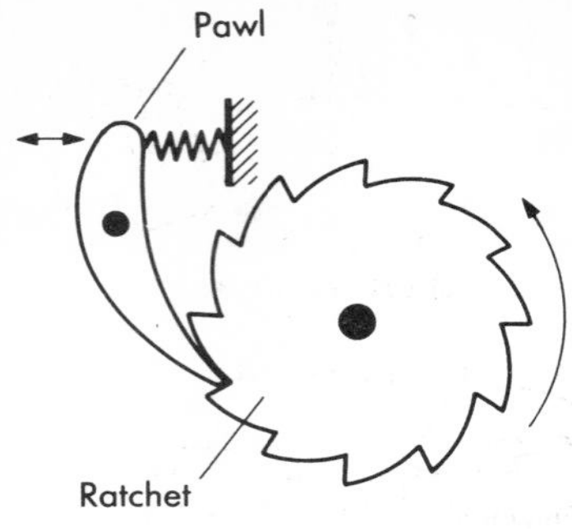

Fig R.4 Ratchet and pawl

REACTANCE

◀ Electrical circuits ▶

REALISATION

To bring an idea to reality. To make an idea in a material or combination of materials.

REBATE

A small step in a piece of wood to allow a panel to be fixed neatly (Fig R.5). Often used where the edge of the panel is to be hidden.

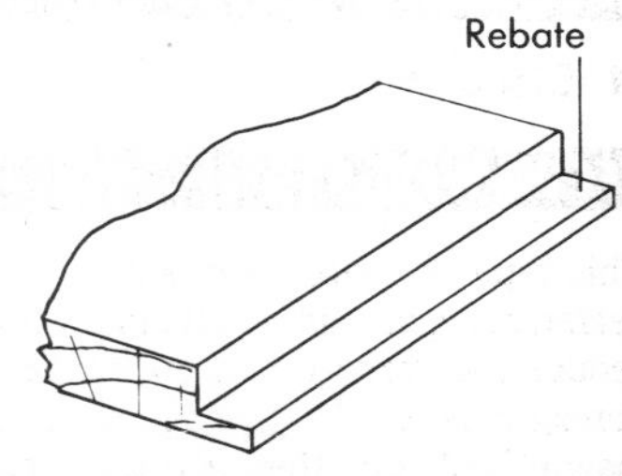

Fig R.5 Rebate

RECIPROCATING MOVEMENT

Moving backwards and forwards in a straight line. Pistons and connecting rods move backwards and forwards. This linear movement is often converted into rotary movement in a car engine by the cam and follower (Fig R.6).

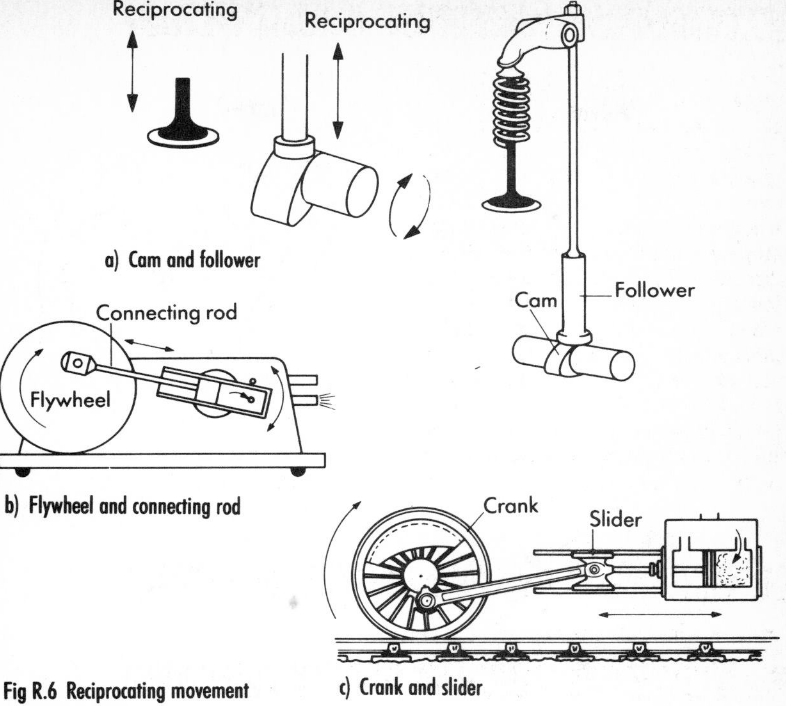

Fig R.6 Reciprocating movement

RECTANGLES

A rectangle is a four-sided plane figure.

RECTIFIERS

◄ Diode ►

REED SWITCH

This type of switch contains two reeds made from a ferromagnetic material sealed in a glass tube. The glass tube contains an inert gas such as nitrogen to reduce the corrosion of the contacts. The reeds can be easily magnetised or demagnetised. If a magnet is brought near the reeds, they become magnetised, i.e. they attract each other and close the contacts. When the magnet is removed, the reeds become demagnetised and the reeds spring open (Fig R.7). Some reed switches are inside a coil of wire so that when a current is passed through the wire a magnetic field causes the reeds to attract.

Reed switches can be used in alarm systems, measuring rotational speed and indicating a rotational position (e.g. North, South, East, West, etc. of a weather vane). They are relatively small and can be used in situations where explosive gases may exist (the sealed tube prevents any sparking from coming into contact with the surrounding air). It is able to operate at 2000 times a minute and it has a long life. ◀ **Relay switch** ▶

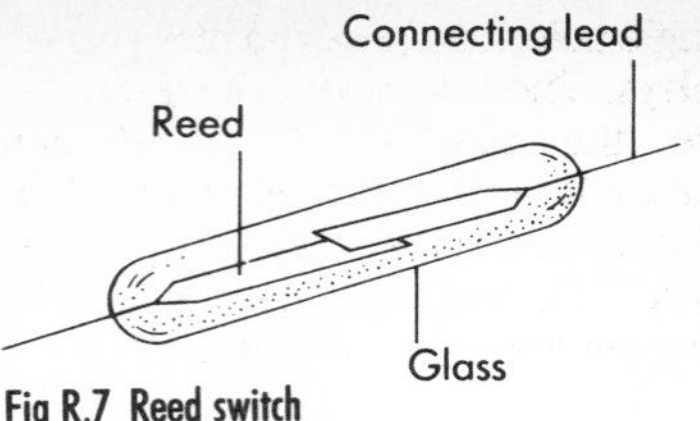

Fig R.7 Reed switch

REFLEX ANGLE

An angle between 180° and 360° (Fig R.8).

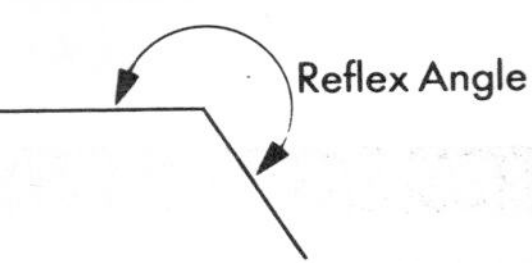

Fig R.8 Reflex angle

REFORMING PROCESSES

◀ **Casting, Enamelling** ▶

REGULAR POLYGONS

◀ **Polygons** ▶

REINFORCE

Some materials, such as cured polyester resin or concrete, are quite able to resist loads or impacts. However, their resistance to damage is considerably increased if another material is embedded in them. The embedding takes place when the material is in a liquid state. In resin, glass fibre in the form of strand mat, ribbon, rovings, etc., is embedded into each layer. This produces a light, but very tough material. **Glass Reinforced Plastics** are used in boat building, the front of high speed trains, cars, etc.

In *concrete,* metal bars or grills are embeded. This is done by pouring the concrete over the metal that is suspended in position, so that the concrete flows all round it. *Reinforced concrete* is used in buildings, bridges, and any structures that have to withstand heavy loads.

RELAY SWITCH

This is an automatic switch that is operated by a current in a coil. The magnetic field attracts an iron armature which moves the contacts to open changeover or closed positions (Fig R.9). The advantage of relays are that a smaller current can be used to control a larger current, and the two circuits are independent of each other.

Transistorised relays that require well as solid state relays which have enclosed in a coil are operated by very low input currents are available, as no moving parts. **Reed switches** that are a low current input and are available as single pole, two pole and changeover relays. The two most common types are the moulded PCB (Printed Circuit Board) mounting, and the DIL (dual in line) relay which looks similar to a TTL logic module and can be plugged into a TTL socket.

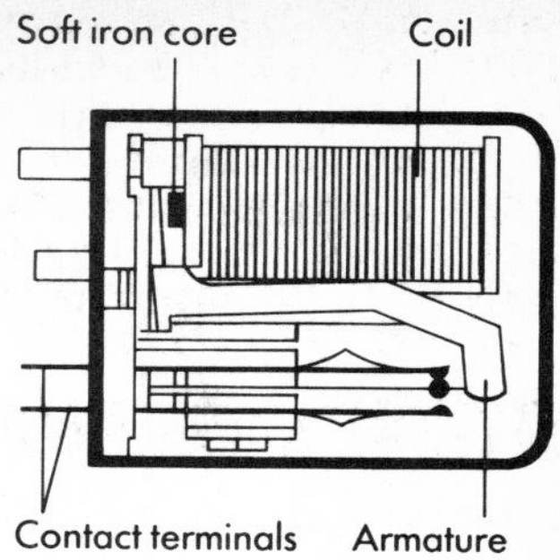

Fig R.9 Relay switch

REMOVED SECTION

This is a section view that has been moved to the side of the view of the component (Fig R.10). The advantage of such sectioning is that several positions can be used to show differences of internal detail in one object.

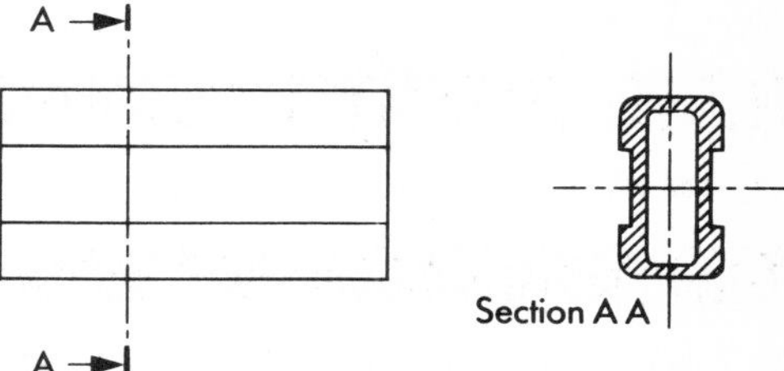

Fig R.10 Removed section

RENDERING

The application of a treatment to a surface. For CDT this mainly applies to illustrate work, where effects of smoothness, roughness, etc can be achieved. A building with rendered brickwork is shown in Fig R.11.

Fig R.11 Rendering

RESEARCH

This means the same as investigation. It does however, suggest that the information is obtained more by *reading* than by trial and testing.
◀ Investigation, Primary investigation ▶

RESISTANCE

The resistance of a material usually refers to its ability to allow or prevent a current passing through it. Resistance is measured in **Ohms, Ω.**

The resistance of a material can be calculated if the current and voltage are known. For example, a current of 1 amp with 10 volts applied has a resistance of 10Ω.

The important formula to remember is that $R = \frac{V}{I}$ or

$$\text{Resistance} = \frac{\text{Voltage}}{\text{Current}}$$

◀ Ohm's law ▶

RESISTOR

This is a device for reducing current in an AC or DC circuit. There are several types of resistors, e.g. wire-wound, carbon composition, film type, cermet, fusible, and nonlinear.

Resistors are made to have a *known resistance.* They can then be used in circuits to provide a limited current flow to devices that would overwise get over heated and damaged. Because resistors are physically small, a *colour-coding system* is used ot identify their resistance. The standard colour code is given below:

Colour	*Value (Ω)*	*Colour*	*Value (Ω)*
black	0	green	5
brown	1	blue	6
red	2	violet	7
orange	3	grey	8
yellow	4	white	9

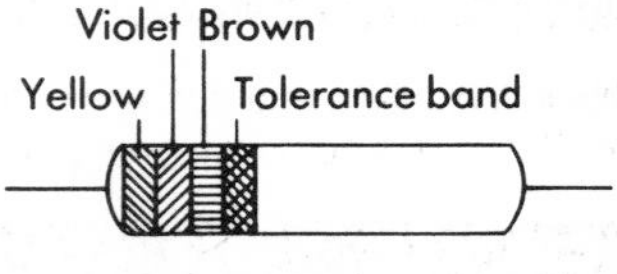

Fig R.12 Resistor

To read the value of a resistor, you start from the colour band that is near to one end of the device. Then read from left to right. The first two bands state a value. The third is a multiplier, i.e. how many noughts to place after the first two figures; the fourth band is a tolerance value. The resistor in Figure R.12 shows the first three bands, and indicates how its value is calculated:

yellow	violet	brown		
4	7	×10	=	470

The resistance therefore equals 470Ω.

The resistance of a resistor need not be quite the same as the colour bands indicate. It could be slightly more, or slightly less. This difference is known as the *tolerance*. The tolerance level is given as a percentage value of the colour code. A resistor with a colour code 2200Ω could have a tolerance value of ± 10%. This means that the resistance could be 10% above, or 10% below, the colour coding value. Since 10% of 2200 = 220, the upper value could be 2420Ω and the lower value could be 1980Ω.

The colour coding for the tolerance level is gold for ± 5% and silver for ± 10%. Preferred resistor values that have a ± 10% tolerance are: 10, 12, 15, 18, 22, 27, 33, 39, 47, 56, 68, 82, and decimal multiples of them. For example 22, 220, 2200 and 22000. There are resistors that have as little as 0.1 to 2% tolerance, but these are more expensive.

REVOLVED SECTION

A section view that has moved through an angle 90° about its central axis is a revolved section. It is drawn within the outline of the component. If it has been moved off the component, then it is called a removed and revolved section.

RHOMBUS

A four-sided figure that has all sides equal in length, with the diagonals meeting at right angles. ◀ **Quadrilateral, Parallelogram** ▶

RIGHT ANGLE

An angle of 90°. It is perhaps the most commonly used angle in the construction world. Devices such as engineers square, try square and set sqaure are all concerned with the 90° angle.

RIGHT-ANGLED TRIANGLE

This is a triangle that has *one* of its angles equal to 90°. A 45° set square and a 60°, 30°, set square are examples of a practical use of a right-angled triangle.

RIGID

A rigid structure is one that is not flexible. Materials vary in flexibility, i.e. some bend some more easily than others. But materials can be made more rigid by *folding*. The *corrugations* (grooves and rounds) in a sheet material help make it quite rigid. Some frame structures are made rigid by putting a *diagonal strut* or tie to form a triangle. ◀ **Triangulation** ▶

ROD

A solid round section of metal or plastics material. The term rod is often replaced with the word 'dowel' for round section wood.

ROM

The abbreviation for Read-Only Memory. They are the details that have already been programmed by the manufacturer and cannot be added to or changed. They can only be used in the 'read' mode. Information can be located by following the correct address procedure. If however the ROM can be programmed by the user, it is called a *Programmable Read-Only Memory* (PROM); and if information can be erased, it is known as an *Erasable Programmable Read-Only Memory* (EPROM).

ROTATE

To go round and round. It is a circular movement that ends where it started. A rotating mechanism is one that is going round about a central point or axis, e.g. a wheel, drill chuck, pulley, etc.

SAFETY

Whenever you are working with materials such as using equipment, testing, applying a finish, etc. you must follow what are known to be *safe procedures*. There is always a correct way of soldering, drilling, casting, moulding, etc. and this is the way in which all practical and experimental work should be carried out.

Good planning, concentration on what you are doing, and following all safety procedures, (such as wearing the correct protective clothing and *never* using a machine without a guard in place) are ways of avoiding an accident.
Remember: When in doubt, always ask your teacher and *never* take risks.

SAFETY COLOURS

Colours used to indicate danger, warning, safe condition, etc. are standardised. There are five main groups of colour signs.

Danger identification

These are fluorescent orange-red, or yellow-and-black bands that go round the edge of an area. They indicate that there is a risk, e.g. a hole in the road may be temporarily fenced with a length of black-and-yellow-banded material attached to the fencing (Fig S.1). In a workshop, such lines are painted on the floor on a low beam.

Prohibition signs

These have a background colour white, with red for the circular band and diagonal. Red must cover at least 35% of the signs shown in Fig S.1. Wherever these signs are used, you must obey them or you may be prosecuted.

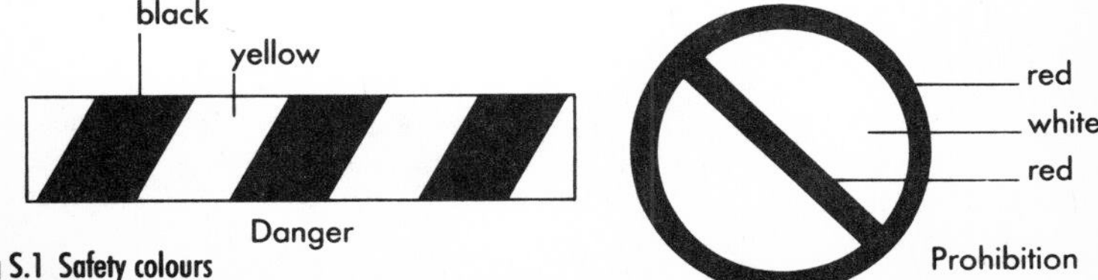

Fig S.1 Safety colours

Warning signs

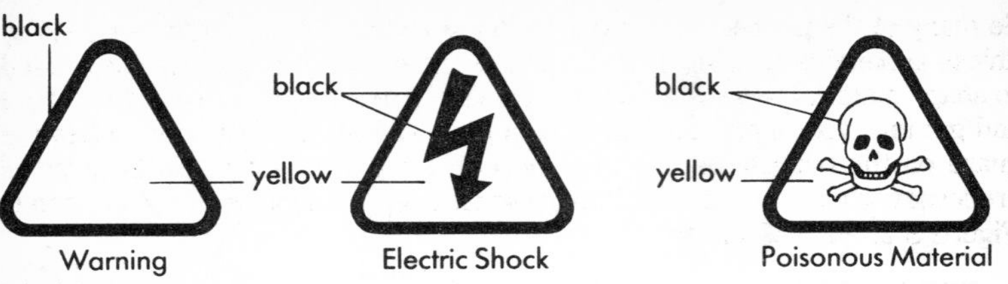

These are triangular in shape with a black band round the edge and a yellow middle. The symbol is placed in the middle of the triangle and coloured black. At least 50% of the safety sign is yellow. These signs are used to make you aware of a danger, i.e. risk of an electric shock, risk of poisonous material, etc.

Mandatory signs

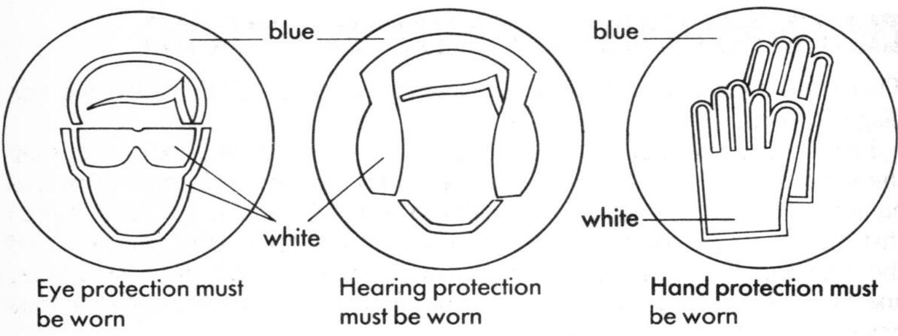

The background colour is blue. The symbol is white and placed in the middle of the sign. At least 50% must be blue. These signs are used to remind you that certain protective clothing must be worn.

Safe condition signs

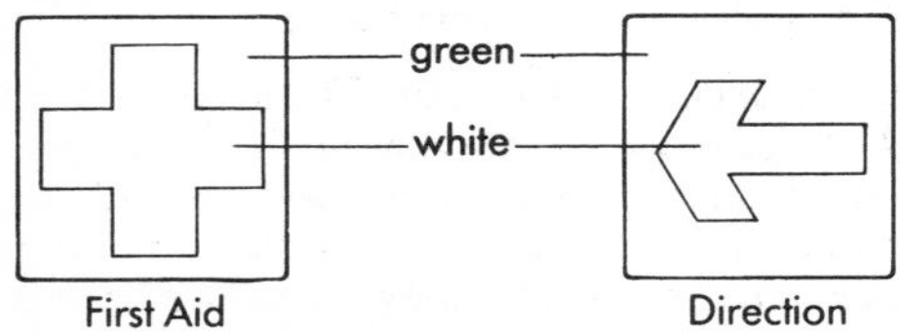

The background colour is green and the symbol is white. The sign must be rectangular and at least 50% of the sign green.

For more information you should refer to BSI PP7307, *Graphical Symbols* for use in schools and colleges, Tables 9, 10, 11, and 12. Table 17 also contains signs to show that a product has been approved as safe and reliable.

SAFETY EQUIPMENT

So many of the processes carried out in a practical activity could cause injury unless protective clothing or equipment is worn. Wherever a machine is used to shape material there is a risk that some of the waste material will fly about and get into your eyes. So *goggles* or a *visor* should be worn, even when the guard on the machine is in place. There is a range of safety clothing for all processes where there is a risk to personal safety; examples are illustrated in Figure S.2. ◀ Valves ▶

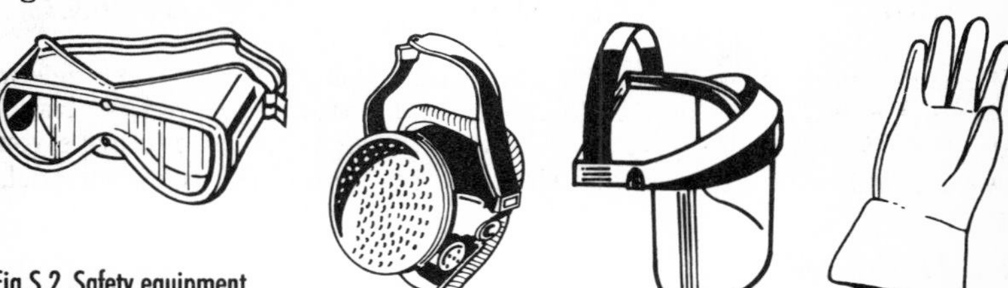

Fig S.2 Safety equipment

SCALE

There are two types of scale in common use, the *plain scale* and the *diagonal scale.*

For the diagonal scale, if the drawing and the object are the *same size,* then the scale is written 1:1. If the drawing is *larger* than the actual object, then the number of times it is bigger is written as the first number i.e. 2:1. This means that the drawing is twice as big as the object. There are preferred scales, and the recommended scales for enlargement drawings are 2:1, 5:1, 10:1, 20:1, and 50:1. The recommended scales for drawings smaller than the original object or view, are as follows:

1:2, 1:5, 1:10, (Working drawings);
1:20, 1:50, 1:100 (Detail of small components);
1:200, 1:500 (Builder's site plan);
1:1000, (Block plan);
1:5000, 1:20,000, (Plan of a town or city);
1:250,000, (Approximately 4 miles to 1 inch. Road atlas);
1:2,000,000, (Small scale maps of countries),

Plain scales are drawn using a metric ruler. The length of the scale should be just longer than the longest line on the drawing. The first division on the scale is subdivided, so that units of less than 1 can be measured, i.e. 0.2, 0.4, 0.6, etc. The scale can be put on the drawing, usually near the bottom and the measurements transferred by using a compass or, better still, dividers.

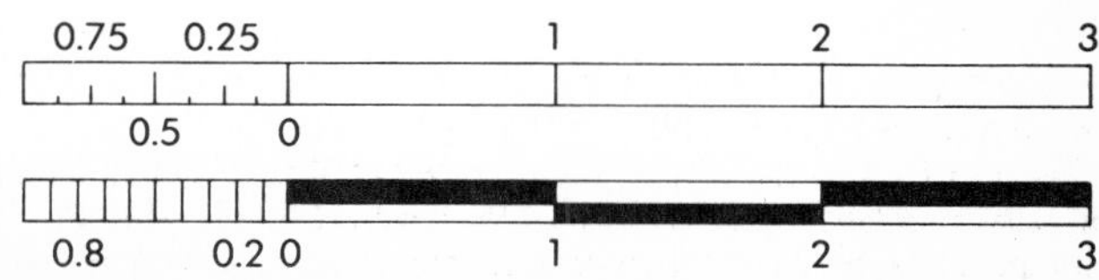

Fig S.3 Scales

SCHMITT TRIGGER

This is a name given to a circuit which behaves in a way similar to a switch. It is always used in sensing circuits that are connected to logic circuits. The purpose of the Schmitt Trigger circuit is to activate (trigger or flick over) another circuit or component abruptly. In circuits that do *not* have a Schmitt Trigger, the sensing circuit can be in a state of indecision and oscillate many times. In a device that was controlled by counting, this would cause havoc and ruin its reliability. The Schmitt Trigger allows the sensing device to provide an input voltage level that has to reach the 'rising threshold voltage' *before* it will trigger abruptly. The same applies for the 'falling threshold voltage'. However, there is a gap between the two thresholds where nothing happens, and this is called the 'Deadband' or 'Hysteresis'. It is this deadband that eliminates the indecision or oscillation and so provides a *clean change* from logic 0 to 1 or 1 to 0.

You can recognise a chip that has a Schmitt Trigger circuit by the symbol ⎍, the design of which is based upon the two graphs of the rising and falling thresholds.

SCREW

A screw is a sloping plane that is wrapped round a cylinder. As it turns (rotates) in another component, it moves forward or backwards in a line (linear movement). This simple mechanical principle is commonly used in mechanisms.

SCREWS

These are devices used to hold materials together. They are available in different lengths, diameters or gauges, materials, shape of head, and type of thread.

The length of a screw will depend upon the shape of the head. The round-headed screw is longer than a countersunk-headed screw, even when the length of the shank and threaded part are the same (Fig S.4).

The diameter of a wood screw is given by a gauge number. The higher the gauge number, the bigger the diameter. Gauge numbers 4 and 6 are in common use for light general work; 8, 10 and 12 are used for more sturdy structures.

Steel is the most common **material** used for the production of screws, especially where corrosion is not likely to occur. Brass screws are more expensive but are used in furniture and where brass fitings are used. Most electrical screws are made from brass. Nylon screws are also in use, mainly to hold plastic materials together.

Screws are identified by the shape of the head, e.g. round-head, countersunk-head, dome-head, etc. They are also identified by the shape of the slot or cavity in the head e.g. Philips, Pozidrive, slot, hexagonal, etc. (Fig S.5).

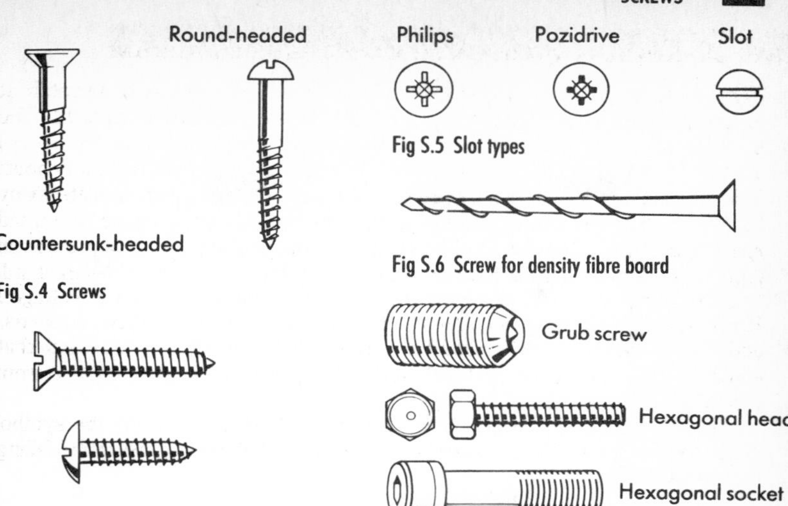

Fig S.4 Screws

Fig S.5 Slot types

Fig S.6 Screw for density fibre board

Fig S.7 Machine screws

Fig S.8 Differing head designs

There are two common forms of thread for wood screws. The most common is the thread which is used on screws designed for natural timber. It has quite a sharp edge on the crest to enable it to cut into the wood (self-tapping screw). The second type of thread is similar, except that there is a wider space between the thread (i.e. the root is much wider). With a lower number of threads per inch or 25 mm, there is less resistance and this makes it easier to turn. This type is designed for use on manufactured boards, such as medium- and high-density fibre boards (Fig S.6).

Machine screws are designed for use in holding metal components together. The form of the thread is standardised and since there is a variety of different threads it is important that the threaded hold of a component or nut be the same for a fit to be possible. British Association (BA) and Whitworth are still in common use, but these are now being replaced by a metric thread. The profiles of these threads are different and it is for this reason that screws *cannot* be used with nuts of identical gauge, but different thread. The design of the head of many machine screws is the same as for a wood screw (Fig S.7). The design of the head differs in the following: hexagonal; hexagonal socket; no head i.e. grub (Fig S.8). A spanner is required for the hexagonal-headed screws and an Allen key for the hexagonal socket screw.

SCREW TAPPING

Internal threads can be cut in holes and external threads on rods by using a special set of tools called 'Taps and Dies' (Fig S.9). The material, mainly metal, is first drilled with a tapping size drill, and then the first of a set of three taps is used to cut a thread. It is known as the *taper tap* because the end has

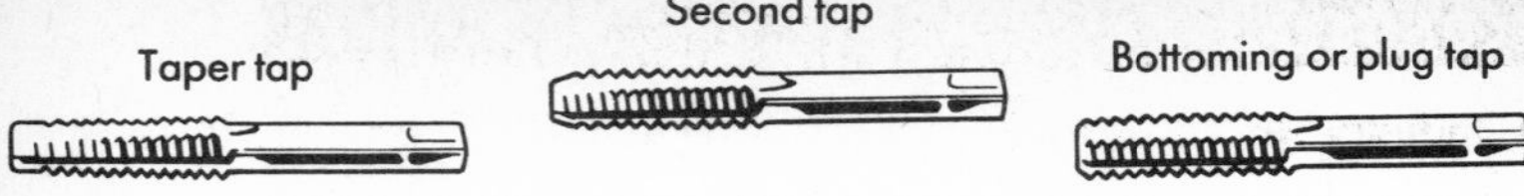

Fig S.9 Screw tapping

no thread and is tapered. This makes it easier to get started. The second tap is used to clean out the thread cut by the taper tap, and to take the thread down a little further where the taper hardly cuts any thread. The third tap, known as the *plug* is then used to give the threaded hole a final finish.

SCREW THREADS

There are four main types of thread. Acme, Buttress, Square and V (Fig S.10). The Acme is used where thrust is in two directions; the buttress for thrust in one direction; the square for thrust in two directions; and the V thread is used where moderate thrust is applied in either direction.

Since the Acme transmits linear motion, it is used on the lead screw on a centre lathe; a buttress thread is used on a gripping device such as an Engineers Vice; a square thread is used on a screw jack; V threads are used on screws, bolts and nuts, etc.

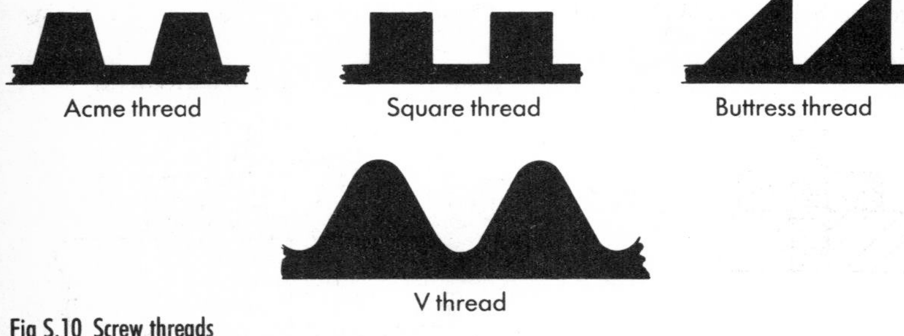

Fig S.10 Screw threads

SCRIBER

This is a marking out tool used on metal (Fig S.11). If the work is bright mild steel, a coating of engineer's blue helps the mark made by the scriber to stand out more clearly.

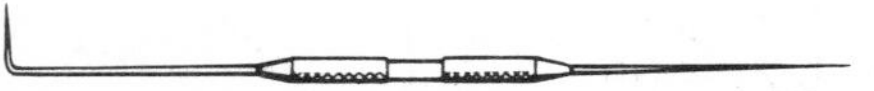

Fig S.11 Scriber

SEASONING

◄ Artificial seasoning, Natural seasoning ►

SECONDARY INDUSTRY

◀ Industry ▶

SECONDARY INVESTIGATION

When you read *someone else's findings* you are reading material that has already been primarily investigated. So if you use this material you are using it as secondary material. Material that comes from reading books, magazines, etc. is all secondary information. When secondary information is used, it must be acknowledged by completing a bibliography (a list of the books used). Much of the material in this referece guide is obtained from secondary research.

SECTIONING

When the internal details of a component cannot be clearly presented by dotted lines on an Orthographic Projection, the process of sectioning is used. A section is an *imaginary cutting plane*. The section view is what you would see when one piece has been removed to expose the cutting plane. The imaginary cutting plane is shown by hatching lines that are at an angle to the outline of the components, usually at 45° (Fig S.12). Look at the examples in Fig S.13 and note what happens when two or more components are next to each other. There are components or parts of components that would not provide helpful detail by sectioning. These are not sectioned even if a cutting

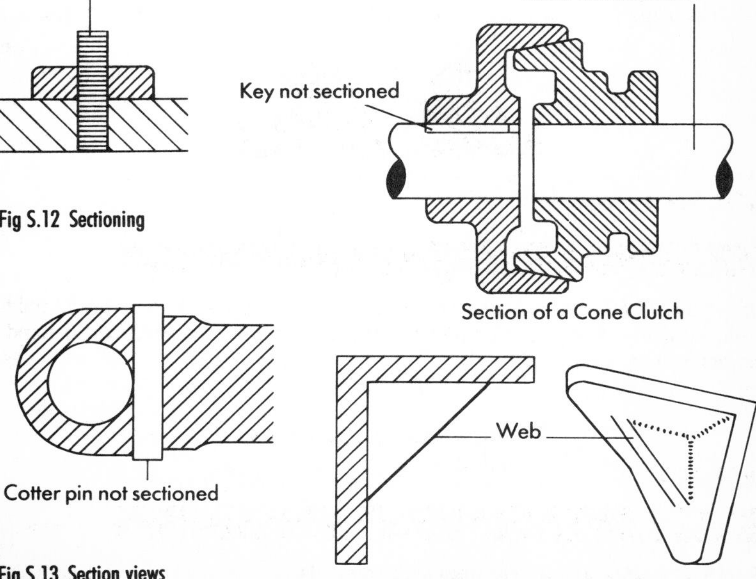

Fig S.12 Sectioning

Fig S.13 Section views

plane passes through them. For example, the detail of a section through a cotter pin, nut and bolt, shaft, rib, web, rivet, key in a keyway, etc. would *not* provide helpful information. If ribs and webs of castings were sectioned, the information would be misleading because it would give the impression that the casting was solid.

Remember: All hatching lines are drawn with thin lines so that the outline is the strongest and most obvious line.

SECTOR

This is a portion of a circle that has two sides formed by the radius of the circle, an arc formed by part of the circumference and an internal angle less than 90°. When the internal angle is 90° the sector is called a *quadrant.* ◀ Circle ▶

SEGMENT

A segment is formed by a straight line with ends that meet on the circumference of a circle. This line is called a chord, and has an arc that is less than half of the circumference. When the arc is equal to half of the circumferemce, the straight line passes through the centre and is called a diameter; this figure is then a semi circle.

SEMICONDUCTORS

Semi means half. So a material that is a semiconductor cannot be as good at conducting as a material that is known as a conductor. Nor is a semiconductor as good at insulation as materials that are known as insulators. Therefore semiconducting materials, such as copper oxide, selenium, gallium arsenide, germanium and silicon, etc. are *halfway between* being a conductor and an insulator.

Germanium and silicon are the two most commonly used semiconducting materials in **transistors**. Both these materials are 'tetravalent' elements, i.e. they have four electrons that can be shared in their outer atomic shell. They have a strong binding force and germanium and silicon crystals are very similar to diamond crystals.

The first and well-known semiconducting device was the 'cat's whisker' on a crystal invented by Pickard in 1906. But it was not until the 1940's that sufficient development in the use of semiconducting materials led to a major revolution by the replacement of 'Thermionic' valves with semiconducting devices. The development of the transistor led to major changes and development in electronics and digital microelectronics. ◀ Transistor ▶

SENSORS

These are devices that are highly sensitive to change. They are used in measuring instruments, warning devices and control system. The device can convert a non electrical stimulus (light, sound, pressure, etc.) into an electrical signal. Or they can convert electrical signals into non electrical signals (sound, light, etc.)

Semiconducting devices are used in measurement and detection instruments. Temperature measuring devices, such as a thermistor (an electronic thermometer), are used to operate water temperature gauges in cars, and to detect a rise in temperature to operate a relay in a fire alarm bell, etc. **Three port** and **five port valves** are activated by mechanical pressure, i.e. push-button, lever, roller trip, diaphragm plunger, etc. Cylinders, like the *double acting cylinder* can be used as a temperature-sensitive device to operate the opening and closing of windows in a green house.

◀ Transducers, Thermistors, Valves, Cylinders ▶

SEQUENTIAL CONTROL

All this means is the *order* in which things must happen. In the case of a pneumatically-operated mechanism, there may be several functions in a process to produce the end product. It is most important for each function to be done in the correct order, so that the next function does not start until the previous function is completed.

Sequential control can be in a *single cycle*, i.e. start, fuction, stop or run *continuously*, i.e. the function repeated until a programme has been completed.

SERIES CIRCUITS

When components in a circuit are connected end to end they are said to be *in series*. When resistors are connected in series, the total resistance equals the sum of the resistors. Total resistance $= R_1 + R_2$. Therefore the total resistance of two resistors in series with a resistance of 2Ω and 3Ω is 5Ω.

SHADING

This is a technique for *toning* a drawing to give it a three-dimensional quality. The tone values of light and darkness are governed first, by the angle and direction of the source of light, and then by light reflected from other objects or surfaces. This means that a surface *not* receiving direct light will be in shade, though it will be receiving some light bouncing off other objects (Fig S.14).

Even where two adjacent surfaces have similar light values, you can use some artistic licence to add a little highlight to stop the two surfaces merging. Remember that light shading, if done correctly, can give a drawing more of a three-dimensional feeling than a lot of dark shading which is done incorrectly.

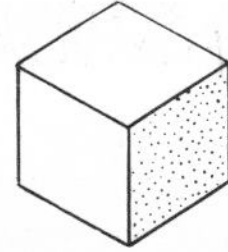
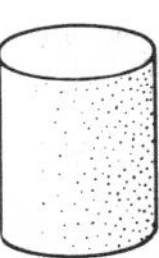
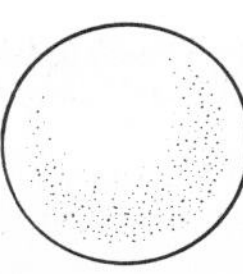

Fig S.14 Shading

SHADOW

The area where light has been *prevented* from falling on a surface. All opaque (cannot be seen through) objects cast a shadow when light has been directed at them. The two main sources of light are sunlight and artificial light. There is a greater variety of positions from which artificial light can be projected onto an object, giving more dramatic effect. Sunlight usually comes from above and from the left or the right (Fig S.15). The most straightforward method for drawing shadows is when the single source of light is from above and to the left or the right of the object.

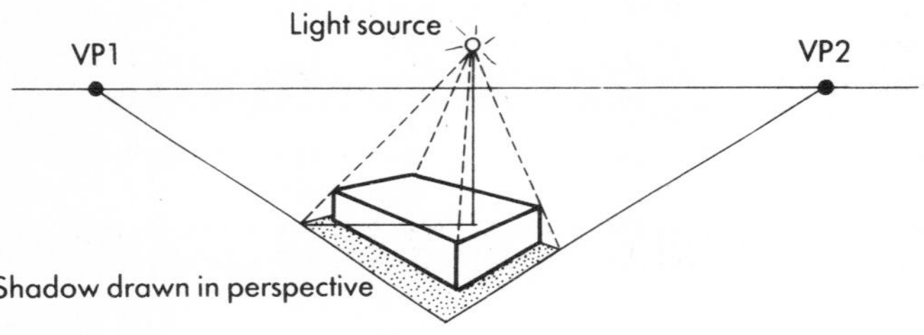

Fig S.15 Shadow

SHAFTS

A shaft is a component which transmits (mainly rotary) motion to other mechanical devices. The driving force is commonly an electric motor which is often linked to a mechanism via a pulley system and a shaft. When a shaft is in line with another shaft, the shafts are said to be 'aligned' and can be joined with a rigid coupling, e.g. flanged or muff coupling. When shafts are *not* aligned, a flexible coupling is used, e.g. rubber trunnion, ball and socket, Hook's type universal joint, etc. ◀ **Couplings** ▶

SHAKES

These are splits that occur in natural timber. They are usually found in timber that has not been seasoned properly and where timber has been exposed to constantly changing wet and dry conditions. They can also occur during the growth of the tree. In windy conditions, a tree can be subjected to very strong forces and these can cause the cells to separate. The *star* and *cup* shakes are the two most common forms of shake (Fig S.16).

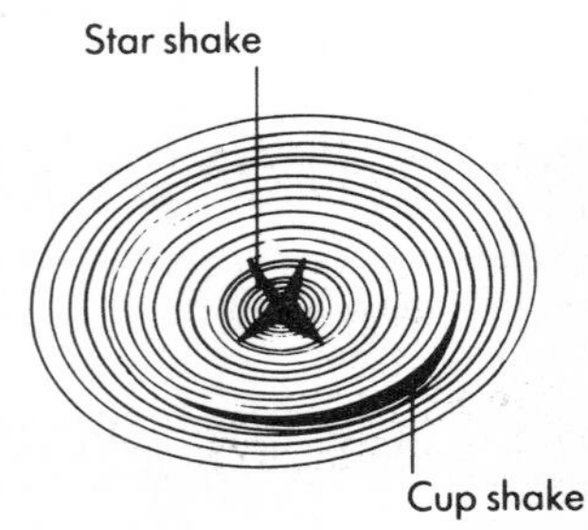

Fig S.16 Shakes

SHEAR FORCE

When two opposite forces that are nearly, but not quite, in line are placed upon a material, the material is said to be *sheared.* Tools such as garden shears, scissors, guillotine, etc. 'shear' material. Structures have to withstand many forces, one of which is the shear force.

SHELF LIFE

Once the container for a synthetic resin, such as polyester (a 'laying up' resin used in GRP work), has been opened, there is a limited period of time for it to be used. This may vary from 6 to 9 months, and be even shorter in warm temperatures. Once the resin has been exposed to the air, the **curing** process has started even though a catalyst has not been added. Buying small containers may be more expensive, but could be much less wasteful.

SHELLAC

Shellac is the substance dissolved in methylated spirits with a little resin to make French Polish. The shellac is obtained from the lac beetle.

SHOULDER

This is the part of a joint that is compared with the shoulders of a human being. They stand out at right angles to the rest of a joint and take a major share of the forces acting on the joint (Fig S.17).

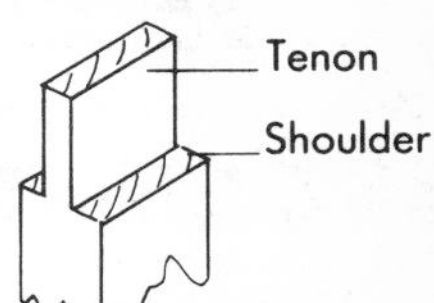

Fig S.17 Shoulder

SHOULDER PLANE

A plane especially desinged for cleaning end grain and getting into corners.

◀ Planes ▶

SHRINK-WRAPPING

This is a method of heating a plastic material, placing it over a product, and allowing it to shrink round the product to provide a close fit.

SHUNT RESISTORS

These are resistors connected in parallel. This type of circuit is often found in **ohmmeters** that are desinged to allow a low ohms reading.

SHUTTLE VALVE

A shuttle valve is one that will allow a single acting cylinder to be operated from two independent positions (Fig S.18).

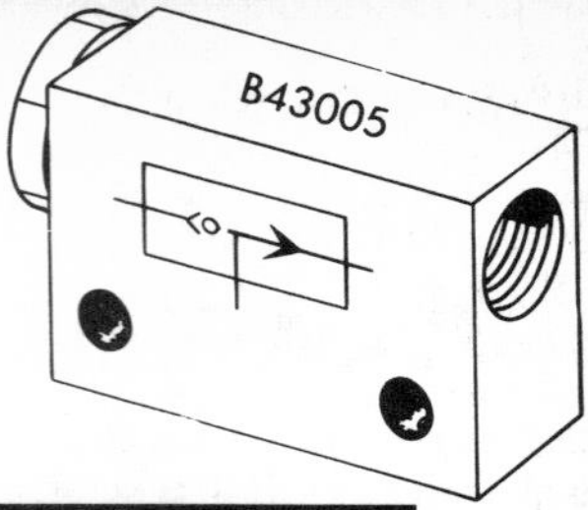

Fig S.18 Shuttle valve

SI UNITS

SI stands for 'System International d'Unites'. It is an internationally accepted system of units of measurement based upon the metre, kilogramme, second, ampere, kelvin, etc. This was done at an international conference in 1960 and replaced the Imperial units of measurements of foot, pound, and second, and modernised the centimetre, gram and second that existed in Europe.

Larger or smaller quanities are formed by multiplying or dividing these base units by 10, 100, 1000 and 1000000 etc. To aviod having lots of figures, the *initial letter* of the multiple or divider is used, e.g. mega (M), a million times; kilo (K), a thousand times; milli (m) a thousandth part of; micro (μ), a millionth part of, etc.

SIGNAL

A *signal* is a variation in voltage or current.

SIGNS

A sign is a pictorial representation or a symbol that is used to communicate an instruction or an identity. Signs are used to convey a piece of information without the use of words. ◀ **Ideograms, Pictograms, Symbols** ▶

SILICON

Silicon (Si) is a non-metal and is the most abundant element in the earth's crust, after oxygen. In its purest form it is hard material that looks like metal but has the crystal structure of diamond. when 'doped' (impurities added) silicon becomes a semiconductor. Small chips form the basis of **integrated circuits** used in solid state electronic devices such as computers, calculators etc. It is also used in solar cells to provide electrical energy. It has the atomic weight of 28.08 and an atomic number of 14.

SILVER

Silver (Ag) is mainly used as a precious metal because of its whiteness and resistance to corrosion. It is also malleable and easy to shape. Had it not been popular as a metal for making precious jewellery, it would have been more greatly used for its excellent conducting properties of heat and electricity. It has the atomic weight of 107.87 and an atomic number of 47.

SILVER SOLDER

Silver solder is an alloy of silver an other metal which lower its melting point. An alloy of 50% silver with 15% copper, 16% zinc and 19% cadmium produces a silver solder that has a melting range between 620°C and 640°C. A silver solder 75% silver has a higher melting range, between 720°C and 765°C.

A range of silver solders from Easy Flow No 2, Easy, Medium, Hard and Enamelling, make it possible for a number of soldering joints to be done on a single product. The high melting point solder (Enamelling solder or Hard solder) should be used first. Then, by using a lower melting point solder on the next stage, the first joint should not melt.

SILVER STEEL

This is a precision-ground steel that is available in 330 mm lengths. The name silver has nothing to do with its ingredients, only with its appearance. It is bright and is used mainly for making tools and components that have to be made with precision. The sectional shape is either square or round.

SILVER STEEL K.E.A.

This is a bright steel that has all the qualities of silver steel with the added advantage of being easily machined.

SINE WAVE

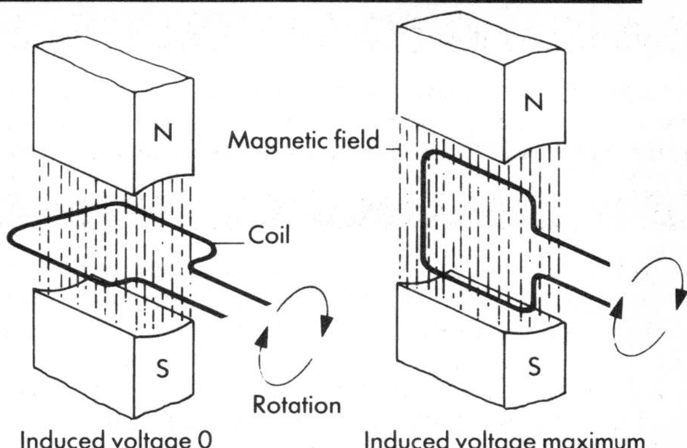

Fig S.19 Coil rotating in a magnetic field

When an alternating current is produced, the voltage changes continually from negative to positive polarities and back again. It can vary in amplitude (value) and time. A complete change from a zero value to a maximum positive amplitude, back to zero an on to a maximum negative amplitude and back to a zero value, is known as a *cycle*. This can be shown on the screen of an oscilloscope and the wave pattern (see Fig A.3) is known as a sine wave. The sine wave is produced as a result of a coil rotating in a magnetic field (Fig S.19). Though the sine wave may vary its form, it is easily recognised and all waves that have this appearance are known as 'Sinusoidal'. This distinguishes them from other wave forms. ◄ **Wave forms** ►

SINGLE ACTING PNEUMATIC CYLINDER

Cylinders are devices for producing a force in a linear motion. The bicycle pump is an example of a pneumatic cylinder. If air were blowin into it from the end where air comes out when it is used as a pump, the handle will move out in a linear motion. This is exactly how a single acting cylinder works.

When air is forced into the cylinder, the piston rod moves out, and when the air pressure is released the spring forces the piston and piston rod to return to its original positon. These cylinders are only used where little force and motion are required, e.g. operating a press switch. ◄ **Pneumatics** ►

SINGLE PLATE FRICTION CLUTCH

A *clutch* is a mechanical device for transmitting rotary motion smoothly from a *driving source* to another mechanical device that is to be *driven*. The single plate friction clutch is a simple mechanism which can be used in light powered systems.

SINGLE POINT PERSPECTIVE

All lines representing horizontal planes that are going away from the viewer meet at a *single vanishing point*. This point is always on the eye level (or the horizon line). A useful method for drawing rooms is sometimes called the *interior perspective*. ◄ **Perspective** ►

SOFT SOLDER

This is a group of solders that are an alloy of lead and tin. They melt at much lower temperatures than silver solders and are extensively used in electronic circuits.

Cored soft solder has a core of non-corrosive flux. This melts when heated and can flow over the electrical join before the solder melts and flows to complete the process. Only non-corrosive fluxes must be used on electrical/electronic work. Where much larger surfaces are to be joined using a soft solder, e.g. 'sweating' a copper base to a container or joining a tin plate lap joint, soft solder sticks or paints may be used. Because all surfaces of the metal to be joined must be chemically cleaned, a corrosive flux may be used. It can be easily washed after soldering has been completed and so prevent any remaining flux from attacking the metal.

Soft solder is available as a stick, wire, or a paint. The melting point ranges between 183°C and 276°C. Wire solders are used for fine work. Stick solders are used where a generous supply of solder is needed in joining metal sheet and pipes, etc. Paint solder is a powdered solder in a liquid flux and can be painted onto the surface to be joined. It can be used for general soft soldering but not for electrical work becuase of the corrosive flux.

SOFT SOLDERING PROCESS

As with any soldering process the metal to be joined must be clean. Clean means that the metal must *not* have a layer of oxide, which forms on most metals when exposed to the air, making them dull or tarnished. It is this oxide that has to be removed. Oxides can be removed *physically*, using a file or abrasive cloth, or *chemically*, using zinc chloride. There is no barrier then between the solder and the metal to be joined. Zinc chloride is corrosive, so do not use it on electrical work. Resin or tallow are two non-corrosive fluxes and are conveniently contained in the centre of the solder so that the soldering process is done in a single operation.

Soldering using a soldering iron

- The bit of the iron should be 'tinned' (have a coating of solder melted over its surface). The heated bit will melt the solder and make it ready for use. The bit is held against the parts to be joined, sufficiently long to allow to heat to be conducted to the work. When, and only when, the parts are at a temperature at which the solder will melt does it begin to 'run' from the bit. To replace the used solder, the bit will have to be touched with the end of the solder stick or wire as and when needed. As soon as the bit is removed from the work, it will cool and the solder solidify.

Soldering using a gas torch

- The torch gently heats the area to be joined by moving the flame to side. Touching the surface with the solder will quickly show whether or not the work is hot enough. As soon as the solder shows signs of melting, be less generous with the heating but try to maintain just sufficient to allow the solder to 'run'. As soon as the join appears to be sufficiently supplied with solder, remove the flame and the solder will quickly solidify.

If a paint is used, this can be heated by either using a soldering iron or a gas torch. The surface to be joined is painted while it is cold. The work is then gently heated until the solder melts and 'runs'. When using a *gas torch* there is always a danger of over heating the work and make it impossible for the process to be successful. Remember that the red heat is approximately 700°C, and you are only wanting a temperature around 200°C. ◀ Soldering iron ▶

SOFTWARE

This is the programme of instructions which are stored in the memory to enable a computer to work, i.e. respond to specific funtions such as moving a cursor. You may think of software as that which you cannot see. Anything that *can* be seen, is called hardware. ◀ Hardware ▶

SOFTWOOD

A botanical identification of wood that comes from coniferous trees (trees that have cones, needle-shaped leaves and are evergreen). The term can generally apply when comparing 'hardwoods' that come from deciduous trees, i.e. ones that have broad leaves which are replaced each year. However, there are some exceptions to the rule. *Pitch pine* is classified as a softwood, yet is much harder than many hardwoods. *Balsa* is a hardwood, yet it is softer and lighter than any soft wood.

Cedar, Larch, Yellow pine, Pitch pine, European redwood, Yew, Douglas fir and Sequoia are examples of softwoods that are in general use. They are different from hardwoods in that they have resin cells and, as in the case of Pitch Pine, can be sticky to handle and difficult to plane because the resin blocks the plane.

SOLAR ENERGY

Though almost all forms of energy source can be traced back to the sun, solar energy is energy which is trapped directly from the sun's rays in solar cells. These are electronic devices that convert radiation into electrical energy, e.g. a p-n junction. They are the most important power supply for satellites and space vehicles. They are made from a range of semiconductors, including silicon, gallium, arsenide, selenuum-cadmium sulphide, etc. Becuase of the low level of electrical output, solar cells are only used in devices that require a low level source of energy to function, e.g. watches and pocket-sized calculators.

SOLDERING

◀ Brazing, Soft soldering process, Soldering iron ▶

SOLDERING IRON

These are devices used in the process of soft soldering. There are two types: one is heated in a gas flame; the other is heated electrically, with the heating element forming part of the soldering iron. *Gas heated irons* are mainly used for large work, such as soldering copper, tinplate, and zinc coated steel sheet material. *Electrical irons* are used for soldering fine work, as in electrical circuits.

SPECIFICATION

Most **design briefs** contain precise requirements, i.e. details which have already been decided and are on no account to be changed. 'Precise detail' usually refers to types of material, sizes, quantity, etc. If a container has to be designed using acrylic, must be no larger than 250 mm × 300 mm × 50 mm, with 20 units to be made, then these details are very exacting and could be considered as a Specification or 'Spec' for short.

SPEED RATIO

◀ Velocity ratio ▶

SPIRAL ARCHIMEDEAN

Sometimes referred to as the *Archimedean Screw*. This engineering device was invented by a Greek mathematician who lived 287 – 212 BC, i.e. just over 2200 years ago. It was then used as a device for lifting water from one level to another. Such devices still exist on the banks of the River Nile to raise water for the irrigation of fields. The principle is also used to force molten plastic materials in the extrusion of pipes, rods etc (Fig S.20). ◀ Screws ▶

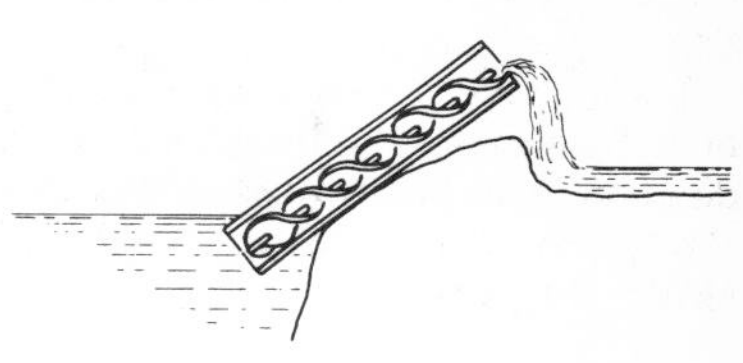

Fig S.20 Spiral Archimedean or Archimedean screw

SPLIT PATTERN

A pattern that is used in a casting process, it can be made of more than one piece. In which case it has to be designed so that the parts can hold together easily and be separated easily. The halves of a pattern can be held together with lugs. Split patterns are only necessary where it would be impossible to remove a pattern from a mould if it were in one piece. ◀ Pattern ▶

SPROCKET AND CHAIN

Many drive mechanisms use a belt or chain to transmit rotary motion from one component to another; the sprocket and chain has the advantage of not slipping. The most well-known example of its use is on the bicycle, where direct positive drive is important. However many machines use sprocket and chain drive systems (Fig S.21).

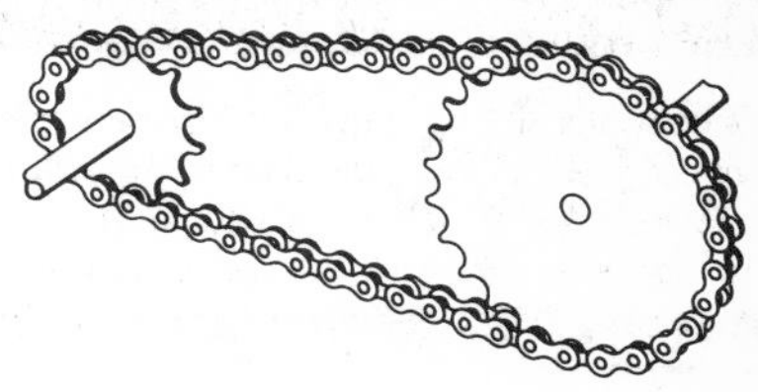

Fig S.21 Sprocket and chain

SPRUE HOLE

This is the hole made in a sand mould to allow molten metal to flow into the cavity made by a pattern, and to rise up another hole when the cavity is full. ◀ Casting ▶

SPRUE PIN

This is the tapered length of round-sectioned wood that is used to make a sprue hole in a sand mould. There are normally two pins, one a little fatter than the other. The fatter one is used for the *pouring hole*, i.e. the hole into which the molten metal will be poured. The thinner one is used to make the *rising hole*.

The reason for the difference in size, is simply that it is important for the molten metal to get into the cavity without delay; the riser is only there to allow air to escape and to show when the mould is full.

SPUR GEARS

These are *gear wheels* that have teeth, and the teeth of one wheel are shaped so that they will mesh (fit) with the teeth of another wheel. The size of the teeth must always be the same, no matter what the size of the gear wheel. Gear wheel sizes are known by their number of teeth. By being able to select gear wheels of different sizes, some **shafts** can be made to rotate more quickly or more slowly. A gear wheel with 40 teeth driving a gear wheel with 20 teeth, means that for one complete revolution of the 40- toothed gear, the 20-toothed gear will have to revolve twice. This means that it will be rotating twice as fast. ◄ Gears ►

STEEL

Steel is an alloy of iron and carbon. Freshly smelted iron may contain as much as 5% carbon and in this state it is difficult to use. It is extremely brittle and hard and will not respond to hammering and machining. When the level of carbon reduced to as little as 1.7% or less, it is called steel. Steel, although an alloy, can alloy with other metals such as nickel, chromium, tungsten, molybdenum, manganese, copper, vanadium, etc. *Stainless steel* is an alloy of steel, nickel and chromium, and is ideally suitable for cultery since it does not rust and is easy to keep clean. **High speed steel** is an alloy of steel and tungsten and, because it is tough and resistant to high temperatures, it is ideally suited for lathe turning tools, drills, etc. The cutting can be done at high speeds without the tool getting blunt, hence the name 'High Speed Steel'.

STENCILS

A stencil is an aid to drawing things quickly and with uniformity. At one time the most common stencils were for letters of the alphabet. But with the growth in the use of symbols, letters form a small proportion of the wide range of stencils/templates are now available. There are stencils for drawing circles, ellipses, hexagonal-headed bolts and nuts, parabolic curve, computer diagrams, furniture, etc. (Fig S.22). Though these are aids to improve the quality of presentation and the speed of drawing, considerable care is still needed to produce good results.

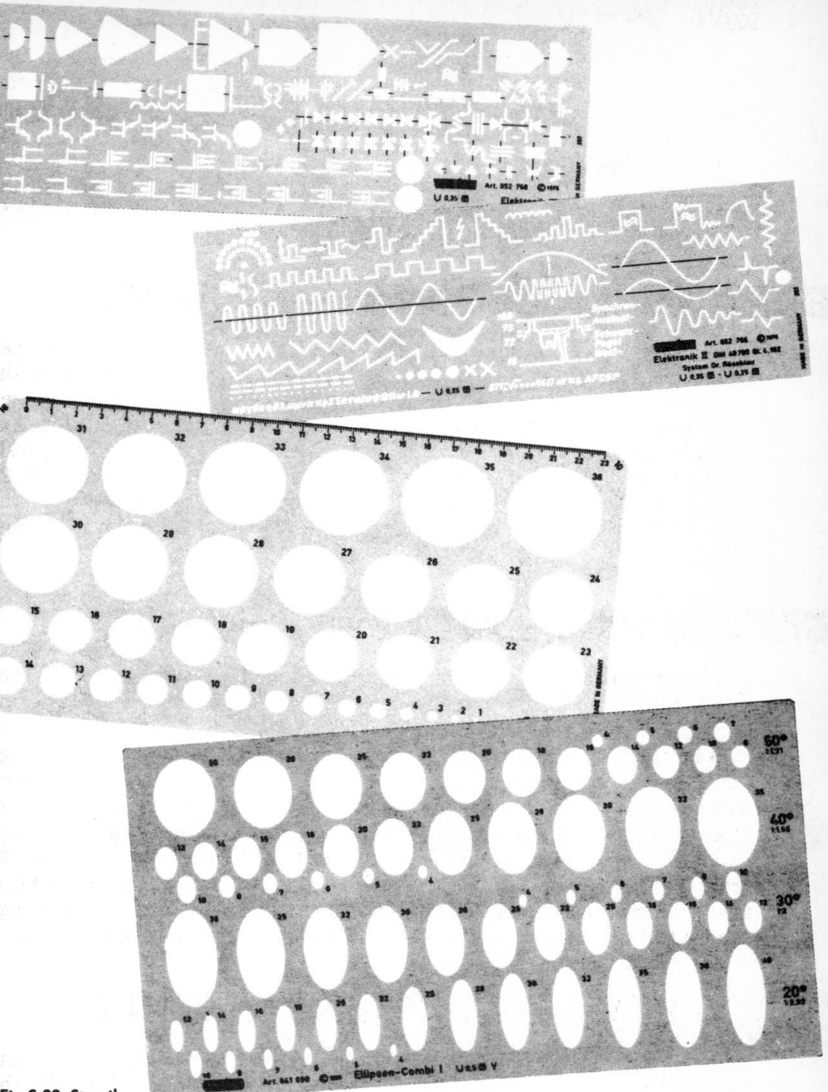

Fig S.22 Stencils

STRAIN

When a material is under strain it changes size and shape. Strain is caused by an external force, e.g. tension (pulling), compression (squeezing), torsion (twisting), etc. ◀ **Hooke's law, Modulus of elasticity, Stress** ▶

STRAIN GAUGE

This is an instrument used to measure the strain of a solid material at its surface. When a solid material is under strain, its electrical resistance is lowered, and a measurable current can be detected.

The resistance strain gauge

This has a fine wire that is attached to the surface of a material. As the material responds to a strain, so the voltage difference in the wire will indicate the strain in the material.

The electromagnetic strain gauge

This has a soft iron armature that is attached to the surface of the material, but free to move inside an inductive coil. As the surface moves, so the armature moves inside the coil, causing a variation in the inductance in the coil.

The piezoelectric strain gauge

This has a quartz crystal attached to the surface of the material. When a force is applied to the material, so that force will act upon the crystal. As the strain on the crystal increases, so the voltage difference increases.

Strain gauges are used to test the effects of loads on materials, especially when they form part of a structure. They are also fitted permanently to structures such as bridges, so that a constant watch can be maintained.

◀ Piezoelectric effect ▶

STRATEGY

The method or plan by which a project, assignment, or problem may be resolved. How a piece of work is to be completed.

STRENGTH

The strength of a structure can depend upon a number of different factors, such as the properties of the material, the type of construction, the arrangement of component parts and the accuracy of construction. A weak structure can be the result of just one of these factors being wrong.

STRESS

The force acting on an object divided by its area.

◀ Hooke's law, Strain ▶

STRUCTURE

There are two main groups, natural and man-made structures.

NATURAL STRUCTURES

Natural structures are designed to perform specific functions. The bole (main trunk) of a tree has to support branches and provide the channel for conveying water and mineral salts to the leaves. It has to make sure that the leaves of the tree receive sunlight, so that *photosynthesis* can take place, with carbon dioxide from the air combining with the water and mineral salts that have been taken in via the roots. This process makes the sugars that provide the food for the tree to grow. This over-simplified description should begin to show you that a tree is an example of complex structure and that each component part has an important role to play for the tree to live.

Trees are also designed to withstand changes in the seasonal climate. Trees find it difficult to take in water during the cold season, so the parts that require water stop functioning, either by dropping their leaves or by having a needle-shaped leaf that requires very little water. The bole of trees is shaped to withstand sideways forces from wind, by being wider at the base where greater forces have to be taken. Branches hang downwards in regions where it is very cold and where there is a lot of snow. The downward slope allows the branch to bend even further with the weight of the snow so that the snow slides off. If you look more closely into the design of trees and other natural things, including animals, plants, insects, fish, etc., you will see that they survive because of their suitable design to cope with the environment.

MAN-MADE STRUCTURES

Man-made structures are those where man has made changes from a natural environment to make survival easier and more comfortable. Anything that is *not* a natural structure is a man-made structure, but man has used natural structures or materials from which to make his own structures, such as buildings, machines, artefacts, etc.

SUBDIVIDE

To divide something more than once.

SUB-SYSTEMS

A sub-system is an important part of a much larger system. An **integrated circuit** is a sub-system of a computer system, the braking system is a sub-system of a bicycle, etc.

SURFACE DEVELOPMENT

This is a *two-dimensional shape* which, when bent or folded, will take on a *three-dimensional form*. Most packaging starts off from a flat piece of sheet material. Only when the surface development is worked out and drawn can the material be cut to shape, ready for bending.

SURFACE TREATMENT

This covers a wide range of treatments, such as painting, polishing, rendering, sealing, punching, enamelling, etc. Any activity which results in a surface changing its appearance has been *treated* in some way or another. ◀ Finishes ▶

SWITCHES

Switches are devices that either connect or disconnect an electrical circuit so that a current may flow or cease to flow. The connecting device is a conductor and is controlled by the movement of an insulated lever, button, knob, etc. Or, as in the case of **reed switches**, by a magnet or an energised electromagnet.

The *toggle switch* is the type that operates a light in the home. The *rocker switch* does the same thing and is an alternative design which can be operated more easily by handicapped and elderly people. *Push-button switches* either stay normally open, as for example in the door bell, or can be pushed to stay closed (On) and pushed again to open (Off), as found on radios, computers, television sets, etc. *Rotary switches* can have many switching patterns, and these are found on heating devices such as hot-plates or ovens that require different settings. ◀ Reed switch, Relay switch ▶

SYMBOLS

The increased need for communication between people who speak a different language that has led to a growth in symbols that anyone can understand. Symbols need to be clear and precise. This is achieved by keeping a symbol simple and by using shapes that can be easily recognised.

British Standards publication PP7307 contains examples of most of the symbols you are likely to need. You are recommended to use these since they are nationally accepted.

SYMMETRICAL/SYMMETRY

When one half of an object or pattern is the *mirror image* of the other then the object or pattern is said to be symmetrical (Fig S.23). Symmetry is often thought of as balance. When things are balanced they are restful and aesthetically acceptable. When things are not balanced, they are less restful and usually are aesthetically difficult to accept.

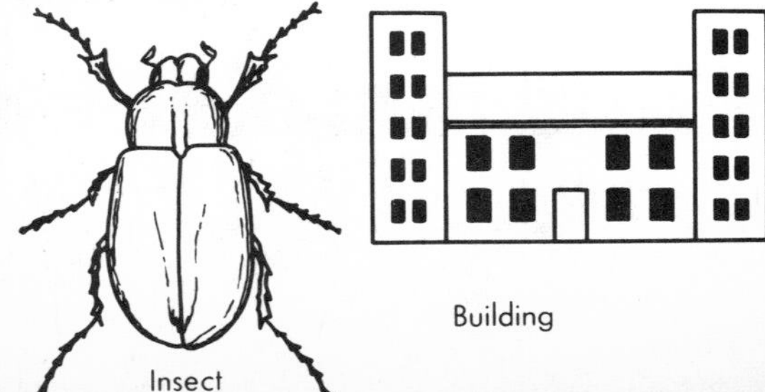

Fig S.23 Symmetry

SYNCHRONISATION

This is the process of keeping a number of activities taking place at the same time. A group of dancers or synchronised swimmers carry out identical movements and pauses at the same time as each other. Electronic systems use circuits in which to generate a pulse at regular, accurate intervals. Many transmitting and receiving devices depend on the exact timing of a pulse, i.e. the pulses are synchronised. These pulses are called 'sync' pulses or 'strobe' pulses.

SYNTHESIS

The bringing together of all the parts. The opposite of analysis. When you are involved with desiging, solving a problem, etc., you will have obtained information during the research and have developed a number of solutions. To synthesise is to bring the information and ideas together, selecting what is worthwhile and rejecting what is not suitable. In other words, you are making decisions that will solve the problem.

TANGENCY

This is the point where a tangent to a circle just touches the circumference. When arcs are joined to straight lines it is important to know the point of tangency, so that a smooth transition is achieved (i.e. you can't see the join) (Fig T.1). When joining straight and curved lines, it is always easier to draw the curved line first and the straight line or lines second.

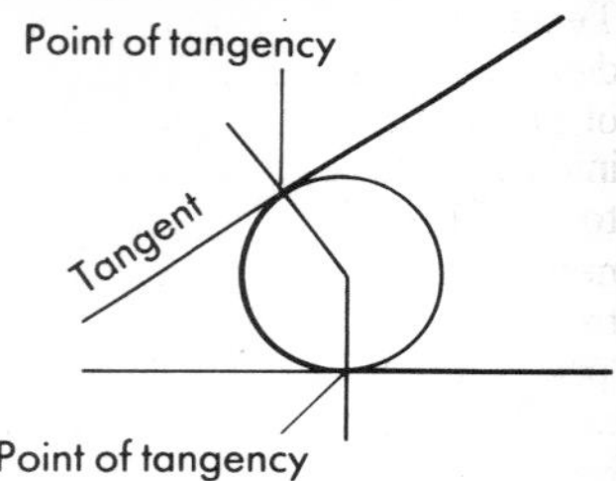

Fig T.1 Tangency

TAPER

A taper is where a rod or bar keeps its cross-sectional shape but gets smaller as it gets nearer the end. Tapers are used where a good tight fit is required, e.g. drills in drilling machines, lathe centres. If a force is applied to push the tapered drill into a tapered hole, it will hold more tightly against the sides of the tapered hole. It is important that the taper on the drill matches the taper hole in the column of the drilling machine. Tapers are given a *Morse taper number* from 1 to 6 (Fig T.2a)). Where taper numbers are not identical it is possible to use a *morse taper sleeve* to make up the difference (Fig T.2b)).

The tapering of a piece of metal is done more for aesthetic reasons than functional reasons (Fig T.2c)). Tools are often tapered to reduce bulk and to make the tool lighter and easier to use (Fig T.2d)).

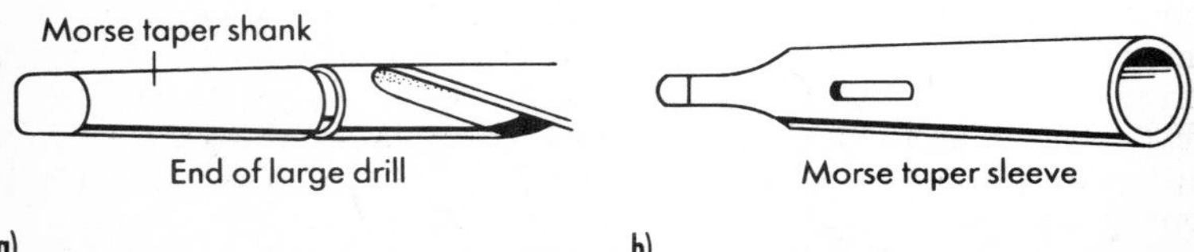

a) b)

Fig T.2 Taper

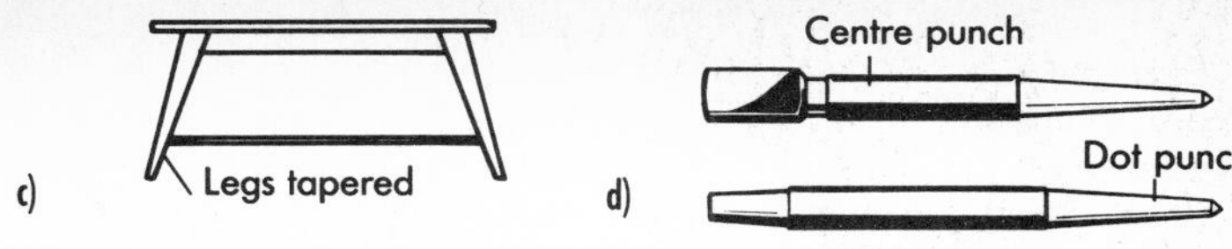

TAPS

◄ Dies ►

TECHNOLOGY AND SOCIETY

Technology has made considerable advances in the last 50 years. The developments that now enable you to see and hear someone on the other side of the world, or indeed in space, have come largely through new technologies involving television and satellite communication. These events were thought to be impossible less than a century ago. Nevertheless it is increasingly necessary to examine the advantages and disadvantages of gaining so much technical knowledge, since all new developments only came at a 'price'. This 'price' must include more than just money. The price of having electrical energy generated by atomic energy is very high when people lose their lives because of radiation leaks, or when fields become contaminated and unsafe to use even by animals. The aerosol sprays make it easy to apply a paint or a hair lacquer, but are they worthwhile when the propellants are known to damage the ozone layer that protects us from the damaging rays of the sun?

The two aspects of *advantage* and *disadvantage* have to be considered for every new development. You could do this with any item that *you* choose, whether it is the motor car, the high-speed train, the laying of a new piece of motorway or something as basic as eating food grown using chemical fertilizers.

Always try to *identify* the advantages and disadvantages and then try to reach a *conclusion* when answering questions based upon this wide topic. The important point is to show that you do take the various aspects into account. Even if an examiner disagrees with your conclusion, he can at least see *how aware you are* about the effects of technology upon society.

TEMPERATURE MEASUREMENT

The need to know the temperature in the heat treatment of metal is quite critical if the desired results are to be achieved. Much of the measurement in annealing, hardening and tempering is judged by *colour*. Colour is achieved on bright tool steel by heating and watching the oxides form on the surface; the first colour to appear is a yellow to pale brown colour, and this appears at approximately 230°C. As the temperature rises, so the colour changes to brown, dark brown, purple and blue at about 295°C.

At much higher temperatures a metal will glow from dull red to bright red, then orange and on to white. This is again judgement by colour and is only helpful to a person with a well-trained eye.

More accurate ways of measuring temperature can be done by using an instrument such as *Thermocouple, Thermometer* or an *Optical Pyrometer.* Thermocouples are useful for measuring a wide range of temperatures; thermometers for measuring temperatures in the lower range; and optical pyrometers in the higher range. ◀ **Thermocouple, Thermometer** ▶

TEMPERING TOOL STEEL

This is usually the second stage of hardening and tempering.
◀ **Hardening and tempering** ▶

TEMPLATE

An aid for drawing letters, figures and symbols such as those used in flow diagrams, electrical and electronic circuits, etc. The term **stencil** is also used. Templates can be made to suit a particular need. It could be for marking out a shape that is going to be repeated many times, as in batch production, or for marking out the position of the centre of holes to be drilled on a number of identical pieces of material. Templates are only useful where work is repetitive. They are aids to lessen the time to perform a function, such as drawing or marking out, and to produce identical shapes, measurements, etc. The more times a template is used, the more it helps to justify the time, energy, cost, etc of producing the template.

TENON

The protruding part that fits into a mortice is called the tenon. The proportions are important for strength. Figure T.3 shows the recommended proportions used in solid timber constructions.

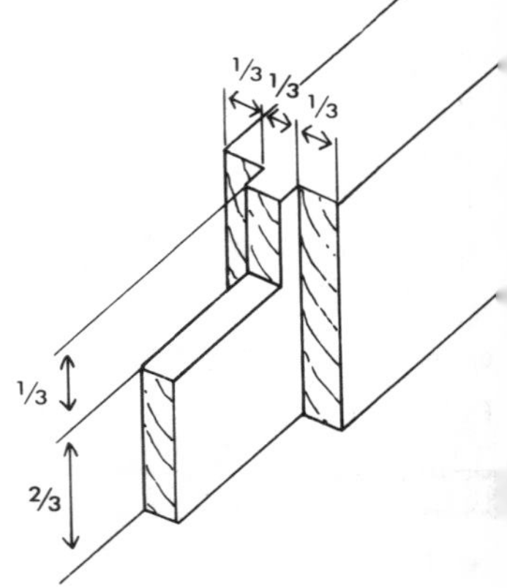

Fig T.3 Tenon

TENSILE STRENGTH

A tensile force is a pulling or stretching force, and the tensile strength of a material is measured by its resistance to being pulled apart. Materials can be tested on a *tensometer* which will measure the load required to fracture a material of a standard size. It is important that the size of the materials being tested to be the same, so that a proper comparison can be made. The tensometer records the changes (Fig T.4).

As the load increases, you see that the material gets longer. At first there is little change, but when the material reaches its **elastic limit**, i.e. the point where it will not return to its original length, it gets longer more quickly.

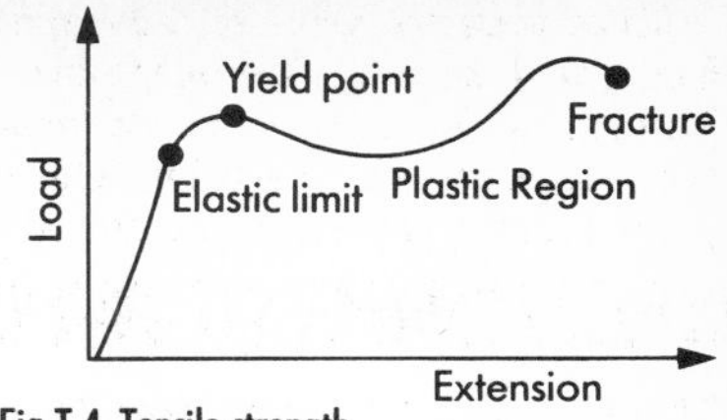

Fig T.4 Tensile strength

Eventually it has little resistance to the stretching load and then has no resistance (*yield point*) and stretches very easily until it breaks. The graph is a scaled-up version of what happens to the material so that the points of change can be identified easily.

◀ Material characteristics ▶

TENSION

Any component in a structure that is said to be in tension is being pulled. The diagonal piece in the construction in Figure T.5a) is in tension.

It is important to remember that tension is the opposite to **compression**. By *combining* a structure with bulky members to support compression, with members that are often much thinner to withstand tension, a stable construction is possible (Fig T.5b)). Struts support compressive forces. Ties withstand pulling forces.

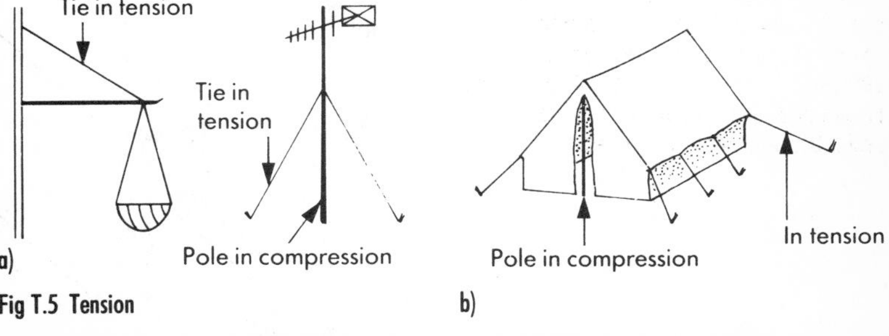

Fig T.5 Tension **b)**

TERTIARY INDUSTRY

◀ Industry ▶

TESSELLATIONS

These are patterns made by repeating a shape called a *tessera*. The simplest tessera is a square, but other geometric forms such as quadrilateral, equilateral triangle, regular pentagon, regular hexagon, etc. can be used to form tessellations (Fig T.6). Isometric grid or square grid paper can be used to create tessellations.

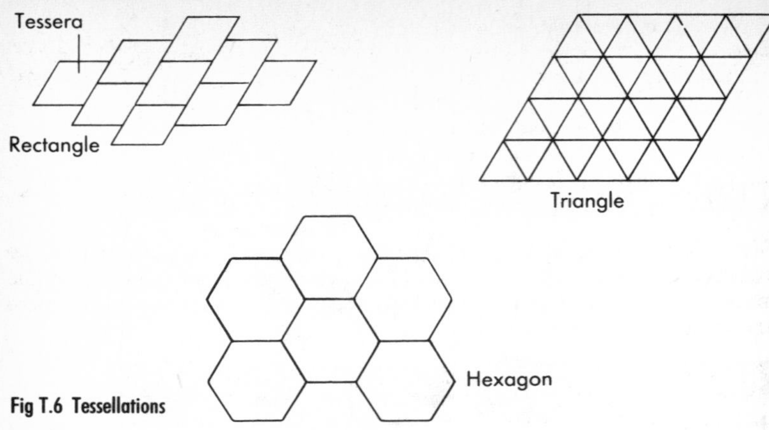

Fig T.6 Tessellations

TEXTURE

The texture of a surface is measured by how it feels if you rub your hand across it. It may feel smooth or rough or be of varying degrees of roughness, i.e. coarse, very coarse, etc. Texture can also apply to techniques of drawing and colouring where the medium is itself textured by adding a texture paste to create a rough surface. The impression of texture can also be created by careful use of a pencil or pen and ink (Fig T.7). You must be careful when applying these techniques to consider tones, as in light and shade, and to remember how light falls on a three dimensional object.

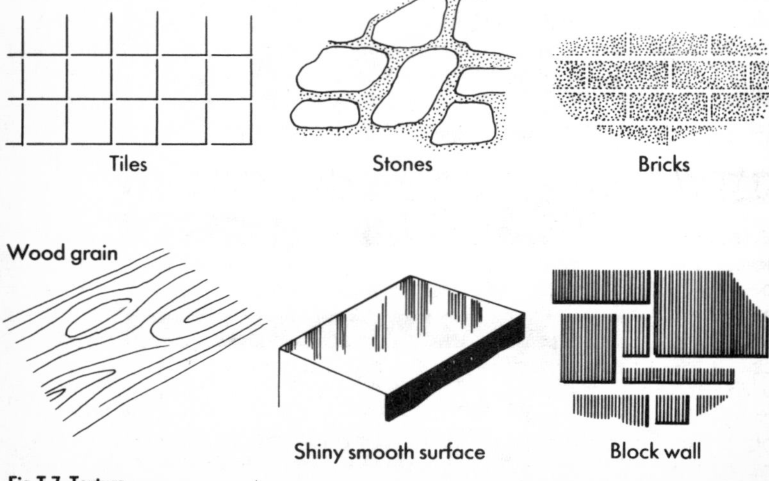

Fig T.7 Texture

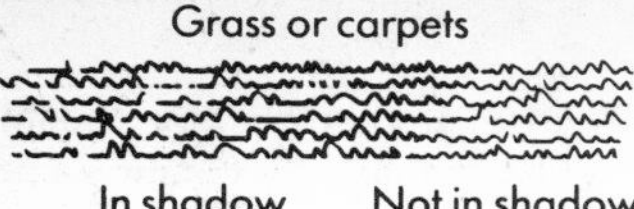

In shadow Not in shadow

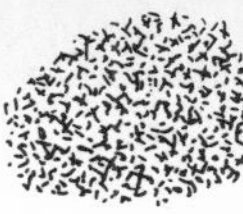
Fabric

Woven fabric

THERMAL ENERGY

Also referred to as heat energy. Heat in a material is dependent upon the vibration of the molecules or atoms. The faster they move, the hotter the material. Because this type of energy is dependent upon *movement*, it is also known as *Kinetic Energy*.

THERMAL INSULATION

Heat flows by *conduction* through solid material; by *convection* where the air forms a current (e.g. hot air rising and cool air replacing it from below; and *radiation*where heat rays pass directly through the air. To prevent this flow is to *insulate* the movement. Insulation can also be made possible by removing air so that heat loss is not possible by convection. In the case of a *vacuum flask*, a silver reflecting glass is used to stop heat loss by radiation.

Natural materials that are good thermal insulators includes wool, eider down (from the eider duck), fir from animals, etc. *Synthetic materials* that are good thermal insulators include expanded polystyrene, silver-surfaced fibres of asbestos, etc.

THERMISTOR

Thermistor is short for *Thermal resistor*, It is very sensitive to temperature changes and is used in temperature-sensing circuits. It has a high negative temperature coefficient, so that as the temperature rises, its resistance gets less. Thermistors are semiconductors made of ceramic material and they are available as discs, washers, beads and rods. They are used to either detect temperature changes or to measure temperature changes.

THERMOCOUPLE

A thermocouple is an electrical thermometer. When two dissimilar metals are joined together, they produce an electric current. The hotter the joined end becomes, the higher the current of electricity. If the free ends are connected in a circuit that includes a meter, the needle will deflect showing that a current is flowing. If the meter is calibrated in degrees Celsius, a temperature reading can be made. The advantage of using a thermocouple is that it can cover a wide range of temperatures. It can also be used in small places, and the meter can be some distance away from the temperature being measured. The range of the temperatures to be measured depends on the nature of the dissimilar metals used. ◀ Heat-sensitive circuit ▶

THERMO FORMING

Many materials become soft and flexible when heated, i.e. they become plastic, and it is at this stage they can be easily formed into a desired shape. **Thermoplastic materials** are easily shaped when heated. They can be vacuum-formed or blow-moulded into shape and, when cool again, become rigid, keeping their new shape.

THERMOMETER

The Thermometer is used to measure temperatures, A commonly used design is one with a quantity of mercury contained in a glass tube that has a narrow bore and seal at both ends. The lower end contains a small reservoir of mercury, sufficient to occupy the full length of the marked or calibrated tube.

When the temperature rises, the mercury expands. When the temperature falls, the mercury contacts (gets smaller). Because the change in temperature and the movement of the mercury are related, this is sometimes referred to as an *analogous system.*

Thermometers are calibrated in either degrees Celsius (Centigrade) or Fahrenheit. On most thermometers the Centigrade scale starts at zero degrees and ends at 100 degrees; the Fahrenheit scale starts at 32 degrees and ends at 212 degrees, the lowest reading being the freezing point of water and the highest reading being the boiling point of water.

To *convert* from the Fahrenheit scale to the Celsius scale you take away 32 and multiply by 5/9. For example, to convert 68°F to Centigrade:

$$68 - 32 = 36 \times 5 = 180 \div 9 = 20$$

Therefore 68°F = 20°C

THERMOPLASTICS

A thermoplastic material is one that becomes soft when heated. Examples include Acrylic, Nylon, Polystyrene, Polythene, Polypropylene, Polytetrafluorethylene (PTFE), Polyvinyl Chloride (PVC).

Uses include lenses, safety glass, clothing, insulation, washing-up bowls, guttering, plumbing, carrier bags, packaging, etc.

THERMOSETTING PLASTICS

Thermosetting plastics start off as a resin and, when a chemical is added, become set or 'cured'. Once this has happened they cannot be softened by heating or by any other means. Examples include: Urea Formaldehyde, Phenol Formaldehyde, Melemine Formadehyde, Polyester Resin, Epoxy Resin, and Polyurethane.

Uses include laminated plastics sheeting, electrical fittings such as plugs switches, adhesives, Glass Reinforced Plastics, paints etc.

THICK FILM INTEGRATED CIRCUIT

In this type of IC the resistors and capacitors are formed into a ceramic layer, but transistors are added as discrete chips.

THIN FILM INTEGRATED CIRCUIT

In this type of IC all the components are evaporated onto an insulated material such as ceramic or glass. This helps to isolate each component.

THIXOTROPIC RESIN

A Thixitropic resin is one that will cling to a vertical surface. They are often called gel resins because they have a sticky quality and jelly-like appearance. They are used as the first coat or layer of resin in GRP work. They form the outside and smooth surface of GRP laminations.

◀ Gel coat ▶

THREAD

The word *Thread* has a different meaning according to its use: e.g. the thread of a *screw* is referring to the profile of the thread, whether square, vee, or buttress, and possibly the number of threads there are to the inch. Thread in *enamelling* is a length of very small diameter glass used to create patterns

THREE-DIMENSIONAL DRAWING

This is where three sides of an object can usually be seen. You can see a top and two sides. Perspective, isometric projection, oblique projection, and planometric projection are graphical examples of three-dimensional presentation.

THREE PORT VALVE

A *port* is a threaded hole, and a three port valve is one that has three threaded holes. The ports are numbered 1 to 3, port number 1 is where the main air supply is fitted. The cylinder is fitted to port numer 2, and port number 3 is for the air to escape (i.e. the exhaust) (Fig T.8).

These valves can be operated by a push button, plunger, or a roller trip.

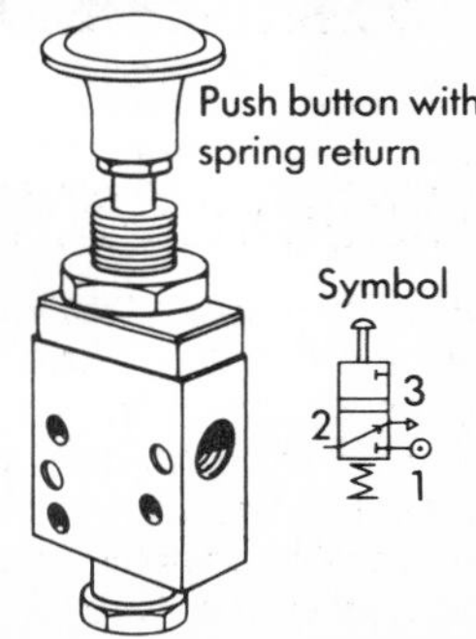

Fig T.8 Three port valve

THROW

Throw in a circuit usually means to change the direction or route of a gas, liquid or electric current.

TIDAL ENERGY

The tide of a sea is a natural source of energy. When tides are used to generate electricity by the movement of water turning turbines, this is tidal energy which can be converted into electrical energy. This system has been widely developed in France and much research has taken place to develop a tidal generation scheme in this country in the River Severn.

TIME BASE

When a voltage increases and decreases at regular intervals, at a constant rate, it is referred to as a time base. The *sawtooth wave* form shows a gradual voltage increase and a sudden fall to its starting value. The time taken for it to complete a cycle is known as the time base. (Fig T.9).

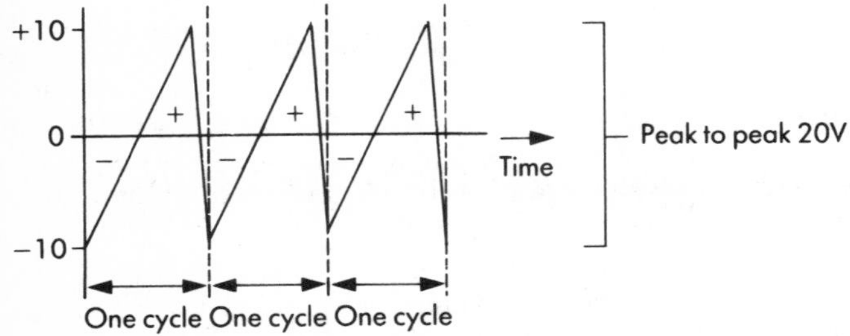

Fig T.9 Time base

TIME CONSTANT

This is the time required for a one-way electrical flow to change after a rise by approximately 63% or a fall by approximately 36%. The time constant is the time for an operation to take place in a device or a circuit. Circuits that contain capacitance or inductance can have a time constant (r) of a few seconds, e.g. a circuit containing a resistance R ohms, in series with a capacitance of C farads, is written as:

$r = RC$ seconds

When a circuit contains a resistance R in series with an inductance of L henrys, the time constant r is written as:

$r = L/R$ seconds

TIME DELAY

This is the time taken between the transmission of a signal and the receiving of a signal.

TOGGLE CLAMP

These are mechanical devices used for securing material while it is being worked upon, e.g. holding acrylic in a vacuum mould. The advantage of such a device over other holding devices is the *speed* with which it can be applied and released. By moving a lever through a small arc of 90°, the material can be secured; by moving the lever in the *reverse direction* you can release the material (Fig T. 10). This principle is also used in a device that folds when the tension has been released, e.g. umbrella, some folding chairs, hoods on prams, etc.

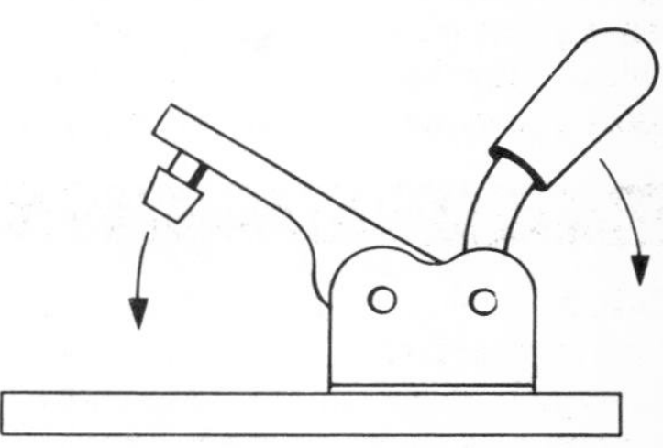

Fig T.10 Toggle clamp

TOLERANCE

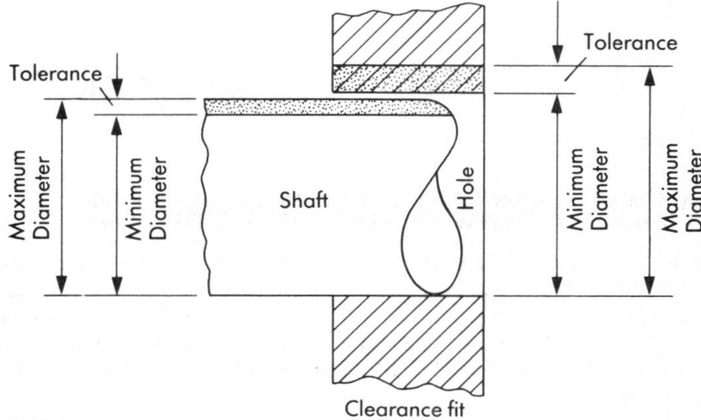

Fig T.11 Tolerance

In general terms tolerance is the range that is acceptable. In *electronic* terms this means that a device will have a tolerance level at which it will function. A resistor may be rated as having a *tolerance level* of plus or minus 10%. This means that the resistor's tolerance will go 10% above its coded value and 10% below. Therefore when a resistor has a *coded resistance value* of 25,000 ohms and a *coded tolerance value* of ±10%, it means that the resistance value may go up to 27,500 ohms, or down 22,500 ohms.

Tolerance in *engineering* terms is the level of accuracy that is acceptable for one component to fit inside another. The tolerance is the *difference* between the maximum measurement and minimum measurement of, say, a *hole*, and the maximum and minimum measurement of a *shaft* that has to go inside the hole (Fig T.11). The three levels are a 'Clearance' fit so that a shaft can run freely (see Fig T.11); a 'Transition' fit so that it can be easily pushed backwards or forwards; or an 'Interference' fit, where considerable force is required to fit the shaft in the hole. An interference fit occurs when the shaft diameter is larger than the diameter of the hole.

TORQUE

A twisting or turning force. ◀ Forces ▶

TOUGHNESS

The toughness of a material is its ability to withstand forces such as compression, tension, shear and torque. Do *not* confuse this term with hardness. A hard material such as iron or glass is hard but also brittle, and will easily break if a force is applied.

TRAMMEL

A trammel is a narrow strip of material, usually paper, used to plot the path of a moving point about a fixed point. Often used to construct an ellipse and to solve loci problems.

TRANSDUCERS

A device that changes a non-electrical property such as sound, light and pressure into an electrical signal. Many sensing devices are transducers, e.g. strain gauge, photocell, microphone, thermistor, etc.

TRANSFORMER

An apparatus for reducing or increasing the voltage of an alternating current.

TRANSISTOR

The term transistor comes from the first part of *trans*former and the last part of resistor. The transistor is a semiconducting device. there are two main groups the n–p–n (i.e. negative – positive – negative) and the p–n–p (i.e. positive – negative – positive).

The leads on a transistor are b base, e emitter, and c collector. Each lead must be identified so that it can be used in a circuit the correct way round (Fig

T. 12). The transistor is quite small; it is less than 1 cubic cm in volume and, in micro-integrated circuits, several hundred can fit into a silicon chip 1mm square. Transistors can function as either switches or amplifiers.

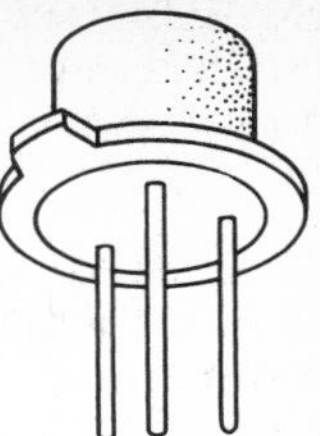

Fig T.12 Transistor

TRANSISTOR-TRANSISTOR LOGIC (TTL)

This is a group of high-speed integrated logic circuits. There are two families of logic gates, the TTL that are identified by numbers that start with 74, and the CMOS family that uses numbers in the 4000 range. These devices can be designed to perform simple switching functions, as on a washing machine, or high-speed functions, as in a calculator or a digital computer system. In this case information may be stored and retrieved as well as counting functions taking place.

TRANSMISSION

This is the movement of a function from one place to another. In *electrical* terms, it may be as simple as operating a switch so that an electric light will operate. In *engineering* or *mechanical* terms, this will mean the transferring of a movement from one part to another in a machine, e.g. the rotation of an armature of an electric motor leading to the rotation of a drill bit.

Transmission is achieved through such devices as pulley systems, gears, couplings, clutches, rack and pinions, shafts, and cams, etc. Reduction of speed and increase of speed is achieved through gears and pulleys. In pneumatics, transmission is achieved through air pressure, cylinders, valves, flow regulators and logic devices.

TRAPEZIUM

This is a four-sided figure that has two parallel sides of different length.
◀ Rectangle ▶

TRIANGLES

These are three-sided figures. The internal angles add up to 180°. There are three types: Equilateral, Isosceles and Scalene (Fig T. 13). As a structure, the triangle is the most stable unit. In such constructions as bridges, electric pylons, cranes, rooves, etc. the stability is achieved through a *combination* of triangular shapes. When one member comes under compression, another member provides an equal and opposite force by being in tension.

Fig T.13 Triangles

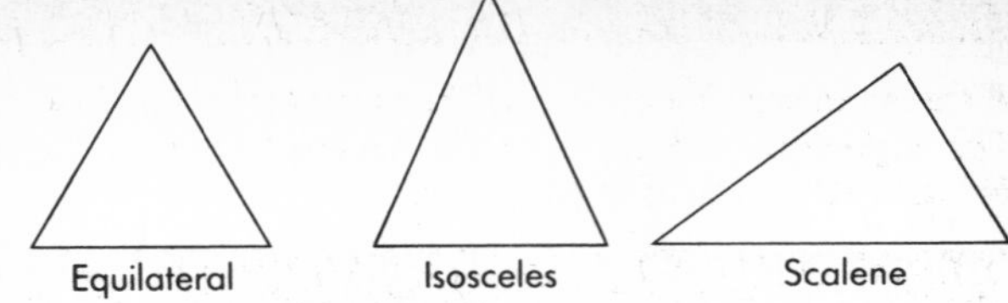

TRIANGULATION

A *triangular* frame is a very rigid structure, no matter what angle the force. Making use of this knowledge in design is called *triangulation*.

TRUE LENGTH

The true length of a line can only be seen when it is parallel to either a horizontal or vertical plane. A line that is *not* parallel to either of these two planes will appear to be shorter than its actual length. To obtain the true length of such a line will require it to be moved until it *is* parallel with one of the planes.

TRUE SHAPE

The surfaces of an object are true shapes (where all lengths of sides and angles are the same as the object) when seen at right angles to the object. It is important to know the true shape of a surface when preparing a two-dimensional development of a three-dimensional object (Fig T.14).

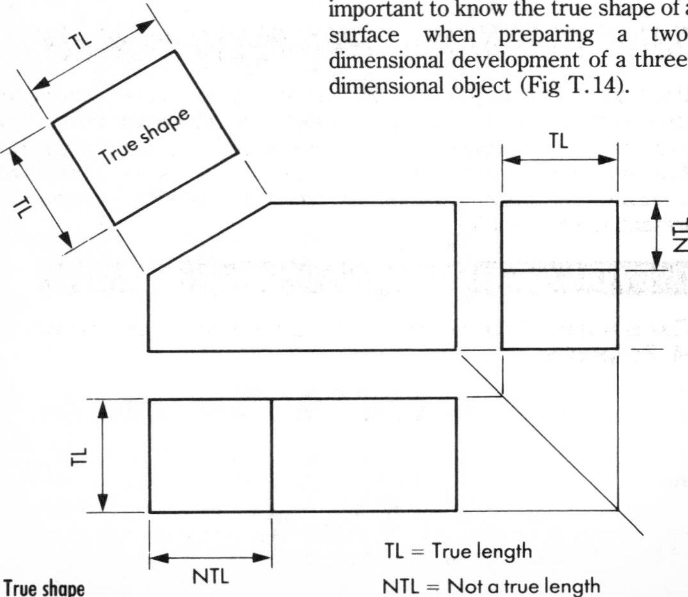

Fig T.14 True shape

TRUNCATED/TRUNCATION

A truncated solid is one that has been cut through and the top part removed. The angle of the cut can vary, but the most common angles are at 30°, 45°, 60°, and 90° to the horizontal plane.

TURNING FORCE

A turning force is one that will cause a beam on a pivot to rotate. This turning force is also known as a *moment*. ◀ Moments ▶

TWIST DRILLS

The flutes of a twist drill give the appearance of a material that has been twisted. It is this characteristic that distinguishes it form *flat drills*.

The flutes are designed to carry away the waste so that the cutting part of the drill is kept clear. This helps the drill to keep cool. The flutes form a helix. There is a *standard helix* which is common to most twist drills, such as 'Jobbers' Drills, but there also exists a *quick helix* suitable for drilling **thermoplastic** and a *slow helix* for drilling **thermosetting plastics** (Fig T.15).

Fig T.15 Twist drills

TWO-DIMENSIONAL DRAWING

This type of drawing produces flat drawings. In any single drawing they only show height and width, height and thickness, length and width, etc. The views given in an **orthographic projection** are all drawn to show only *two* types of dimension, e.g. height and width, etc. This type of drawing is quite simple and is suitable for quick sketches, for the early stages of designing and for presenting your first ideas.

TWO POINT PERSPECTIVE

This is a type of *three-dimensional* drawing that has two vanishing points. ◀ Perspective ▶

UNDER CUT

In carving, this means to cut away below or beneath. Such cutting away produces shadows to emphasise pattern, shape and form. This term is used in making patterns for casting. When a mould has been made it must, in the case of sand casting, be possible for the pattern to be removed without damaging the mould made in the sand. Similarly, with metal moulds, it must be possible to remove the casting from the mould without damage. To make sure a pattern or casting *can* be removed from a mould, it must not have any undercuts (Fig U.1).

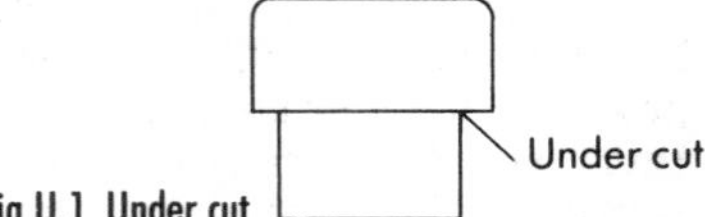

Fig U.1 Under cut

UNIFORMITY

All aspects the same. This may refer to size, shape, colour, texture, etc. When items are mass produced they all look the same, and are uniform in size, etc. To achieve uniformity in producing a product it is necessary to use templates, patterns, jigs, moulds, etc.

UNIVERSAL JOINT

These are used to join *shafts* that are not always in line. They may be at a fixed angle, or at an angle that is constantly changing. In order that the rotation of one shaft can be transmitted to another shaft, a *flexible joint* is needed. Figure U.2 shows some methods that are used.

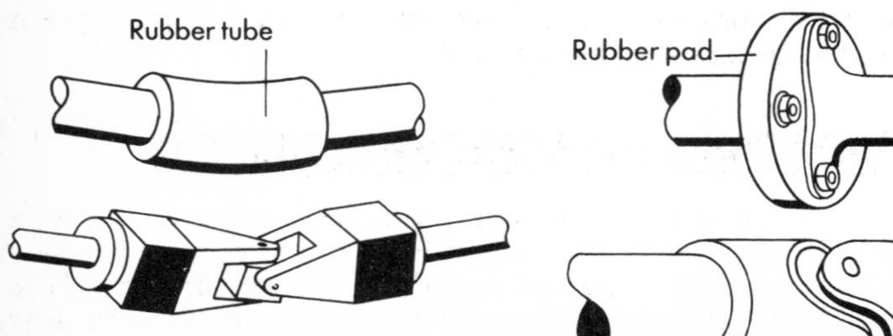

Fig U.2 Universal joints

VACUUM FORMING

This is a process that is used to form **thermoplastic** sheet material when it is hot and pliable. A sheet of thermoplastic material is held in a frame, heated till soft and placed over a mould. Air is drawn away from the underside of the sheet by a vacuum pump, and the soft plastic material forms itself closely round the mould. After a few seconds, the sheet will have cooled sufficiently for it to become rigid again so that it can be removed from the mould.

This process is suitable for producing shapes that do not have sharp corners but do have a draw angle between 2 – 5 (Fig V. 1). At an industrial level this process is used for items such as the insides of refrigerators, acrylic basins, baths, etc. At a school level, much smaller products can be produced, e.g. body work for model vehicles, toys, containers and dishes, or it can be used in making moulds from which plaster or resin casts can be taken. If thin polystyrene sheet is used, a mould can be made that is to be thrown away after it has been used. The product can then have under cuts, does not require a draft, and have a greater choice of form.

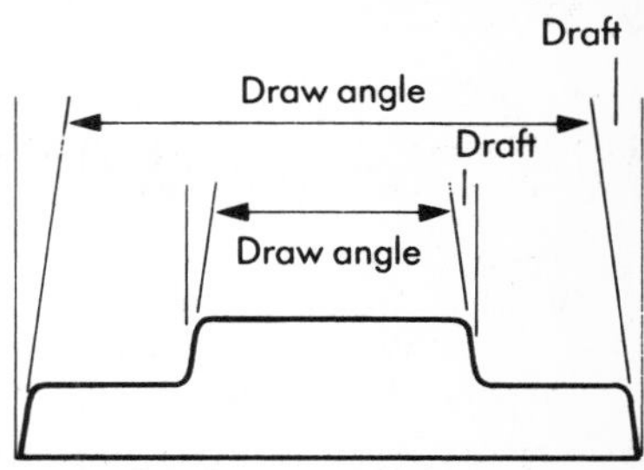

Fig V.1 Vacuum forming

VALENCE

A measure of the combining or replacing power of an atom of the substance as compared with the standard hydrogen atom.

VALVES

In pneumatic circuits, work depends upon compressed air. In such a system there is need for control and safety, and valves are designed to perform these functions. The most common valves include the following: **three port** and **five port** valves, shuttle valve, safety valve, pilot valves, solenoid valves, amplifier or step-up relay, etc. Here we look at a number of valves.

AMPLIFIER VALVE

This valve has a sensitive diaphragm that responds to a low pressure signal and is able to control the flow of high pressure in a pneumatic circuit (Fig V.2). Employing such a valve produces a quicker response than a three port valve with a standard diaphragm. It is also called a step up relay.

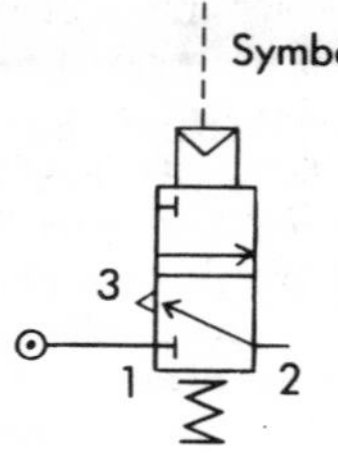

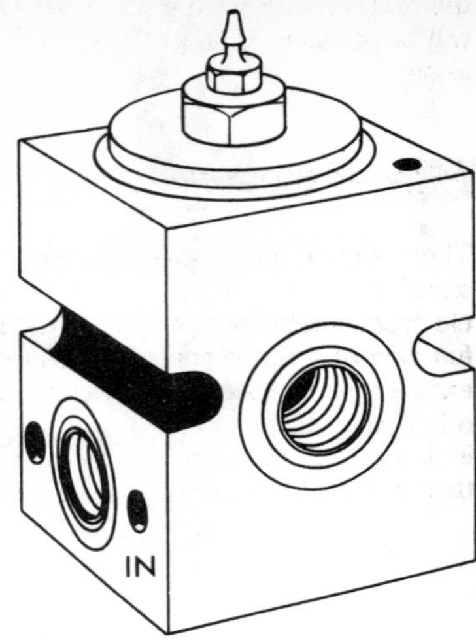

Fig V.2 Amplifier valve

PILOT VALVE

These are valves that are used to control a control valve from some distance away (Fig V.3). They are **five port valves** and can be used to perform a variety of operating functions on single and double acting cylinders. Pilot valves can be identified in a circuit by the dotted or broken lines indicating the pipe lines.

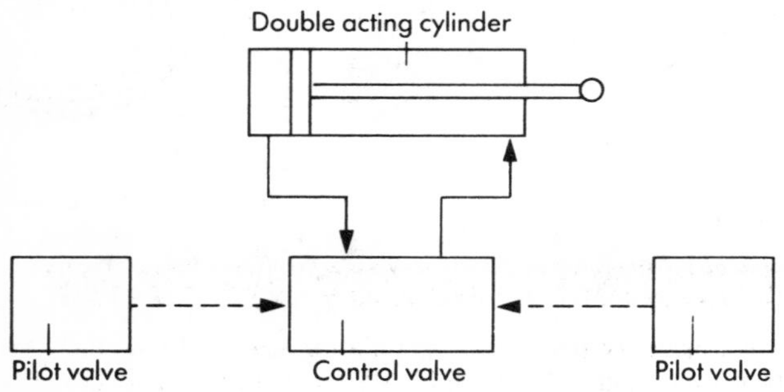

Fig V.3 Pilot valve

SAFETY VALVE

A safety valve is designed as the weakest part of the circuit. In this respect it is the same as a *fuse* in an electrical circuit. It is attached to the receiver (a steel storage tank) so that if the compressor builds up too much pressure in the receiver, because a pressure switch has failed, then the compressed air will be released. The pressure in the receiver will then fall and the valve will close.

SOLENOID VALVE

These can be **three port** or **five port** valves that are controlled by an electric signal in a coil. When a current passes through the coil, it produces an electromagnetic force sufficient to move a soft iron armature. In so doing, the function of a three port valve can change form closing a valve and allowing exhaust air to escape, to opening the valve and providing a main supply to other parts of the circuit (Fig V.4). The advantage of using this type of valve is that electrical signals are quicker and cheaper, can travel longer distances than pneumatic signals and also use less space.

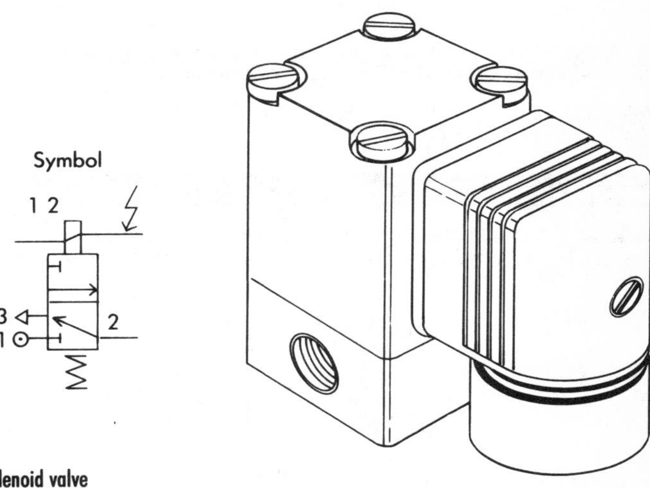

Fig V.4 Solenoid valve

VECTORS

A vector is a quantity that has magnitude (or size) and direction. These can also involve speed and force. Speed however, does not have direction, it only has magnitude.

These quantities can be represented by *lines*. The *length* of a line represents *magnitude* and the *angle* represents *direction*. The effect of adding the forces can be done using a vector diagram. Imagine a boat wanting to cross a river 3 Km wide. If the boat travels at 3 Km per hour, but the current of the river is flowing at 4 Km per hour, the boat will be carried down the river. What velocity will the boat require to get to the other side? This can be calculated by the vector diagram (Fig V.5). ◀ **Lines** ▶

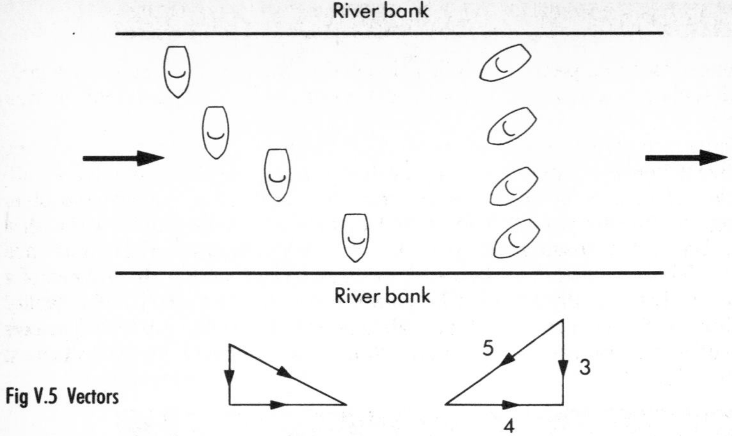

Fig V.5 Vectors

VELOCITY

Velocity is concerned with the distance a mechanism moves and the effort required to make it move.

VELOCITY RATIO

Velocity ratio is concerned with the distance moved by the effort compared with the distance moved by the load. This can be written:

$$\text{Velocity Ratio} = \frac{\text{distance moved by effort}}{\text{distance moved by load}}$$

In the case of a third class lever shown in Figure V.6a), the VR = $\frac{100}{50}$ = 2:1. In the case of the two pulley wheels shown in Fig V.6b), the *driver pulley* has to rotate once to make the *driven pulley* rotate twice; the Velocity Ratio is therefore 1:2.

The rotary velocity is concerned with the speed or number of times a pulley wheel rotates in one minute. This is expressed as revs. per min. Since the ratio of the effort is the same, then if the driver wheel rotates 100 revs per min., the driven wheel will rotate 200 revs. per min. (i.e. the Velocity Ratio = 1:2).

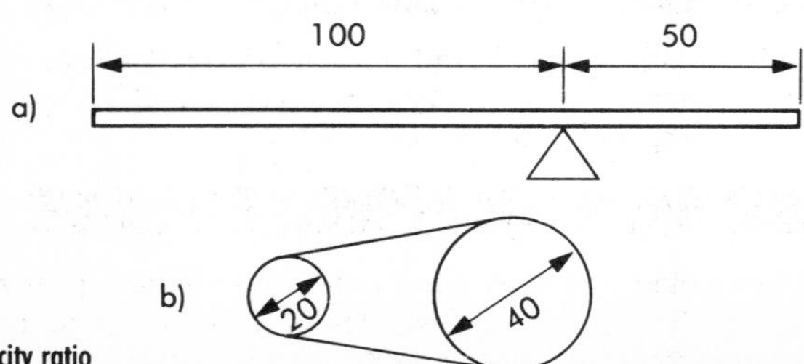

Fig V.6 Velocity ratio

VENEER

A veneer is a thin piece of wood. It is used in the manufacture of plywood. Solid timber is often covered with a veneer from an attractively grained timber.

There are two methods of producing a veneer. The method used for producing veneers for general use, involves turning a log on a giant lathe with a wide blade that is forced against the rotating surface. The veneer peels off in a long, continuous ribbon. The second method involves slicing a log with a large blade, the result being that the attractive features of the grain are shown. These veneers are then kept for the external surface or surfaces of a piece of plywood. Plywood with *decorative veneers* is used for hight quality furniture such as doors, table tops, cabinets, etc. Plywood with *peeled veneers* are put to general use, e.g. flooring, shuttering, and work that is to have a painted finish.

VENTILATE

The movement of air or the freedom for air to escape is important and necessary in some processes. In *sand casting* it is necessary to allow hot air to escape when the molten metal is being poured into the mould. If this cannot happen, the trapped air will prevent the molten metal occupying all the space in the mould, and the casting will have a pitted or hollow impression in its surface. To prevent this from happening, small holes are made in the sand to allow the hot air to escape.

Several processes give off fumes that are unpleasant and can, in some cases, cause headaches or eyes to run. In such circumstances the rooms should be well ventilated by either windows being open or an air ventilation system being used. Good ventilation is needed for the following processes: GRP work, casting, respraying, welding, forging, etc.

VENTS

The small holes in moulds to allow air to escape. Venting a mould used in *vacuum forming* helps the hot thermoplastic to form closely round the mould. Venting in *sand casting* helps the air to escape when the hot metal is poured into the mould. ◀ **Casting** ▶

VERTICAL

At 90° to the horizontal. A vertical plane is at 90° to the horizontal plane. The side view or front view of an object is drawn on what represents the *vertical plane* in **orthographic projection**.

VIEW

The drawing of an object as seen from a known position, e.g. from above, from the side etc. The term 'view' has the same meaning as *elevation* in **orthographic projection** but 'view' is more commonly used.

VISUAL DISPLAY UNIT (VDU)

This is the piece of equipment that shows information on a screen, such as a television screen, computer screen, etc. Often abbreviated as VDU.

VOLT

The SI unit of electrical potential. It is the measurement of the work an electric charge from one point to another that has a higher potential.

VOLTAGE

Voltage is the potential difference between two points of a circuit or device. Voltage equals current (I) times resistance (R). e.g. when I = 2 amps and resistance = 3 ohms, the voltage = 6V. It must be remembered that there mut be a **potential difference** between the two points, otherwise the electrons will not flow to produce a current.

VOLTAGE MEASUREMENT

One volt (V) is the potential difference across a resistance of one ohm that has a current of one amp. As a unit of measurement, the Volt is suitable for many applications. But in electronics, this unit is too big, especially when the current can be a few thousandths or even millionths of an ampere. So it is necessary to use a prefix e.g. milli (m) for one thousandth or micro (μ) for one millionth. Hence one 5000th of an amp is written 5mA; one 15,000,000th of a volt is written 15 μV.

VOLTMETER

A voltmeter is used to measure the potential difference across a resistance. In the moving coil meter, the needle is deflected when a current passes through a coil that is free to rotate in a magnetic field. A spring returns the needle to zero when no current is flowing. The movement of the needle is *proportional* to the amount of current flowing in the coil.

Before the voltmeter can be used, the selector switch has to be set in the appropriate voltage range. This will cause a full scale deflection (fsd). If the setting is for 10 volts, then the deflection will go from one end of the scale to the other, giving a reading of 10 volts. If the setting is for 25 volts, then the fsd of the needle will give a reading of 25 volts (Fig V.7).

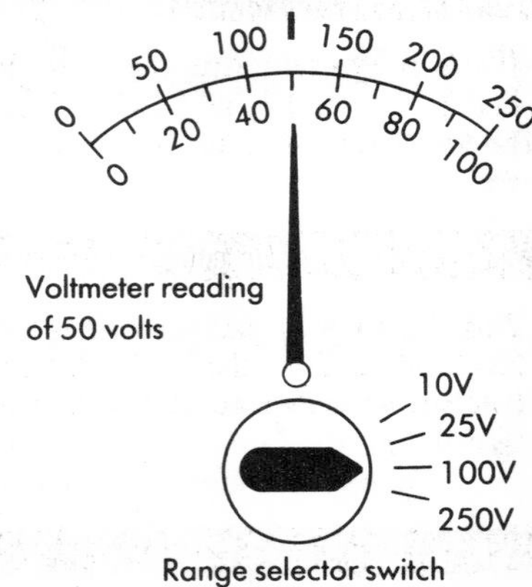

Fig V.7 Voltmeter

WALL ATTACHMENT DEVICE

◄ Logic gates ►

WANEY EDGE

The *waney edge* of a piece of timber is an edge that still has the bark of the tree. Though this is normally removed, it is kept for use in rustic furniture, especially for table tops.

WARP

The movement of a flat piece of timber. A twist. A warped piece of timber is *not* flat or true.

WASTE

Waste in general terms applies to that which is no longer required. It may be in the form of 'Off Cuts', in which case further use may be made, or it may be in the form of shavings, dust, etc., which have little or no practical use.

WASTE AREA

Waste area is a part that is to be removed and is shown by cross-hatching on the waste side of the line (Fig W.1).

Fig W.1 Waste area

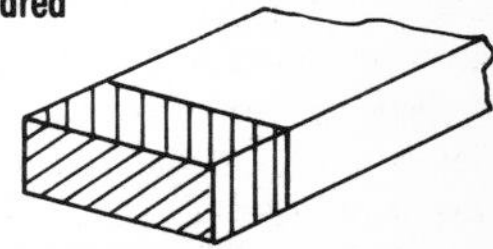

WASTING PROCESS

This means that the method of shaping is done by *removing material with a cutting tool,* such as a saw, plane, lathe, milling machine, drilling machine, etc., as opposed to casting, bending, twisting, forging beating, etc.

WATERCOLOUR

Watercolour paints are used to *tint* a drawing by applying a wash (single coat) of watercolour to a surface. They can also be used to provide a background, e.g. just colour the outside edge of the object, or it can be used to colour a surface so that it is slightly darker than the other surfaces, giving depth to the drawing.

Watercolours are *translucent* and should not be used to cover over mistakes, because the mistakes will still show no matter how many washes are applied. For an *even* wash, the paper should be damp, before making horizontal stokes with the brush from top to bottom. Each stroke should just overlap in the previous stroke. If the last stroke is darker than the previous strokes, then blotting paper should be used to remove excess watercolour.

WAVE

A wave is a displacement of particles in a medium. The displacement can be continuous and repeated over a period of time.

WAVE FORM

A wave form is a graph that shows the variation of wave strength over a period of time, including the *amplitude* (peak to peak or trough to trough) (Fig W.2). The *cathode-ray oscilloscope* is an electronic apparatus that is used to examine wave forms which are displayed on a screen. The most common wave form is the *sine wave*. Other wave forms that you are likely to meet are Square, Pulse, Sawtooth, Ripple, and trapezoidal. ◀ Sine wave ▶

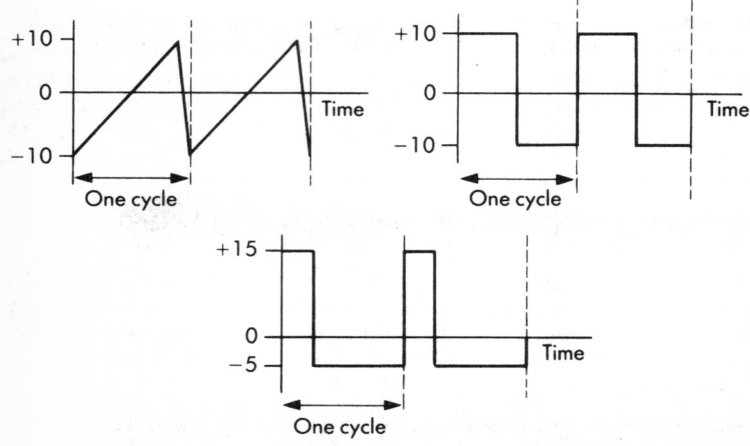

Fig W.2 Wave form

WAX

The main sources of wax are insects such as bees, and plants. *Carnauba wax*, which comes from the Brazilian Palm, is a very hard wax and is used in most furniture polishes. It provides a hard, glossy protective coat.

WEAR

When one material is in contact with another and there is movement some particles are removed. This constant removal or particles reduces the size of the material. Wear takes place in most mechanical devices; it is reduced by various methods of lubrication and by the use of bearings. The methods used to reduce *friction* between moving parts also reduces wear.

◀ **Lubrication** ▶

WEB

This is a term used in casting. It is the name given to the part of a casting that acts as a support (Fig W.3).

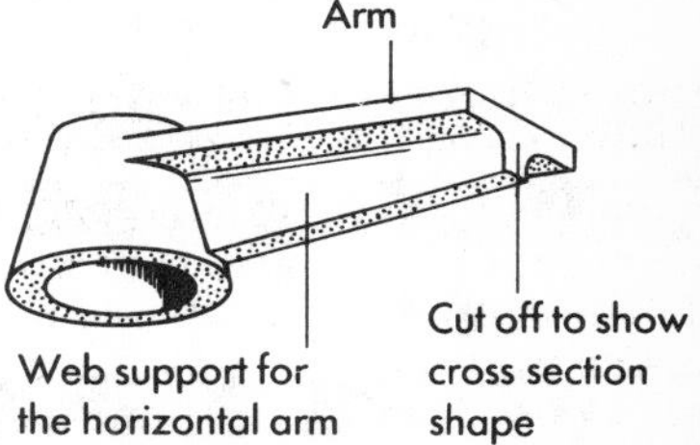

Fig W.3 Web

WEDGE

The wedge is an example of the *inclined plane*. It is a way of moving a load more easily than the effort required to lift the same load vertically. The wedge has many applications. It can be used as a force to cut wood when using a chisel, plane, knife, etc. When the inclined plane is wrapped round a cylinder, it is known as a *thread* and can be used to apply a load for holding devices, such as screws and cramps, and for lifting devices, such as jacks. This is a mechanism that gains considerable **mechanical advantage**.

WELDING PROCESS

This is the joining of like materials by the application of heat. The heat melts the surfaces of the material to be joined and the additional like material fills any gap. The term *welding* is mainly given to the joining of **ferrous** metals and some **thermoplastics** such as nylon and Polyvinylchloride (PVC).

◀ **Arc welding, Oxyacetylene welding** ▶

WELDING ROD

This is material used to join other materials during welding and to fill any grooves or fillets that form part of the design of the welding joint.

WELDING SYMBOLS

Some examples of these are shown in Fig W.4.

Fig W.4 Welding symbols

Square butt
II
Symbol

Single-V butt
V
Symbol

Fillet
Symbol

Spot
Symbol

WET AND DRY

◀ Abrasives ▶

WHEEL

The wheel is one of the most commonly used mechanical devices. Like the lever, it can move loads with considerable **mechanical advantage**. This is shown mainly in **gear** and **pulley** mechanisms.

WOOD WORM

This is a general term used to describe a family of insects that live mainly in sap wood. They go through a life cycle of egg, larvae, pupae to beetle. During this life cycle the wood worm (larva) bores holes to gain food, and so weakens the wood, making it useless. Millions of pounds worth of damage are caused every year to buildings that use wood as a construction material. Several types of beetle also attack wood; beetles are the House Long Horn, Powder Post, Furniture, and Deathwatch (Fig W.5).

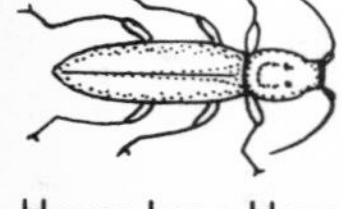
House Long Horn

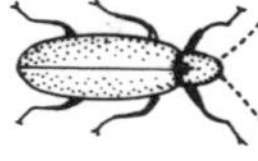
Furniture

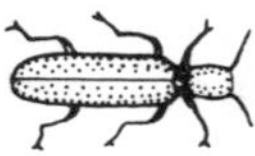
Powder Post

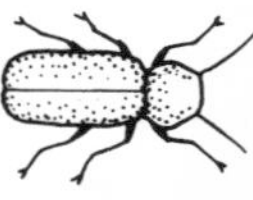
Deathwatch

Fig W.5 Beetles

WORK HARDENING

When some metals are put under pressure, e.g. the blow of a hammer, they become hard. They can become so hard that they begin breaking or cracking. To *prevent* this happening the metals are **annealed** (softened) by heating and cooling. Aluminium, copper, gilding metal are examples of materials that become hard with continous beating with a hammer or mallet.

WORKING DRAWING

A working drawing is one that contains *all* the information that is necessary to make a product. **Orthographic projection** is a suitable way of presenting information and is widely used. However, it is not the only way and for such items as sculpture and circuitry, an alternative method should be used. Providing the drawing contains at least sufficient information for the work to be completed, it can be regarded as a working drawing. Materials, sizes, construction, components, fittings, finish are some of the details that you would expect to find on a working drawing. Where possible, a working drawing should be drawn the *same size* as the end product, and show true shape views. Such a drawing is helpful for marking out and checking.

WORKING PROPERTIES

Some materials are easier to cut, saw, plane, chisel, bend, twist, mould, etc., than others. A material that is easy to work is said to have good working properties. A material that is difficult to work is said to have poor working properties. Selecting a material on the basis of its working properties may not only prove to be a good choice, but also a wise choice. Generally speaking, working with a material that has good working properties often means that you can achieve a better quality finish in a shorter space of time, than working with one that has poor working qualities.

WORM GEAR

◀ Gears ▶

YIELD POINT

◀ Material characteristics ▶